K & Block

November 1977

# The Origins and Course
# of Psychopathology

# The Origins and Course of Psychopathology

*Methods of Longitudinal Research*

Edited by

**John S. Strauss** and **Haroutun M. Babigian**

*University of Rochester*
*Rochester, New York*

and

**Merrill Roff**

*Professor Emeritus*
*University of Minnesota*
*Minneapolis, Minnesota*

**Plenum Press · New York and London**

Library of Congress Cataloging in Publication Data

Main entry under title:

The Origins and course of psychopathology.

    Includes index.
    1. Psychiatry—Longitudinal studies. I. Strauss, John S. II. Babigian, Haroutun. III.
Roff, Merrill Flagg, 1909-     [DNLM: 1. Psychopathology. WM100 069]
RC337.073           616.8'9'007                     77-2874
ISBN 0-306-31028-7

© 1977 Plenum Press, New York
A Division of Plenum Publishing Corporation
227 West 17th Street, New York, N.Y. 10011

Printed in the United States of America

# Acknowledgments

The editors wish to thank Ms. Patti Sanderl, Nancy Ryan, Sue Willis, and Dolores Jones for their assistance and dedication in preparing this volume. We also wish to thank Drs. Martin Katz and Robert Hirschfeld of the Clinical Research Branch, National Institute of Mental Health; the Department of Psychiatry of the University of Rochester, Dr. Lyman C. Wynne, Chairman; Roche Laboratories, and the Sandoz Corporation for their support of the conference from which this volume is derived.

In addition, we acknowledge the following:

Figure 1, Chapter 1. Reprinted by permission of the authors and the editor, from Weissman, M.M. and Kasl, S.V.: Help seeking in depressed outpatients following maintenance therapy. British Journal of Psychiatry, vol. 129, pp. 252-260, 1976.

Figure 1, Chapter 5. From Dohrenwend, B.P.: The social psychological nature of stress: A framework for causal inquiry. Journal of Abnormal and Social Psychology, vol. 62, pp. 294-302, 1961. Copyright 1961 by the American Psychological Association. Reprinted by permission.

Table 2 and Figure 1, Chapter 12. Reprinted by permission of the authors and the editor from Hogarty, G.E.; Goldberg, S.C.; Schooler, N.R.; and Ulrich, R.F.: Drug sociotherapy in the aftercare of schizophrenic patients. Archives of General Psychiatry, vol. 31, pp. 603-608, 1974. Copyright 1974, American Medical Association.

Figure 1, Chapter 14. From Gunderson, J.; Carpenter, W.T., Jr.; Strauss, J.S.; and Scott, W.: Borderline patients - A comparative study. American Journal of Psychiatry, vol. 132, pp. 1257-1264, 1975. Copyright 1975, the American Psychiatric Association. Reprinted by permission.

Table 2, Chapter 14.  Reprinted by permission of the authors and the editor, from Carpenter, W.T.; Strauss, J.S.; and Bartko, J.J.: A flexible system for the identification of schizophrenia: A report from the International Pilot Study of Schizophrenia.  Science, vol. 182, pp. 1275-1278, 1973. Copyright 1973 by the American Association for the Advancement of Science.

Chapter 16.  This paper has been published as part of a series of program reports of the National Institute on Drug Abuse supported research on evaluation of treatment for drug abuse, in Sells, S.B. and Simpson, D.D., Eds., The Effectiveness of Drug Abuse Treatment, Volume III. Further Studies of Drug Users, Treatment Typologies, and Assessment of Outcomes During Treatment in the DARP.  Cambridge, Mass.: Ballinger Publishing Company, published in June, 1976.

This work has also been supported in part by NIMH Grant No. MH-00006-01.

# Preface

The Society for Life History Research in Psychopathology
is a group of investigators from many disciplines who share
an interest in studying the longitudinal aspects of psychiatric disorder. Sociologists, psychologists, statisticians,
psychiatrists, epidemiologists, and others each bring to the
study of life history the expertise and vantage point arising
from his or her unique training and experience.

This volume, the fifth in a series, is devoted to explor-
ing the methods used to contribute to the understanding of the
complex unfolding of a human life as it avoids, copes with, or
succumbs to psychiatric disorder. We hope that by describing
these methods, their current status, advantages, and shortcomings, this volume can serve as a guidepost to all who are
involved in our field to help understand it further and to
generate solutions for the many crucial problems we face.

J.S.

H.B.

M.R.

# Contents

SECTION I
CONTROLLED VS. NATURALISTIC APPROACHES

CHAPTER 1

CHAPTER 2

CHAPTER 3

CHAPTER 4

SECTION II
LIFE EVENTS

SECTION III
STUDIES OF CHILDREN AT RISK

SECTION V
RELATIONSHIPS AMONG VARIABLES AFFECTING DEVELOPMENT
AND COURSE OF PSYCHOPATHOLOGY

# Introduction

Limitations in methodology have provided a major hindrance to discovering the causes of psychiatric disorder and evaluating treatment effectiveness. Clinical and research reports often have not established the reliability of crucial variables and investigations have often used relatively crude methods for determining the roles and interactions of factors investigated. Patient diagnoses, for example, have frequently been based solely on the criterion - if any criterion was specified at all - of "hospital diagnosis," without recognizing the vast differences within and across hospitals of how diagnostic labels are applied. Statistics, when used, have often been applied in an unsophisticated way (Spitzer and Cohen, 1968). These problems have been particularly serious in longitudinal research where the need to measure changes in subjects over time has complicated the development of optimal research designs.

More recently, the methods available for research in psychopathology have advanced considerably. Improved techniques for collecting clinical data, new laboratory procedures, and increased access to computer facilities have all contributed to the development and differentiation of several methods for longitudinal research. With these approaches, it has been possible to advance our knowledge of the effects of genetics, early environment, stress, biochemical variables, treatment, and recent environment on the development and course of psychiatric disorder. These advances make it possible to proceed beyond earlier knowledge to specify crucial factors with increasing detail, and to determine their roles and interactions (Strauss, in press).

Development of still more effective research methods is essential, however. Groups focusing on one area need to keep abreast of progress elsewhere so that advances in one approach can contribute to development in the others.

For these reasons, the most advanced methods need to be made known to all investigators.

To further these goals, this volume describes recent methodological advances in five major areas of longitudinal research in psychopathology. In the first section, one of the most basic issues is considered, the relative advantages and limitations of controlled and natural history approaches to longitudinal research. The manipulation of subject cohorts in the controlled approach and the non-intervention of the natural history method have crucial ramifications in current psychiatric research. This is especially important in situations where experimental manipulations are either unethical or impossible, such as in the study of severe stresses or in the evaluation of generally accepted but unproven treatment methods.

Sections two through four involve more specialized topics regarding factors that cause or affect the course of psychiatric disorder. Section two focuses on the methodology of life events studies. These include studies of so-called precipitating events, not as simple an area as it once seemed. Methodology and findings to deal with the complexity of this topic have undergone especially rapid development in the past few years.

The third section describes issues and advances in methods of high-risk research - an approach to understanding psychopathology that focuses primarily on defining the lasting traits that determine vulnerability. This approach provides a complement to life events studies which concentrate on the specific precipitating situations acting on the person's traits and personality organization. High-risk research has provided a major advance for avoiding the serious problems of post-hoc reasoning and retrospective falsification.

The fourth section focuses on follow-up studies of patients with demonstrated psychopathology. These studies have their greatest value in revealing the factors, including treatment, that affect the course of psychiatric disorder. This more traditional research area has also undergone considerable change in recent years, including development of more adequate approaches to assessing the many aspects of outcome.

The last section is concerned with methods for understanding the relative importance and interaction of the
diverse elements affecting the onset and course of psychopathology. There has been general recognition that longitudinal research must deal with many variables simultaneously. However, until recently, this recognition has generally
been limited either to a somewhat off-hand noting of the
importance of factors not in one's area of specialization,
or to attempts to relate only globally the diverse relevant
variables. Many methods for defining precisely the relative
importance and interaction of numerous variables have been
developed recently and are crucial for weaving together the
specific findings from the various approaches considered
earlier.

                                                    J.S.

                                                    H.B.

                                                    M.R.


                          REFERENCES

1.  Spitzer, R, and Cohen, J.  Common errors in quantitative
    psychiatric research.  International Journal of
    Psychiatry, 1968, 6, (2): 109-131.

2.  Strauss, J.S.  Untangling the antecedents of schizo-
    phrenic behaviors.  In Siva Sankar, D.V. (ed.),
    Psychiatric problems of childhood.  PJD Publications,
    in press.

# Section I

# Controlled vs. Naturalistic Approaches

CONTROLLED VS. NATURALISTIC EXPERIMENTS: APPLICATION OF
THE LIFE TABLE METHOD[1]

Myrna M. Wiessman
Department of Psychiatry
Yale University School of Medicine
100 Park Avenue
New Haven, Connecticut

I would like to discuss this subject by drawing from
my own experiences, which may present a familiar topic from
a different vantage point. I'll describe research on the
outpatient treatment of primary depression, in which I've
collaborated since 1967 with Drs. Gerald Klerman and Alberto
DiMascio, and Ms. Brigitte Prusoff. This research is relevant to the topic since it included a twenty-month study
with both controlled and naturalistic phases. I will also
draw upon my training in epidemiology, where procedures for
the study of cholera or the statistical techniques used for
obtaining mortality data can be useful models for psychiatric
research. This discussion will illustrate that the limitations and advantages of naturalistic and controlled experiments are not that clear. Moreover, the statistical technique of life tables can be used to approximate quasi-
experimental conditions for the analysis of data collected
naturalistically.

---

[1]Appreciation is expressed to Gerald L. Klerman, M.D.,
Alberto DiMascio, Ph.D., and Brigitte Prusoff, M.P.H., for
the use of collaborative data and to Gerald L. Klerman , M.D.
for comments on the material presented in this paper. This
research was supported by U.S.P.H.S. Grants MH 13738, MH
15650, and MH 17728 from the Psychopharmacology Research
Branch, National Institute of Mental Health, Department of
Health, Education, and Welfare.

## CONTROLLED VS. NATURALISTIC EXPERIMENTS

First let us review the distinctions between controlled and naturalistic experiments. Basically there are two approaches to testing hypotheses: controlled or experimental studies and naturalistic or observational ones. In any controlled study the investigator examines the impact of varying a factor which is under his or her control. This usually involves selecting a number of individuals who are alike in specific characteristics, excluding others and subjecting randomly chosen subgroups to an experimental treatment or a disease-producing situation, and finally comparing the outcome on treatement or the occurrence of disease in the experimental and control groups. In practice the experimental manipulation of disease-producing situations is not possible in human subjects although it is used in animal studies, e.g., Dr. William McKinney and the Wisconsin group experimentally produce situations of loss and observe the occurrence of symptoms in monkeys exposed to these conditions. Since controlled experiments in humans involve the manipulation of therapeutic interventions, e.g., drugs, an education program, psychotherapy, etc., we will restrict the discussion to these studies, although, even here, ethical questions about the withholding of effective treatments or the use of experimental treatments must be carefully considered.

Controlled treatment studies generally follow one of two models. There are experiments testing treatment for acute or ongoing disorders in symptomatic subjects (therapeutic trials) or for the prevention of disease or the recurrence of symptoms in asymptomatic subjects (prophylactic or maintenance trials).

The controlled experiment is the strongest approach to hypothesis testing. The selection of subjects can be precise. Allocation to treatment is random, and one can expect the groups formed to be generally alike at the beginning of the experiment. Since subjects do not select their own assignment to treatment, the effect of the intervention can be measured without the confounding influence of self-selection. In many studies the expectations of investigators or participants, as a source of error, can be controlled by double-blind techniques. Moreover, the type, amount, quality, and timing of the intervention can be

controlled. The assessments of outcome can be structured,
predetermined, and well-defined. Nonetheless, controlled
experiments have their limitations. They are time-consuming,
can pose ethical concerns, and even in the best co-ordinated
study, subjects may drop out before the predetermined time
and in ways which are not random.

For these reasons, observational or naturalistic experiments are more common. They are less costly and raise
fewer ethical questions. In these studies the investigator
observes the occurrence of disease or the effects of treatments or of time, in people who are already segregated into
groups on the basis of some experience or exposure. Allocation into groups is not under the investigator's control
but is natural.

Naturally occurring groups may confound results since
persons tend to segregate themselves and may differ in
characteristics other than the factors under study. For
example, people who seek different treatments may not only
differ in the exposure to the treatment but in the length
and severity of illness and a whole host of other factors
which led them to select the specific treatment in the first
place. Because of these confounding influences the role of
the specific factor under investigation is more difficult to
demonstrate. While information may be gathered about the
behavior of persons, that would be useful in planning care,
little may be learned about the efficacy of treatment or
exposures leading to the development of a disease.

The separation between controlled and natural experiments is not that distinct nor their limitations that clear.
While controlled experiments can establish the efficacy of
treatment, aspects of controlled experiments can become
naturalistic and subject to the same problems of self-
selection. As mentioned previously, patient attrition in
controlled treatment is often nonrandom so that subjects
remaining, as well as those leaving early, are to some
extent self-selected. In therapeutic trials patients may
select their treatments overtly or covertly. As we often
find, patient attendance in psychotherapy or consumption of
experimental medication can vary considerably. On the other
hand, certain naturalistic experiments can provide clear
understanding of disease etiology. Outside of psychiatry,
naturalistic studies are the most common type, e.g., the

association between smoking and lung cancer was an observation made by naturalistic experiments.  However, naturalistic experiments require powerful factors to detect associations since many sources of variance are introduced.  The
risk factor or the treatments must be powerful to overcome
these sources of variation.  Although I could find no publishe
figures, several investigators agreed that the risk factor
or treatment should contribute more than 10% of the variance
to outcome to detect an association (Colin White, M.D.,
Gerald Klerman, M.D., personal communication, 1975).  Smoking
is one such powerful factor in lung cancer.  Similar ones
are rarely found in psychiatry.

## NATURALLY OCCURRING EXPERIMENTS

There is one group of natural experiments which deserve
mention because they can be important tools and have been
underutilized in psychiatry. These are naturally occurring
experiments.  The most famous naturally occurring experiment
was reported by John Snow over a hundred years ago. On the
basis of extensive study of the epidemiology of cholera, he
found that rates were particularly high in areas of London
supplied with water by the three companies which drew their
water at points heavily polluted with sewage.  He observed
that when one of the companies relocated their source to
less polluted areas, the incidence of cholera declined
substantially in the area fed by that source, but did not
change in the areas fed by the other two companies.  This
observation led him to dismantle the pumps from the polluted
areas to control the epidemic and demonstrated the value of
searching out unusual circumstances to test hypotheses.

Cholera is, of course, a long way from psychiatric
disorders.  However, there have been natural experiments in
psychiatry that have yielded important information as well.
These have included rigorously defined studies around
significant or predictable events which have occurred naturally such as survivors of a disaster (Lindemann, 1944);
children of schizophrenic biologic parents adopted at birth
by normal parents (Rosenthal & Kety, 1968); or as a result
of administrative changes such as urban renewal and forced
relocation (Kasl, 1972); automation of a factory (Cobb,
Kasl, Connelly, 1966); planned social reform (Campbell,
1969); and abrupt discharge of psychiatric patients during a
strike (Barrett, 1969).

Research strategies can be developed around identifying such stressful social events which have consequences for the mental health of the persons involved, and can be studied in their natural setting. The individual's exposure to such events takes place with a minimum of self-selection, and adequate comparison groups can be found who have not been exposed to the events. In these cases a truly natural experiment exists and the risk following exposure to disease-producing situations, which cannot be produced experimentally can be observed.


THE NEW HAVEN-BOSTON COLLABORATIVE DEPRESSION STUDY

Against this background, this report describes a study which is typical of controlled and naturalistic experiments in psychiatry and which illustrates the limitations of both designs, as well as the strategies used to overcome their limitations. This was a twenty-month study with both controlled and naturalistic phases. The purpose was to determine the optimum maintenance therapy for patients recovering from a depressive episode.


## Design

The design of the study, in brief, was a 3 x 2 balanced factorial in which 150 acutely depressed women who had received symptomatic relief with amitriptyline were assigned at random to eight months of controlled maintenance amitriptyline, placebo or no pill with or without psychotherapy (Figure 1). After the controlled treatment phase, patients were followed for twelve additional months in a naturalistic phase.


## Attrition

Dropout of patients in a long-term treatment study must be expected. In the New Haven-Boston study, 150 patients were the cohort of the controlled study and, of this total, 44 patients terminated the controlled treatment before the eight months. Moreover, attrition was not random across treatments as more patients relapsed in the no-drug groups. As frequently occurs in long-term trials, the original

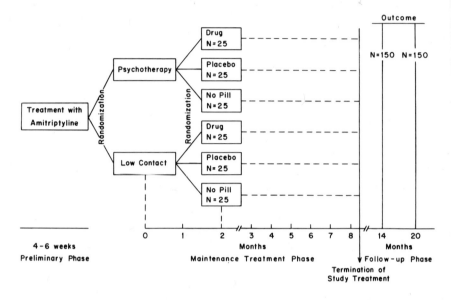

Figure 1.   Design of the Study

conditions of randomization no longer held because of differential dropout usually due to relapse.   Various approaches
to handling attrition were undertaken.

## Life Table Method

The life table method for handling attrition has been
used extensively in epidemiology in mortality studies
especially for estimating mortality risks in cancer.   It has
been used infrequently in psychiatric cases.   This neglect
is unfortunate since the life table method is particulary
useful in longitudinal studies, especially in a controlled
experiment with a well defined outcome such as relapse
(Greenwood, 1926).   This method allows calculation of probability of outcome for separate groups while correcting for

the change in a number of subjects in each group over time
(Table 1 shows the formula).  Using life tables, it is
possible to calculate the probability of relapsing within a
specified time period for each treatment, while adjusting
for patients who dropped out for reasons other than relapse,
by including them in the analysis only during the period
when they were observed (Mausner and Bahn, 1974).  Therefore,
no patient is left out of the cohort.  Gerald Klerman first
pointed out the applicability of life tables for calculating
relapse rates in long-term psychiatric treatment trials.
Table 2 shows the results using the life table method and
shows that drug therapy significantly reduced the probability
of relapse (Klerman, et al., 1974).

Table 1

Life Table Calculations:
Cumulative Chance of Relapse

For interval x to x+1

$O_x$ = Number of patients under observation at the beginning
of interval

$d_x$ = Relapses during interval

$w_x$ = Withdrawal during interval

$$q_x = \dfrac{d_x}{O_x - \dfrac{w_x}{2}} = \text{Chance of relapse during interval}$$

$p_x = 1-q_x$ = Chance of surviving during interval

$P_x = (p_1)\,(p_2)\,(p_3)\ldots(p_x)$ = Cumulative chance of survival

$$\text{Standard Error (S.E.) of } P_x = \sqrt{\sum \dfrac{q_x}{O_x - W_x - \dfrac{d_x}{2}}\, P_x}$$

Table 2

Cumulative Chance of Relapse in the
Different Treatment Groups (N=150)

|                    | Cumulative Chance of Relapse | |
|--------------------|---------|--------|
|                    | %       | S.E.   |
| Drug               | 12.2    | .05    |
| Placebo            | 29.2    | .07    |
| No Pill            | 26.6    | .06    |
| No Drug            | 27.9    | .05    |
|                    |         |        |
| High Contact       | 19.5    | .05    |
| Low contact        | 26.2    | .05    |

Drug vs. Placebo   p   .05
Drug vs. No Drug   p   .05

High vs. Low Contact – N.S.

## End Point and Survivor Analysis

While the life table analysis was useful in determining
relapse rates between groups, other outcomes such as clinical
symptoms and social functioning were also tested.  For those
outcome data we used an end point analysis as an alternate
method of handling attrition. In this type of analysis early
terminators from the trial are rated at the point of termination and their rating is included in all subsequent analyses.
The rationale behind this approach is that the status of
patients at dropout is the best prediction of their status
at termination of the trial.  In addition, we used a survivor analysis which included only the 106 persons who
completed the full eight months of treatment and then
compared the results of these different analyses (Weissman,
Prusoff, Klerman, 1974).

## THE NATURALISTIC PHASE

Patients were followed up six months and one year after the eight month period ended to see if there were differential treatment effects and to examine the patient's long-term clinical course. Information was obtained on all 150 patients at both follow-ups. Such a response rate is unusual and probably was related to the fact that the patients had already been in our care for an extended period and had demonstrated their stability, cooperativeness and loyalty. Most follow-ups have to deal with considerable attrition and surely we would have had to in other circumstances.

The patient's stability, however, was limited to their willingness to be interviewed. In all other regards they took divergent courses. Because patients had sought out a variety of treatments, there no longer existed any pure treatment groups. Therefore, it was impossible to interpret any differential treatment effects of the controlled treatment once it was no longer controlled.

### Life Table Method

We had used life tables in the controlled phase of the study for calculating the probability of relapse in the different treatment groups. We also had made monthly assessments of the patients' clinical status and treatment received during the twelve-month naturalistic phase. While we could not sort out differential effects of the controlled treatment once it ended, we could use the life table method to determine the probability of relapse or remission on the different treatments received during the naturalistic phase. The examination of naturalistic data using life tables has just begun. One analysis illustrating this method is presented in Table 3. For this analysis we looked at the probability of remission with and without tricyclics in patients who were symptomatic when they began the follow-up. Remission was defined as return to an asymptomatic state (global rating of 1 or 2 on a 7-point scale) for three consecutive months. Patients were considered symptomatic at the beginning of the follow-up if they had a global illness rating of 3 to 7. The probability of remission for patients remaining on tricyclics was 86% as contrasted with 66% for the patients off tricyclics (Figure 2). The sample for these

Table 3

Probability of Remission* By Drug Group in Patients
Who Began the Follow-Up With Symptoms**

| | | | | | | | | |
|---|---|---|---|---|---|---|---|---|
| **Patients Remaining on Tricyclics Until Outcome** | | | | | | | | |

| Month | $O_x$ | $d_x$ | $W_x$ | $q_x$ | $p_x$ | $P_x$ | $\dfrac{q_x}{O_x - W_x - \dfrac{d_x}{2}}$ | $(1 - P_x)$ (Cumulative Chance of Remission) |
|---|---|---|---|---|---|---|---|---|
| 9 | 14 | | | | | | | |
| 10 | 14 | 2 | 0 | .142 | .857 | .857 | .012 | .142 |
| 11 | 12 | 3 | 0 | .250 | .750 | .643 | .027 | .357 |
| 12 | 9 | 3 | 0 | .333 | .667 | .429 | .055 | .571 |
| 13 | 6 | 1 | 0 | .167 | .833 | .358 | .033 | .643 |
| 14 | 5 | 1 | 0 | .200 | .800 | .286 | .050 | .714 |
| 15 | 4 | 0 | 0 | 0 | 1.000 | .286 | 0 | .714 |
| 16 | 4 | 0 | 0 | 0 | 1.000 | .286 | 0 | .714 |
| 17 | 4 | 0 | 0 | 0 | 1.000 | .286 | 0 | .714 |
| 18 | 4 | 2 | 0 | .500 | .500 | .143 | .250 | .857 |
| 19 | 2 | 0 | 0 | 0 | 1.000 | .143 | 0 | .857 |
| 20 | 2 | 0 | 0 | 0 | 1.000 | .143 | 0 | .857 |

Probability of remission = 85.7%

| | | | | | | | | |
|---|---|---|---|---|---|---|---|---|
| **Patients Remaining off Tricyclics Until Outcome** | | | | | | | | |

| Month | $O_x$ | $d_x$ | $W_x$ | $q_x$ | $p_x$ | $P_x$ | | |
|---|---|---|---|---|---|---|---|---|
| 9 | 28 | | | | | | | |
| 10 | 28 | 3 | 0 | .107 | .893 | .893 | .004 | .107 |
| 11 | 25 | 1 | 0 | .040 | .960 | .857 | .001 | .143 |
| 12 | 24 | 4 | 0 | .167 | .830 | .714 | .008 | .285 |
| 13 | 20 | 0 | 0 | 0 | 1.000 | .714 | 0 | .285 |
| 14 | 20 | 3 | 0 | .150 | .850 | .607 | .008 | .393 |
| 15 | 17 | 4 | 2 | .235 | .764 | .464 | .019 | .536 |
| 16 | 11 | 0 | 0 | 0 | 1.000 | .464 | 0 | .536 |
| 17 | 11 | 3 | 0 | .273 | .727 | .337 | .034 | .663 |
| 18 | 8 | 0 | 0 | 0 | 1.000 | .337 | 0 | .663 |
| 19 | 8 | 0 | 0 | 0 | 1.000 | .337 | 0 | .663 |
| 20 | 8 | 0 | 0 | 0 | 1.000 | .337 | 0 | .663 |

Probability of remission = 66.3%

*Remission = Any 3 consecutive months global illness score of 2 or less.

**Symptoms = Global illness score greater than 2.

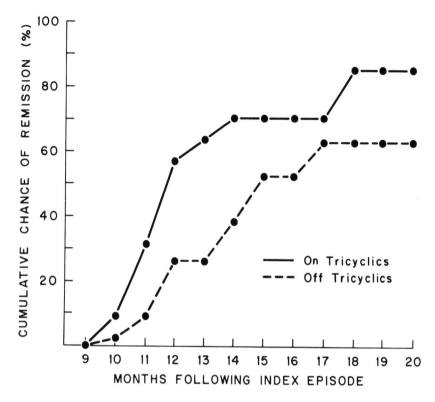

Figure 2
Probability of Remission in Depressed Patients
Who Began the Follow-up With Symptoms

analyses were small and the differences did not reach significance.

The naturalistic data will be explored further in a variety of ways using life tables. The probability of relapse, or recurrence in patients with symptom-free episodes under various treatment conditions will be evaluated. The life table makes it possible to uncover an important sequence in the follow-up. For example, an examination of the data by a cross-sectional approach at the six-month and one-year follow-up showed a significant correlation between use of

tricyclics in the follow-up and the return of symptoms. It
was unclear if symptoms returned in patients who continued
on medication or if medication was received when the patient
had a return of symptoms. The life table clearly showed
that the latter was the case and allowed us to calculate
probability of symptom return as a function of whether the
patient did or did not receive medication up to a point of
symptom return or termination of the observation period.

The life table yields the probability that an event
such as death, relapse, remission will occur in successive
intervals of time (visits, days, months, years) after some
starting point and, conversely, the probability of surviving
each interval. The multiplication of these probabilities of
survival for each time interval for those alive at the
beginning of that interval yields a cumulative probability
of surviving for the total period of study (Mausner & Bahn,
1974). The method has certain requirements. The starting
point and the outcome must be well defined. If a substantial
proportion of the cohort is lost to follow-up, it cannot be
used.

We are impressed with the potential of life tables for
approximating a quasi-experimental condition in the analysis
of data collected naturalistically. This technique could
be applied to ordinary clinic practice with the minor
requirement that systematic information on the outcome
variables be collected at each visit.


## CONCLUSION

Both controlled and naturalistic studies are useful
strategies as long as their limitations are well understood.
Controlled experiments can test the efficacy of different
interventions, but attention must be paid to attrition.
Life tables, end point and survivor analysis should all be
considered and results compared.

Controlled studies for testing risk factors for disease
in humans, while theoretically possible, are ethically
impossible. As pointed out by Mednick and McNeill (1968) in
discussing research on schizophrenics, it is extremely
difficult to construct unequivocal causative statements
without experimental manipulation. Anything else is corre-

lative.  Experimental manipulation is the method of choice
for studying the etiology of disease and for this reason
animal research has been quite important in such disorders
as tuberculosis, lung cancer, poliomyelitis.  There are
limitations to this approach for most psychiatric disorders.
For example, the characteristic disorder of schizophrenics
involves language and thought which are uniquely human
conditions.  Disorders of mood, however, may have their
parallels in certain higher animals and animal research may
provide important information.

     There are alternatives to controlled experimental
studies involving manipulation of risk factors.  These are
naturally occurring experiments which allow testing of
hypotheses about etiological risks.  Natural experiments can
contribute to basic knowledge, and would be impossible to
conduct by plan.  They answer questions which cannot easily
be tested in unselected or broadly based populations because
multiple sources of error obscure associations.  Opportunities
for such natural experiments should be sought and exploited.

     Conventional naturalistic studies, the most typical
kind of research in psychiatry, provide important descriptive
information (a reasonable estimate of what happens to patients).
This information is useful in detecting diagnostic and
clinical changes over time, generating hypotheses and planning
care.  Few risk factors or treatments in psychiatry are
powerful enough to overcome the variances of naturalistic
studies.  However, the life table method which has been used
effectively in assessing survivorship risks in cancer should
be used more frequently in both controlled and naturalistic
psychiatric longitudinal studies.  By this method, information on the effects of treatments may be obtained at regular
clinic follow-up.  If accurate information on the patient's
treatment and clinical status at each visit is recorded, the
probability of relapse or remission or other distinct
outcomes under different conditions, over time, may be
ascertained.  Such a procedure could maximize the data
collected during normal clinical practice and can approximate quasi-experimental conditions.  Neither the naturalistic
nor the controlled experiment is ideal under all conditions
and a healthy skepticism as well as a search for solutions
to their limitations are required.

REFERENCES

Barrett, J., Kuriansky, J., Gurland, B.:  Community tenure
    following emergency discharge.  American Journal of
    Psychiatry, 1969, 128, 945-958.

Campbell, D.T.:  Reforms as experiments.  American Psycholo-
    gist, 1969, 24, 409-429.

Cobb, S., Kasl, S.V., Connelly, W.E.:  The health of people
    changing jobs:  A description of a longitudinal study.
    American Journal of Public Health, 1966, 56, 1476-1481.

Greenwood, M:  The errors of sampling of the survivorship
    tables.  Report on Public Mental Health and Medical
    Subjects #33, Appendix 1, H.M. Stationery Office, London,
    1926.

Kasl, S.V.:  Physical and mental health effects of involun-
    tary relocation and institutionalization on the elderly.
    American Journal of Public Health, 1972, 62, 377-384.

Klerman, G.L., DiMascio, A., Weissman, M., Prusoff, B.,
    Paykel, E.S.:  Treatment of depression by drugs and
    psychotherapy.  American Journal of Psychiatry, 1974,
    131, 186-191.

Lindemann, E.:  Symptomatology and management of acute grief.
    American Journal of Psychiatry, 1944, 101, 141-148.

Mausner, J.S., Bahn, A.K.:  Epidemiology:  An Introductory
    Text.  W.B. Saunders Company, Philadelphia, 1974, pp.
    332-335.

Mednick, S., McNeil, T.:  Current methodology on research on
    the etiology of schizophrenia.  Serious difficulties
    which suggest the use of the high-risk-group method.
    Psychological Bulletin, 1968, 70, 681-693.

Rosenthal, D., Kety, S.S.:  The Transmission of Schizophrenia.
    Pergamon Press, London, 1968.

Weissman, M.F., Prusoff, B.A., Klerman, G.L.:  Drugs and
    psychotherapy in depression revisited:  Issues in the
    analysis of long-term trials.  Psychopharmacology
    Bulletin, 1975, 11, 39-41.

OPEN DISCUSSION

Greenhouse: I don't understand your surprise that these techniques could be applied to naturalistic studies. You can apply any technique you want to naturalistic studies. It's not the question of applicability; it's a question of logic as to the interpretation of meaning of the technique in certain situations. In this particular instance, I certainly would agree that the life table technique seems to be logically appropriate and does seem to work.

Weissman: I think you're quite right, that it should be no surprise, but sometimes you don't think of things right in front of you. Dr. Gerald Klerman suggested we use life table methods for our controlled treatment experiments; Dr. Morton Kramer has applied the life table approach to psychiatric admission rates, and of course it's been used for 30 years with cancer data. But it hasn't been used, I believe, in psychiatric naturalistic studies. I'd be interested in references, because we haven't found any.

Goldberg: What is the relative validity and power of life table approaches compared to other means of looking at data? Certainly you get a result which feels that it might be so, but would you get a more sensitive result, say, with some other method?

Weissman: In the life table, you begin following people at the same point of time, for example in this paper everybody began at the same symptom level, so that you actually select a portion of the sample to look at and to follow longitudinally. Now this has problems; one is that you're only selecting a portion of the sample. The advantage is it summarizes a longitudinal course. When we tried to analyze follow-up study cross-sectionally, e.g., at six months and one year, in a disorder with remissions and relapses, we could not interpret the results. The life table method allowed us to learn something about the course of illness under different conditions. It's not going to be the whole answer.

# THE PSYCHIATRIC CASE REGISTER: A VERSATILE DEVICE FOR THE APPLICATION OF MULTIPLE METHODOLOGICAL APPROACHES

Haroutun M. Babigian and
Dolores Burchell Jones
Department of Psychiatry
University of Rochester Medical Center
300 Crittenden Boulevard
Rochester, New York

The significance of psychiatric case registers as research instruments has been well established. They have been utilized in the planning and evaluation of community mental health services (Gardner, et al., 1964; Miles & Gardner, 1966; Gardner & Babigian, 1966; Gardner, 1967), in epidemiological research (Miles et al., 1964; Babigian & Odoroff, 1969; Babigian, 1970; Pederson et al., 1972; Guggenheim & Babigian, 1974; Pederson et al., 1973; Kendell, et al., 1973) and in clinical research (Babigian, et al., 1965). There has been less focus however, on the research designs that may be employed with register data. Hence, the purpose of this paper is to provide a more complete description of the methodological versatility of the case register has been presented elsewhere (Bahn, 1967; Baldwin, 1970; Wing, 1970; Babigian, 1972; Wing, 1972). Although much of this paper is based on our experience with the Monroe County Psychiatric Case Register, the various research designs below are not specific to it, but can be employed with all similar registers.

The Monroe County Psychiatric Case Register is a longitudinal file of all patients seen in private and public inpatient and outpatient mental health facilities in Monroe County since January 1, 1960. The facilities reporting to the register include a university department of psychiatry with inpatient and ambulatory services; the Rochester Psychiatric Center (formerly the Rochester State Hospital); three community mental health centers; an acute inpatient observation unit; the Veteran's Administration Hospital and outpatient clinic, a children's treatment center; the Monroe County Clinic for Sociolegal Services, and approximately 70 percent of all private practicing psychiatrists. Facilities report patients cared for in their inpatient, outpatient, day treatment, and emergency services separately. The register is described in greater detail by Gardner et al., (1963), Babigian (1972), and Liptzin and Babigian (1972).

Wing (1972) has identified three characteristics of case registers which make them especially important as research instruments. First, the register contains unduplicated counts of the psychiatric contacts of each patient and thus avoids selection biases inherent in data available from one facility. Second, since the register contains information on the population of a particular geographic area, census data can be utilized to calculate rates. For example, the 1973 incidence and prevalence utilization rates per 1,000 by age and race/sex for the Monroe County population presented in Table 1 and 2 show that 2.7 percent of the population in Monroe County received care during 1973. Blacks, especially black males, have higher incidence and prevalence rates of utilization than whites. The age category with the highest incidence rates (15-24) does not vary by race/sex, but there are race/ sex differences in the age group with the highest prevalence rate. Prevalence rates are highest for black and white males aged 15-24, white females 25-44 years old and 35-44 year old black females. Finally, because the data are collected on each patient for every episode of care, the psychiatric history of patients can be determined. Also, because of the manner in which register information is collected, data are not lost because of respondent (patient) noncooperation. Data can be lost, however, if facilities reporting to the register report sporadically or cease reporting entirely. In Monroe County, data has been lost throughout the years because of unreporting by some private psychiatrists. This unreporting increased during 1973.

## NATURALISTIC STUDIES

There are two types of naturalistic studies; cross-sectional and longitudinal. These approaches have been frequently employed in psychiatric research. Basically, they

Table 1

1973 Incidence Rates by Age and Race/Sex*

|  | 0-14 | 15-24 | 25-34 | 35-44 | 45-54 | 55-64 | 65+ | Total |
|---|---|---|---|---|---|---|---|---|
| White Male | 669 | 714 | 406 | 257 | 179 | 108 | 96 | 2429 |
| Rate | 7.02 | 12.84 | 9.62 | 7.08 | 4.73 | 3.78 | 3.58 | 7.53 |
| White Female | 332 | 761 | 512 | 294 | 231 | 124 | 167 | 2421 |
| Rate | 3.66 | 12.53 | 11.86 | 7.86 | 5.53 | 3.87 | 4.06 | 6.98 |
| Non-White Male | 105 | 148 | 79 | 52 | 33 | 7 | 6 | 430 |
| Rate | 9.17 | 33.35 | 20.50 | 18.19 | 17.69 | 7.04 | 8.68 | 16.44 |
| Non-White Female | 79 | 135 | 71 | 49 | 15 | 7 | 6 | 362 |
| Rate | 6.94 | 23.82 | 15.62 | 16.06 | 7.92 | 6.48 | 7.26 | 12.72 |
| Total | 1185 | 1758 | 1068 | 652 | 458 | 246 | 275 | 5642 |
| Rate | 5.65 | 13.90 | 11.39 | 8.19 | 5.49 | 3.92 | 3.96 | 7.79 |

* All rates are adjusted per 1,000 Monroe County (1973) population.

Table 2

1973 Prevalence Rates by Age and Race/Sex*

|  | 0-14 | 15-24 | 25-34 | 35-44 | 45-54 | 55-64 | 65+ | Total |
|---|---|---|---|---|---|---|---|---|
| White Male | 1730 | 2097 | 1430 | 1234 | 1076 | 606 | 392 | 8565 |
| Rate | 18.16 | 37.71 | 33.89 | 34.00 | 28.44 | 21.20 | 14.63 | 26.55 |
| White Female | 762 | 1863 | 1710 | 1442 | 1131 | 682 | 701 | 8291 |
| Rate | 8.40 | 30.67 | 39.61 | 38.55 | 27.07 | 21.29 | 17.04 | 23.90 |
| Non-White Male | 306 | 387 | 296 | 234 | 149 | 55 | 19 | 1446 |
| Rate | 26.72 | 87.21 | 76.82 | 81.84 | 79.86 | 55.30 | 27.49 | 55.28 |
| Non-White Female | 173 | 358 | 256 | 233 | 84 | 33 | 26 | 1163 |
| Rate | 15.19 | 63.17 | 56.33 | 76.35 | 44.34 | 30.55 | 31.45 | 40.87 |
| Total | 2971 | 4705 | 3692 | 3143 | 2440 | 1376 | 1138 | 19465 |
| Rate | 14.16 | 37.21 | 39.38 | 39.48 | 29.26 | 21.95 | 16.39 | 26.88 |

* All rates are adjusted per 1,000 Monroe County (1973) population.

produce descriptive material regarding the flow of patients
through the various psychiatric facilities, diagnostic changes
over time and changes in the population receiving psychiatric
services. Since it is rarely possible to study the entire
population of interest, researchers must indirectly study
the universe in which they are interested through sampling.
With this procedure, there is always uncertainty over whether
the sample drawn is a representative one. This problem is not
as serious for users of register data, for almost every
psychiatric contact is reported. The register can then, for
all practical purposes, be considered a population; one
which is geographically defined - in this case Monroe County
residents - and which is distinguished by some common behavior
or experience; namely, contact with a psychiatric facility.

The cross-sectional design involves the collection of
data at one specific point in time and is utilized to determine the characteristics of a population or of selected subgroups. This approach was used by Gardner et al. (1963) to
describe the first year's psychiatric experience in Monroe
County. They found that about 17 persons per 1,000 population
were psychiatric patients during 1960, sixty-one percent
of whom were given a diagnosis of either schizophrenic reaction,
affective psychosis, or chronic brain syndrome. They also
noted that admission rates were generally higher for men than
women and for nonwhites than for whites. While the population
selected for this study consisted of individuals receiving
psychiatric care during a specified time interval, subpopulations can be selected on the basis of diagnosis, age, race,
sex, or any other variable contained in the register. For
example, diagnosis was used by Guggenheim and Babigian (1974)
as the basis for selection of their subpopulations of all
patients ever to receive a diagnosis of catatonic schizophrenia
from 1960-1966. The relationship between this diagnostic en-
tity and sex, socioeconomic status and relative risk of death
was investigated, as well as length of admission and diagnostic outcome. They found that more women than men were diagnosed as catatonic when compared to the register schizophrenics and that the age-adjusted rates for those consistently
diagnosed as catatonic were much higher in the lower socioeconomic classes. They also discovered that the catatonic
cohort's relative risk of death was 2.6 to 3.6 times greater
than in the age-adjusted county population. Guggenheim and
Babigian's study also illustrates the register's function of
preserving history for the researcher. By recording each
individual's psychiatric contacts, past and present, the

opportunity to investigate particular subpopulations is not
lost with the passage of time.

The psychiatric case register can also be used to conduct longitudinal research. Traditionally, this type of
naturalistic study involves the collection of data at successive points in time. Data obtained in this manner are used
to make comparisons of total populations as well as comparisons of selected subgroups within the total. A longitudinal
study was conducted using register data in which one-day prevalence rates were analyzed for October 1, 1961, 1966, and
1972 (1976). By comparing these three days, information can
be obtained on changes in prevalence rates for various psychiatric disorders by age, race/sex, and treatment modality
(inpatient or outpatient) over the twelve year period. There
are two advantages in utilizing the register to carry out a
longitudinal study. First, since the register contains data
that have been continuously gathered over a period of years,
it permits the researcher greater flexibility in specifying
the particular time frames he wishes to examine. Second,
since the data have already been collected and are immediately
available, the time and expense involved in conducting research
are significantly reduced.

The panel design is another longitudinal technique which
can also be applied to register data. In this approach, the
same subjects are interviewed or measured successively over
an extended period. Because the register contains the psychiatric history of patients, a researcher can use it to
follow or measure repeatedly a population or subpopulation
in which he is interested. In the usual panel design, measurements are obtained at what the researcher considers theoretically relevant intervals. However, when applied to register
data, this approach is limited by the investigator's inability
to control the scheduling of the data collection process.
That is, the investigator can control neither when the first
measurement (first psychiatric contact) will be taken nor
the interval between measurements (succeeding contacts).
However, register data do permit measurement of the same
individuals at different points in time. The panel design
was applied to register data by Babigian, et al. (1965) in
their study of diagnostic consistency. The subpopulation of
interest was comprised of those whose first lifetime psychiatric contact occurred between January 1, 1961 and December 31,
1962. Initial diagnoses (first measurement) were then com-

pared with the diagnoses received as patients were seen in subsequent episodes of care (repeated measurements). This study revealed that while chronic brain syndrome and schizophrenia were the diagnoses given with the greatest consistency, least consistency was found with the affective psychoses. Troublesome patients with repeated contacts were eventually diagnosed schizophrenic and admitted to the state hospital. In a future panel study, we plan to follow patients for a period of ten years after their first hospitalization in 1962. The advantage of employing register data to conduct a panel study is again the reduction in time and expense. In addition, attrition can only occur through death on outmigration rather than through refusal to continue participating the study.

From the previous discussion, it is evident that register data can be quite useful in conducting naturalistic studies. Populations and population subgroups existing at a specified time may be described using cross-sectional research, while longitudinal designs can be employed to describe variations in population characteristics or in the utilization of facilities over time. Panel studies can also be conducted to examine the changes that occur over time in the same group of people. These techniques are helpful in determining incidence, prevalence, and readmission rates, utilization patterns of psychiatric facilities, and characteristics of the population served, as well as information relevant to numerous other problems.

## NATURAL EXPERIMENTS

Campbell and Stanley in Experimental and Quasi-Experimental Designs for Research (1963) have attempted to deal with the peculiar problems social scientists have in securing adequate and proper data. Some of the quasi-experimental designs discussed in their book can be adapted for use with register data.

Natural experiments exist when planned or unplanned conditions or events occur and are so discrete that they can be considered as experimental treatments applied at a particular time to a specific population. In these instances, "the individual's exposure to such events takes place with a minimum of self selection, and adequate comparison groups can be found who have not been exposed to the events" (Weissman,

1975, p. 5). Natural experiments differ from true experiments in that the experimenter has limited control over selecting the people to whom the treatment will be administered,
where it will be administered and when. Because of these
limitations, the results obtained from quasi-experiments are
usually open to conflicting interpretations. However, the
time series design, the nonequivalent control group design
and the multiple time series design adequately control many
of the extraneous variables that can render an experiment
worthless.

One way to help determine the impact of planned or unplanned events on the mental health of a population is to
conduct a quasi-experiment using a time series design.
Utilizing register data, a series of measurements $(0_1$-$0_8)$ or
rates can be calculated for some group before and after the
occurrence of a particular event or treatment $(X)$. The
schematic representation of the design is as follows:

$$0_1 \ 0_2 \ 0_3 \ 0_4 \ X \ 0_5 \ 0_6 \ 0_7 \ 0_8$$

If the difference between $0_4$ and $0_5$ is larger than the difference between any other two pairs of measurements, it may
tentatively be concluded that X has had an effect. Ordinarily, there are two serious problems with this design - its
inability to control the events occurring between measurements (history) and its inability to control the possible
interaction of the measurement scheme and the event of interest (the interaction of testing and X). The advantage of
applying the time series design to register data is that although it cannot ensure that some more or less simultaneous
event did not produce an experimental gain, it eliminates the
interaction of testing and X as a factor jeopardizing external
validity. Because respondents (patients) are not given pre-
tests per se, they cannot be sensitized to the experimental
variable, thus making the results obtained generalizable to
the unpretested population. This design was one of those
used in Babigian's study (in press) of the impact of the
establishment of community mental health centers on the patterns of utilization of services. By comparing data obtained
for the years 1963 through 1973, it was possible to show that
after the establishment of two centers, one in 1967 and the
other in 1968, the incidence and prevalence rates of utilization increased in the catchment areas where these centers
were located.

A nonequivalent control group design is another methodological approach that can be employed using register data
and is diagrammed as follows:

$$\frac{O}{O} \; X \; \frac{O}{O}$$

This design involves an experimental and control group both
of which (1) are administered a pre- and post-test and (2)
are naturally assembled collectives and as such do not have
pre-experimental equivalence. The assignment of X is assumed
to be random and under the experimenter's control (Campbell
& Stanley, 1963, p. 47). This assumption cannot be made
when dealing with register data since the events (treatments)
and people we study through the register are not easily
manipulated. However, this design could still be very
useful especially when the experimental and control groups
are quite similar. Indeed, the greater the similarity, the
more effective this design becomes in controlling the main
effects of extraneous variables that might jeopardize the
validity of the experiment (history, maturation, testing and
instrumentation). When using register data, the nonequivalent
control group design also minimizes the interaction of
testing and X for the reason noted above in the discussion
of the time series design. In addition, the unwanted effect
produced by the interaction of testing and the selection of
subjects is decreased because register data are not obtained
through the administration of tests. The remaining threat
to the validity of this quasi-experimental design comes from
the interaction between differences in the selection of
subjects for the experimental and control groups and history
and maturation (Campbell & Stanley, 1963, p. 48). This
design has not been applied to the register. But, it could,
for example, be helpful in evaluating mental health projects
in schools, mental health services to catchment areas and
programs for alcoholics in industry by comparing the number
of individuals from two similar units appearing in the
register before and at some period after the experimental
treatment (new program or service) has been given to one of
the two units.

One of the best quasi experiments is the multiple time
series design. This design:

$$\frac{O_1}{O_1} \; \frac{O_2}{O_2} \; \frac{O_3}{O_3} \; \frac{O_4}{O_4} \; X \; \frac{O_5}{O_5} \; \frac{O_6}{O_6} \; \frac{O_7}{O_7} \; \frac{O_8}{O_8}$$

contains within it the two designs discussed above and consequently, possesses the merits associated with both.  It
gains superiority from the certainty with which its results
can be interpreted.  Multiple measurements permit the effect
of the treatment to be demonstrated twice - against the control group and against the pre-treatment values in its own
series.  The multiple time series design is particularly
appropriate when there is an availability of repeated measurements obtained in a non-reactive setting (Campbell & Stanley,
1963, pp. 55-57).

    Register data not only meet these two criteria but also
when employed in a multiple time series design greatly reduce this design's two troublesome weaknesses - the inability
to control for the interaction of testing and X and the inability to control for the possible interaction of the selection of subjects and the event of interest (the limitation
of the effects of the experimental variable to that specific
sample).  Because data are not gathered from tests administered to patients, patients' reactions to an experimental
variable cannot become confused with the effect of a previously administered test.  The interaction of the selection
of subjects and X is reduced because the register contains
data on almost every patient who has received psychiatric
care in Monroe County since 1960.  This lack of bias means
that the effect of the experimental variable (X) can be
generalized to other areas like Monroe County.  The interaction of the selection of subjects and X may become a problem however, if patients are given the right to determine
the disposition of their psychiatric records.  In that case,
the results obtained might be valid only for the group studied
because those patients allowing their records to be used
would probably differ in important respects from those who
refused.  And, as a result, their reaction to the experimental variable may be unique and thus be of limited value in
generalizing to a wider population.  This design was also
employed in Babigian's previously mentioned study of the establishment of community mental health centers (in press).
In 1965, Monroe County, New York was divided into four
catchment areas, each area including urban, suburban, and
rural sections.  Figure 1 presents a map of the county's
four catchment areas: A, B, C, and D and the location of the
community mental health centers.  Although there were adequate mental health facilities in the county prior to 1967,
community mental health centers had not yet been established.

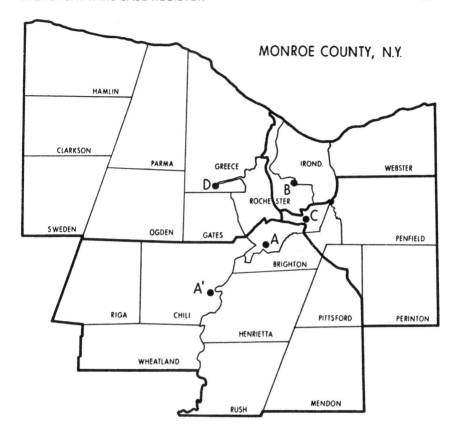

Figure 1

Community Mental Health Centers in Monroe County, New York

A = University of Rochester Community Mental Health Center

$A^1$ = The Convalescent Hospital for Children

B = Rochester Mental Health Center

C = Genesee Hospital Mental Health Center

D = Park Ridge Hospital Community Mental Health Center

Since 1967, the University of Rochester Community Mental
Health Center and Convalescent Hospital for Children in
Catchment Area A (population 180,196/per 1970 census) and
the Rochester Mental Health Center in Catchment Area B
(population 146,963) were developed to serve approximately
one-half the county population. The other half of the
county's population in Catchment Area C (population 146,963)
and D (population 208,704) continued without centers. The
Genesee Hospital Mental Health Center (Catchment Area C) and
the Park Ridge Hospital Community Mental Health Area (Catchment Area D) began operation in 1973 and 1975 respectively.

The multiple time series design was used to evaluate
the impact of these centers on the utilization of services.
Incidence and prevalence utilization rates were obtained for
each catchment area from 1963 to 1973. The rates in the
areas with centers were compared to the incidence and
prevalence utilization rates in the areas without them.
(See Figures 2 and 3. Contrasting catchment area A with C
and catchment area B with D demonstrated that the incidence
and prevalence of utilization was low in B and D - areas
which contained the fewest mental health services - before
1967. After the establishment of one community mental
health center in catchment area A (1968) and the other in
catchment area B (1967), the incidence and prevalence
utilization rates for these two areas rapidly increased
relative not only to their own rates prior to the opening of
the community mental health centers but also relative to the
rates of catchment areas C and D. By using the multiple
time series design, it was possible in this way to show that
the establishment of community mental health centers did
have an effect on the utilization of mental health services.

Although there are other quasi experimental designs,
the three discussed above seem most appropriately applied to
case register data. Basically, these designs consist of
comparing pre- and post-treatment measures to determine if
there has been a post-treatment gain in the experimental
group. The time series, the non-equivalent control group
design and the multiple time series design can be used to
study the impact of new policies, programs, and facilities.

These designs have been employed for several years in
evaluation research. Perhaps this discussion will increase
their application to other questions that might be addressed
using register data.

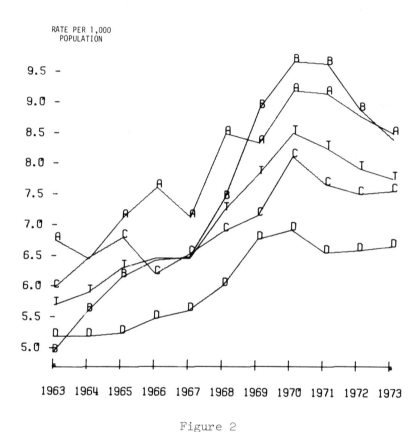

Figure 2

Rates of first lifetime psychiatric contacts for
Monroe County by year and catchment area

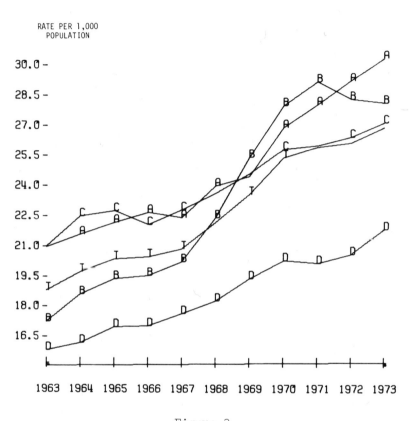

Figure 3

Prevalence rates of psychiatric contacts for Monroe County
by year and catchment area

## ADDITIONAL ADVANTAGES

In addition to its methodological versatility, the psychiatric case register can be of assistance in the initial phase of the research process, in record matching, and in determining the accuracy of diagnoses made in the field.

As Bahn (1967) has suggested, the register can be used in the initial phase of the research process as a sampling frame for in-depth studies. This service is especially useful in psychiatric research since the population of interest is generally not readily identifiable. The Monroe County Psychiatric Case Register was used for this purpose by Hetznecker et al. (1966) to provide a sampling base for a follow-up study of schizophrenic and nonpsychotic males. Pederson et al. (in preparation) interviewed representative samples of psychotically depressed patients to determine their level of functioning and degree of pathology. The Camberwell Register has also been used as a sampling frame for more intensive studies. Dawson (1972) used that register to select a sample of patients admitted under order to investigate the reasons for compulsory admission. Wing (1972) also employed the Camberwell Register to select a sample for the evaluation of the industrial rehabilitation of chronic psychotic patients. Although sampling frames could be obtained from the records of the psychiatric facilities themselves, they would not be as accurate or as unbiased as those provided by the register. Thus, by utilizing the register, selection of the sample can be done more adequately, more efficiently, and with less effort.

Medical, death, police, and welfare records can be matched with register data to increase the number of questions that can be dealt with concerning the etiology, course and outcome of particular disorders, as well as the impact of various community and mental health programs. Cowen et al. (1973) traced the subsequent psychiatric histories, as recorded in the Monroe County Psychiatric Case Register, of individuals who as children in 1950-1961 were participants in the Primary Mental Health Project. They found that children who had been identified as vulnerable later had a disproportionately large number of entries in the psychiatric register. In another study (Babigian & Odoroff, 1969), death certificates of Monroe County residents provided by

the New York State Department of Health were compared to the
register, and the death data for each registered individual
were recorded. They discovered that the relative risk of
death for the register population was more than two times
higher than for the general population for both sexes and
for all causes of death except neoplasms. Even after eliminating the groups known to have high mortality rates, the
relative risk of death still remained 1.5 to 2 times that of
the general population. Thus, the use of register data in
conjunction with information available from other sources
can greatly increase the breadth and depth with which various
questions can be investigated.

Finally, the register can be used to make partial
checks on the accuracy of diagnoses made in the field. That
is, if registers are available it would be possible to see
how many individuals diagnosed as "normal" in field studies,
such as the midtown Manhattan study (Srole, et al., 1962)
appeared in the register. Conversely, we can get an estimate
of untreated mental disorders by seeing how many people
diagnosed as "abnormal" in the field do not appear in the
register. (This might also be an estimate of over-diagnosis).
We can also match specific diagnoses made in the field with
the diagnoses of those who are recorded in the register as
another approach to the study of diagnostic consistency.

The case register is a valuable instrument in the field
of psychiatric research. Its advantages to investigators
include an unbiased study population, unduplicated counts of
psychiatric contacts, longitudinal information on each
patient, immediately useable data and a reduction in the
cost and time involved in conducting research. However,
before interest can be generated in the register as a data
source, potential researchers must have some idea how it can
be manipulated. We have discussed several types of natural
studies that can be applied to register data. These include
cross sectional, longitudinal, and panel approaches, as well
as natural or quasi experimental designs. Perhaps this
paper, which has emphasized the methodological versatility
of the psychiatric case register, will stimulate even more
research utilizing this source of data.

REFERENCES

Babigian, H.M., Gardner, E.A., Miles, H.C., and Romano, J. Diagnostic consistency and change in a follow-up study of 1215 patients. American Journal of Psychiatry, 1965, 121, 895-901.

Babigian, and Odoroff, C.L. The mortality experience of a population with psychiatric illness. American Journal of Psychiatry, 1969, 126, 470-480.

Babigian, H.M. Schizophrenia in Monroe County. Paper read at "Schizophrenia - The Implications of Research Findings for Treatment and Teaching," a conference sponsored by the National Institute of Mental Health and John E. Fogarty International Center, National Institutes of Health, May 31, June 1 and 2, 1970.

Babigian, H.M. The role of psychiatric case registers in the longitudinal study of psychopathology. In M. Roff, L. Robins, and M. Pollack (Eds.), Life history research in psychopathology, Volume 2. Minnesota: University of Minnesota Press, 1972, pp. 155-169.

Babigian, H.M., and Jones, D.B. Variations in one-day prevalence over 12 years. Paper read at the Annual Meeting of the American Psychiatric Association, Miami, Florida. May 10-14, 1976.

Babigian, H.M. The impact of community mental health centers on the utilization of services. Archives of General Psychiatry, submitted for publication.

Bahn, A.K. Research tools for planning and evalution. In R.H. Williams and L.D. Ozarin (Eds.), Community mental health: An international perspective. San Francisco: Jossey-Bass, Inc., 1967, pp. 292-304.

Baldwin, J.A. Discussion. In E.D. Hare and J.K. Wing (Eds.), Psychiatric epidemiology: Proceedings of the international symposium held at Aberdeen University, July 22-25, 1969. New York: Oxford University Press, 1970, pp. 273-275.

Campbell, D.T., and Stanley, J.C. Experimental and quasi-experimental designs for research. Chicago: Rand McNally, 1963.

Cowen, E.L., Pederson, A.,.., Babigian, H.M., Izzo, L., and
    Trost, M.A.  Long-term follow up of early detected vul-
    nerable children.  Journal of Consulting and Clinical
    Psychology, 1973, 41, 438-446.

Dawson, H.  Reasons for compulsory admission.  In J.K. Wing
    and A.M. Hailey (Eds.), Evaluating a community psychiat-
    ric service:  The Camberwell Register 1964-1971.  Oxford:
    Oxford University Press, 1972, pp. 221-231.

Gardner, E.A., Miles, H.C., Iker, H.P., and Romano, J.  A
    cumulative register of psychiatric services in a commu-
    nity.  American Journal of Public Health, 1963, 35,
    1269-1277.

Gardner, E.A., Miles, H.C., Bahn, A.K., and Romano, J.  All
    psychiatric experience in a community.  Archives of
    General Psychiatry, 1963, 9, 369-378.

Gardner, E.A., Bahn, A.K., and Miles, H.C.  Patient exper-
    ience in psychiatric units of general and state mental
    hospitals.  Public Health Reports, 1964, 79, 755-767.

Gardner, E.A., and Babigian, H.M.  A longitudinal comparison
    of psychiatric service.  American Journal of Ortho-
    psychiatry, 1966, 36, 818-828.

Gardner, E.A.  The use of a psychiatric case register in the
    planning and evaluation of a mental health program.
    In R.R. Monroe, G.D. Klee, and E.B. Brody (Eds.),
    Psychiatric epidemiology and mental health planning.
    Washington, D.C.:  American Psychiatric Association,
    1967, pp. 258-281.

Guggenheim, F.G., and Babigian, H.M.  Catatonic schizophrenia:
    epidemiology and clinical course.  Journal of Nervous
    and Mental Disease, 1974, 158, 291-305.

Hetznecker, W., Gardner, E.A., Odoroff, C.L., and Turner,
    R.J.  Field survey methods in psychiatry.  Archives
    of General Psychiatry, 1966, 15, 427-438.

Kendell, R.E., Hall, D.J., Hailey, A., and Babigian, H.M.
    The epidemiology of anorexia nervosa.  Psychological
    Medicine, 1973, 3, 200-203.

Liptzin, B., and Babigian, H.M.  Ten years experience with a cumulative psychiatric patient register.  Methods of Information in Medicine, 1971, 11, 238-242.

Miles, H.C., Gardner, E.A., Bodian C., and Romano, J.  A cumulative survey of all psychiatric experience in Monroe County, New York:  Summary data for the first year (1960).  Psychiatric Quarterly, 1964, 38, 458-487.

Miles, H.C., and Gardner, E.A.  A psychiatric case register. Archives of General Psychiatry, 1966, 14, 571-580.

Pederson, A.M., Barry, D.J., and Babigian, H.M.  Epidemiological considerations of psychotic depression.  Archives of General Psychiatry, 1972, 27, 193-197.

Pederson, A.M., Awad, G.A., and Kindler, A.R.  Epidemiological differences between white and nonwhite suicide attempters. American Journal of Psychiatry, 1973, 130, 1071-1076.

Pederson, A.M., Babigian, H.M., and Barry, D.J.  Follow-up of 569 psychotically depressed patients, in preparation.

Srole, L., Langner, T.S., Michael, S.T., Opler, M.K., and Rennic, T.A.C.  Mental health in the metropolis:  The Midtown Manhatten study.  New York: McGraw Hill, 1962.

Weissman, M.M.  Controlled vs. naturalistic experiments: Advantages, limitations and overlaps.  Paper read at the Conference of the Society for Life History Research in Psychopathology, University of Rochester School of Medicine and Dentistry, Rochester, New York, May 21-23, 1975.

Wing, J.K.  Principles of evaluation.  In J.K. Wing and A.M. Hailey (Eds.), Evaluating a community psychiatric service: The Camberwell Register, 1964-1971.  Oxford: Oxford University Press, 1972, pp, 11-39.

Wing, L.  Discussion.  In E.H. Hare and J.K. Wing (Eds.), Psychiatric epidemiology:  Proceedings of the international symposium held at Aberdeen University, July 22-25, 1969.  New York: Oxford University Press, 1970, pp. 275-268.

Wing, J.K.    An epidemiological and experimental evaluation o
    the industrial rehabilitation of chronic psychotic
    patients in the community.  In J.K. Wing and A.M. Hailey
    (Eds).  Evaluating a community psychiatric service:  The
    Camberwell Register 1964-1971.  New York: Oxford Univ-
    ersity Press, 1972, pp. 283-308.

## OPEN DISCUSSION

Robins:  Have you tried to use the register as a sampling base?  Have you used it to pick a sample which you
then go out and interview or anything of that sort?

Babigian:  Yes.  For example, one study was done in
the mid-sixties by Cumming, Gardner, Turner and Hetznecker.
They identified a population that had been admitted with
the diagnosis of schizophrenia, and then three years later
interviewed them in detail using various evaluative instruments.  They also had a control sample of non-schizophrenic-
psychotic, and non-psychotic individuals.  There have been
other studies, too.

Robins:  The thing that concerns me is whether you can
still do that?  What would you say if someone asked how did
you get my name?

Babigian:  No, we cannot undertake such studies now
because of the complicated issues of informed consent and
confidentiality at this time.

# A SURVEY OF ISSUES RELATED TO THE ANALYSIS OF OBSERVATIONAL DATA IN LONGITUDINAL RESEARCH

John E. Overall
The University of Texas Medical Branch
Galveston, Texas

The primary problems in analysis of data from longitudinal studies arise from the fact the such studies most frequently involve naturally occurring groups, or samples of convenience, rather than random assignment and other features of good experimental design. This fact results in numerous possibly confounded effects that must be disentangled in analysis of the data. Because groups may differ initially on the measures that are to be the basis for evaluation of change, the particular index chosen to define change is more critical than in experimental studies. In this brief discussion, an attempt will be made to survey some of the more controversial issues related to definition of change and the statistical control over a variety of possibly confounding factors in observational type research.

## MEASUREMENT OF CHANGE

The problem of defining an appropriate index of change is especially important in observational type research where significant group differences are likely to be present at the initial or baseline evaluation. In this section, several alternative indices of change will be enumerated primarily to emphasize their essential similarities with regard to the problems that have caused concern in longitudinal research. In considering alternative definitions of change, "longitudinal research" will be conceived to include simple two-point comparisons as well as the evaluation of trends across multiple time periods.

The first point to be made is that <u>all</u> measures of change
involve some type of weighted or unweighted difference scores
The simple pre-post difference score is perhaps the best known
index of change.

$$D = X_1 - X_2$$

or

$$D = X_2 - X_1$$

The use of simple difference scores to measure change has
often been criticized on the grounds that errors of measurement are additive and, thus, difference scores are less
reliable than the original measurements (Webster & Bereiter,
1963). What is frequently not recognized is that this has
no relevance for comparisons of treatment effects or other
group differences. The power of tests of significance is
actually maximum when the reliability of difference scores,
upon which all calculations are based, is zero (Overall &
Woodward, 1975, 1976).

A frequently used alternative definition of change results from the analysis of covariance in which outcome scores
are adjusted statistically to be independent of the baseline
scores. It is sometimes not recognized that the analysis
of covariance is an analysis of weighted difference scores
of the type

$$X_2 = X_2 - bX_1,$$

where b is the coefficient of linear regression relating the
outcome measures to the baseline scores. In fact, if one
knew the true population regression function <u>a priori</u>, the
analysis of covariance could actually be calculated as an
analysis of variance of weighted difference scores (Cochran,
1957). The analysis of weighted difference scores obviously
involves no assumption that the "covariate" is measured without error.

The conception of analysis of covariance as the analysis
of weighted difference scores suggest a whole class of
indices that involve <u>a priori</u> weighted difference scores.
For example, in clinical psychopharmacology research it has

been found repeatedly that ratings of symptom severity tend to be reduced about 50 percent in a short course of drug treatment. Particularly in small sample studies, it may be more appropriate to consider an a priori weighted differ- ence score. Many interesting possibilities exist for using clinical knowledge to provide a predicted outcome for each individual subject. The analysis of covariance and related analyses of weighted difference scores can be conceived as analyses of "deviations about expected outcome."

Concern has been expressed by several writers over im- plications of a "regression toward the mean" phenomenon in the analysis of covariance. It is a well-known fact that individuals with extreme scores on one occasion will tend to have scores closer to their group mean on a second occasion, even though no treatment or other factors produces the change. Formulae presented by Lord (1963), McNemar (1958), and Davis (1961), lead to definition of a weighted difference score that represents an estimate of true change for an individual based on fallible observed scores.

It is not really clear when the attenuation correction should be applied however. As will be discussed, the analysis of covariance is not biased by the presence of measurement error in the concommitant variable. Certain authors who have been most critical of the analysis of covariance with regard to that problem have based their conclusions on Monte Carlo demonstrations in which the covariate was systematically in- fluenced by the factor being evaluated for effect (Campbell & Erlebacher, 1970). They thus erroneously attributed the biases in estimates of change to problems arising from measurement error, when in fact their poor results were due to the fact that the covariate was systematically affected by the treatments or group differences. The analysis of covariance involves a number of complex issues, and it is important to separate them in order to understand what the method can and cannot achieve with regard to controlling for initial differences between groups.

The analysis of covariance (ANCOVA) is so complex and has been so criticized in the psychological literature that an entire volume could easily be devoted to discussion of issues related to that technique alone. Overall and Woodward (1975) recently attempted to survey conditions under which ANCOVA should and should not be preferred as a method of adjusting for initial or baseline differences. The following conclusions appear warranted, accepting validity of the assumptions of linearity and homogeneity of regression.

The ANCOVA does not require that covariates be measured without error as implied by numerous writers (Lord, 1963; Kahneman, 1965; Lubin, 1965; Evans and Anastasio, 1968; Campbell & Erlebacher, 1970). Given random assignment to treatments or nonrandom assignment that is probabilistically contingent on the observed covariate scores, ANCOVA will provide unbiased estimates of true treatment effects irrespective of measurement error in the concommitant variable. That tests of significance are unbiased in the presence of measurement error in concommitant variables is evident in the "residual F-test" procedure discussed by Roy and Bargmann (1958), which is precisely equivalent to ANCOVA. Given nonrandom assignment that is dependent, not on observed covariat scores, but on the true component only, simple change scores provide unbiased estimates of true treatment effects and ANCOVA provides biased estimates. Where "treatments" are actually intact groups measured on the same variables across multiple time periods, simple change scores (or successive differences) provide unbiased estimates of the true difference in trends and ANCOVA provides biased estimates. Thus, whether ANCOVA or simple difference scores should be used to define effects in longitudinal research is a decision that depends upon the conditions under which groups to be compared were constituted. Except in experimental and some types of pseudo experimental research, where nonrandom assignment depends on both true and error components in the baseline measures, ANCOVA is not considered to be the most appropriate correction for baseline differences.

Although the discussion to this point has focused on the measurement of change in simple pre-post comparisons, the analysis of trends across multiple observation periods also involves consideration of weighted difference scores or contrast functions. For example, the linear trend across six equally spaced observation periods can be represented by a single composite score of the following type:

$$Y = 5X_1 + 3X_2 + 1X_3 - 1X_4 - 3X_5 - 5X_6$$

It is easy to appreciate that scores $X_1, X_2, \ldots, X_6$, which manifest a linear decline from first to last, will result in large positive values for Y. Similarly, scores that have a linear ascending trend will results in large negative

values for Y. As is well known, orthogonal polynomial coefficients can be used to represent various additional curvi-
linear trend components. The point emphasized here is that
the trend components are actually equivalent to weighted
difference scores, although this fact may not be obvious in
some computational procedures used for "trend analysis."

   If the shape of a complex non-linear trend can be anticipated in advance, it is possible to define a set of weighting coefficients to represent that trend irrespective of its
form. This can have substantial advantage from point of view
of power of tests of significance as compared with the more
frequent approach of using multiple orthogonal polynomial
components to represent the a priori trend.

   In comparing trends across time for two groups, the
trend weighting coefficients should be chosen to maximize
the difference in mean trend scores. For example, suppose
that a mathematical model or prior empirical data suggest the
likelihood of two groups having trends of the forms shown in
Figure 1. The difference between the complex nonlinear
curves is shown in Figure 2. Suppose that each of a number
of subjects in each group is measured seven times at the
points indicated in Figure 2. The coefficients for the
weighted contrast that should account for most of the a
priori anticipated differences between the two experimental
groups can be obtained by measuring the height of the difference curve at the various observation points and then subtracting out the mean to yield coefficients that sum to zero.
In this example, the nonlinear function, which on a priori
grounds should be maximally sensitive to differences between
the two groups, is of the form

$$Y = -8X_1 - 1X_2 + 6X_3 + 7X_4 + 6X_5 - 1X_6 - 8X_7$$

This single composite variable can be calculated for each
subject from his seven original scores and a simple t-test
or equivalent ANOVA can be used to evaluate the significance
of the hypothesized difference in trends for the two groups.
Again, the detailed example is provided, not so much for the
purpose of showing how the trend analysis should be accom-
plished, but to emphasize the fact that change in multiple
repeated measurements is always defined as some type of
weighted difference score. The actual conversion of repeated
measures to a single composite trend score also lays the

foundation for recognition that no assumption concerning
uniformity of correlations among the repeated measures is
required.

There are other convenient computational methods for
testing hypotheses concerning trends. The weighting coefficients (whether linear, orthogonal polynomial, or complex a priori trend functions) can be entered as dummy vari-
ates (covariates) in a general linear regression analysis.
The variance accounted for by the trend function (dummy
variate) can be tested for significance, and the residual
difference in time-period means after the a priori trend
has been partialled out can be tested for significance to
evaluate "goodness of fit" of the model. The analysis of
repeated measurement designs by the general linear regression
method is discussed by Woodward and Overall (1976) for both
single and multiple dependent variables.

One of the most controversial issues in the analysis of
repeated measurement data concerns the effect of differential serial correlations among the measurements over time
(Gaito & Wiley, 1963). The agricultural spit-plot design,
which is the basis for most univariate analyses of variance
for repeated measurements in behavioral sciences, involves
an assumption that the correlations among observations for
all pairs of time periods are equal. On the other hand, the
transformation of repeated measurements to a priori weighted
contrast functions to be analyzed as a simple randomized
design with one (trend) observation per subject does not imply
such an assumption, although the optimal nature of the contrast functions with regard to discriminating different
group trends does depend to some extent on the pattern of
correlations.

Numerous authors have proposed the use of multivariate
tests rather than univariate tests for repeated-measurement
designs (Bock, 1963). The p repeated measurements can be
treated as p correlated dependent variables in a multivariate
analyses, and this obviates any problem concerning differentia
correlations among scores separated by different periods of
time. If all p original measurements are included as dependent variables, the test is sensitive to average differences
in elevation as well as trends. Morrison (1967, pp. 141-145)
suggests analysis of the p-1 successive difference scores as
dependent variables in a multivariate analysis of variance,

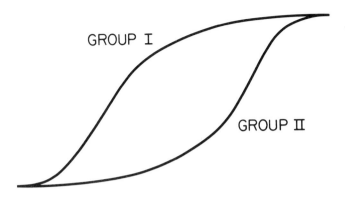

Figure 1

Curves representing anticipated growth trends for two groups.

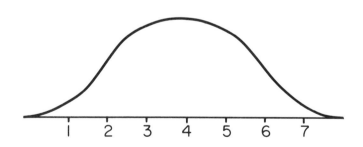

Figure 2

Curve representing the difference in anticipated
growth trends for two groups

or multivariate $T^2$ in the case of two groups. This approach
has the advantage of subtracting out the average elevation
factor and thus being sensitive only to trend effects. Overa
and Klett (1972, pp. 313-314) have discussed reducing the p
original measurements to a set of a priori trend scores representing linear, quadratic, and cubic components and then
analyzing those major trend components as multiple dependent
variables. If there are several observation periods in a
longitudinal study, the transformation of data to a small
number of major trend components prior to multivariate analysis of group differences should in general be expected to
provide more powerful tests of significance than the analysis
of all p-1 successive difference scores.

In point of fact, the distinction between multivariate
and univariate approaches to repeated measurements is not
as great as it might appear. The multivariate ANOVA results
in definition of the weighted combination of the p original
measurements which has greatest potential for describing the
differences between groups, treatment effects, or time period

$$Y = b_1 X_1 + b_2 X_2 + \ldots + b_p X_p,$$

where the $b_i$ are calculated to provide Y which has maximum
potential for measuring group differences or treatment effects
In the simplest case the $b_i$ are discriminant function coefficients, and in more complex cases they are elements of
the solution vector satisfying the matrix equation $(SP_h - \lambda SF_\epsilon)$ $\underline{b} = 0$ in the multivariate analysis of variance. The
similarity of this weighted function of the original measure-
ments to the a priori weighted trend functions discussed
with reference to univariate repeated-measurement analyses is
obvious. Because the multivariate weighting coefficients
are fitted to the data to provide maximum group differences
or maximum time-trend effects, degrees of freedom are appropriately altered and the multivariate test statistic has a
different distribution function; nevertheless, the general
similarity of the hypotheses that are tested is apparent.
In either the multivariate or univariate trend analyses,
one is concerned with a linear function of the original
repeated measurements.

The same can be said of the multivariate analysis of
p-1 successive difference scores because the optimum weights
defined by the multivariate analysis can readily be distributed among the p original measures.

$$Y = b_1 (X_1 - X_2) + b_2 (X_2 - X_3) + \ldots + b_{p-1}(X_{p-1} - X_p)$$

$$Y = b_1 X_1 + (b_2 - b_1) X_2 + (b_3 - b_2) X_3 + \ldots$$

Thus:

$$Y = b_1 X_1 + b_2 X_2 + b_3' X_3 + \ldots + b_p' X_p$$

The advantage of the multivariate analysis of p-1 successive difference scores over the multivariate analysis of $\underline{p}$ original measurements is that the weighting coefficients are defined to test hypotheses about trend differences rather than overall differences which include the profile elevation factor.

If the number of repeated observations in a longitudinal study is large, the multivariate analysis of $\underline{p}$ original measures or p-1 successive difference scores is likely to suffer from low power. It would appear preferable to define q p contrast functions, using orthogonal polynomial coefficients, and then to employ the stepwise F-test procedure described by Bock (1963) and Bock and Haggard (1968). For eight equally spaced repeated measurements, the first five transformed scores would be the following type.

$$Y_1 = 1X_1 + 1X_2 + 1X_3 + 1X_4 + 1X_5 + 1X_6 + 1X_7 + 1X_8$$

$$Y_2 = -7X_1 - 5X_2 - 3X_3 - 1X_4 + 1X_5 + 3X_6 + 5X_7 + 7X_8$$

$$Y_3 = +7X_1 + 1X_2 - 3X_3 - 5X_4 - 5X_5 - 3X_6 + 1X_7 + 7X_8$$

$$Y_4 = -7X_1 + 5X_2 + 7X_3 + 3X_4 - 3X_5 - 7X_6 - 5X_7 + 7X_8$$

$$Y_5 = +7X_1 - 13X_2 - 3X_3 + 9X_4 + 9X_5 - 3X_6 - 13X_7 + 7X_8$$

Depending on the pattern of correlations between various pairs of time periods, these linear contrast functions may

not be statistically independent. The first function $Y_1$
will be recognized to represent the elevation, or average
level, factor in the profile scores. The next four function
represent linear, quadratic, cubic and quartic trend components. It is quite reasonable to expect that any meaningf-
ful true trend effects can be represented by a function no
more complex than a fourth-degree polynomial. If one were
interested in all differences between groups of subjects,
including differences in average profile elevation, a multivariate analysis of variance could be performed on all five
transformed scores. On the other hand, it is probable that
only the differences in trends over time will be of interest
The procedure described by Bock (1963), Bock and Haggard (19
which is based on derivations presented by Roy and Bargman
(1958), provides a test of the average elevation factor.
That factor is then swept out of the matrix to obtain an F-
test of differences between the groups on the linear trend
function with the elevation factor removed. The elevation
factor and the linear trend function are then both swept
out to obtain an F-test of differences between the groups on
the quadratic function, and so on. Because the successive
F-tests are statistically independent, they can be combinted
for an overall test of the multivariate profile (trend) diffe-
ences if one desires.

It is interesting to note that exactly these same tests
can be obtained using a covariance conception of the general
linear model analysis. The significance of group differences
on $Y_1$ is first tested disregarding $Y_2$, $Y_3$, $Y_4$, and Y5. Next,
$Y_1$ is entered as a linear covariate, and the difference
between groups on the $Y_2$ variable is tested with Y partialled
out. Next, both $Y_1$ and $Y_2$ are entered as covariates, and
the significance of differences between groups on $Y_3$ is
tested with $Y_1$ and $Y_2$ partialled out. The procedure can be
repeated, each time adding the previous dependent variable
as a covariate. The general linear regression method for
multiple covariance analysis can be used efficiently for this
approach (Overall, 1972). The stepwise F-test procedure
undertaken on major trend components appears to have all of
the advantages of a complete multivariate analysis, to require no assumptions concerning homogeneity of correlations
among observations at the various time periods, and yet to
provide an intuitively meaningful and powerful univariate
test of trend differences in data from longitudinal studies
involving numerous repeated measurements. On the other hand,
we have here a case where the "treatment effect" is represented in the linear model for the covariate. For example,

in testing the significance of our linear trend component, it is the mean of scores across all time periods that is entered as the covariate. The tests of significance appear valid, but there is a question as to whether the parameters that are tested are really what we think they are. The mean of scores across all time periods will surely reflect to some degree any treatment or group differences that may also be reflected in the linear trend component.

## STATISTICAL CONTROL OVER MULTIPLE CONFOUNDED FACTORS

The choice of an appropriate measure of change is very important in defining true treatment effects or effects associated with group differences over time; however, simply equating groups on baseline scores may not be adequate to remove all irrelevant or biasing sources of variance. In experimental research, random assignment is the strategy used most often to "balance out" the effects of a variety of nuisance factors that may have systematic effects on the parameters of interest. In observational research, where intact groups are the subject of concern, random assignment is not possible. Natural groups, such as schizophrenics and normal controls, may differ in a variety of characteristics that are irrelevant to the interests of the researcher, that are social or other correlates of the disorder which have pronounced but unnecessary effects on the dependent variable, or that are direct manifestations of the disease process. One is faced with a serious rational problem concerning what should and what should not be controlled for.

The fact that analysis of covariance, or some other form of baseline correction, may not be adequate alone is easily illustrated. Suppose that two diagnostic groups being compared in a longitudinal study differ substantially in average age. An analysis of successive difference scores reveals evidence of greater "performance decrement" in one group than in the other. The result may be due to the disease process, or it may be a natural effect of normal aging. To attribute the effect to differences in the disease process when in fact it is due to another factor has been called a "specification error" by some writers (O'Conner, 1973).

It is possible to employ more complex statistical analyses to partial out irrelevant sources of variance, but one must question seriously in each particular case whether such

statistical control is meaningful.  In the above example,
a two-way age x diagnosis analysis of variance could be proposed to separate the effects of age and disease process.
Under a wide range of practical conditions, the two-way
analysis can be expected to estimate the same effects and
to test the same hypotheses that might otherwise be estimated
and tested in a balanced (equal cell frequency) factorial
design involving the same factors.  That is, the after-the-
fact analysis of independent effects of age and disease process can be expected to achieve very much the same thing as
might otherwise be achieved by stratified sampling to equate
diagnostic groups for age (Overall, Spiegel & Cohen, 1975).
The question is whether this is what is really wanted.

The question whether to stratify on a control variable
is similar to the question of whether it would be appropriate
to match subjects within the groups of primary concern on the
variable in question.  In the process of "equating groups
statistically", just as in the case of selective sampling to
match groups, one generates an artificial population that does
not exist in nature.  Any time that significant group differences are identified for one factor with others held constant,
one must realize that conclusions may not generalize to the
natural intact groups which are of primary concern.  It is
easy to construct an example to illustrate this problem.
Suppose that "schizophrenic" and "depressed" patients differ
on a characteristic performance decrement, in average and
that performance decrement relates to age as shown in Table
1.  The unweighted means for the two diagnostic groups are
quite different across both age categories; however, the
means for the two diagnostic groups are equal if age is dis-
regarded.  This is a case where age considered disregarding
diagnosis would appear highly significant in its effect,
diagnosis considered disregarding age would appear to have
no effect, but diagnosis with age partialled out would appear
highly significant.  What is a meaningful conclusion?  The
diagnostic groups do in fact differ in average age; so the
effect of partialling out age is to emphasize selectively
the younger segment of the depressive population and the
older segment of the schizophrenic population.  This could
result in comparing more chronic schizophrenics with less
chronic depressed patients if additional control variables
are not considered.

It is extremely important for the user of analysis of
variance techniques to appreciate the fact that the least
squares regression solutions approximate analyses in which

Table 1

Illustration of Problem of Interpreting Adjusted
Effects in Nonorthogonal Analysis of Variance

|  | Young | Old |  |
|---|---|---|---|
| Schizophrenic | $\bar{X}=20$ | $\bar{X}=30$ | $\bar{X} = 25.0$ |
|  | N=8 | N=2 |  |
| Depressive | $\bar{X}=15$ | $\bar{X}=24$ | $\bar{X} = 19.5$ |
|  | N=2 | N=8 |  |
|  | $\bar{X}=17.5$ | $\bar{X}=27.0$ |  |

Diagnosis disregarding age:
    Schizophrenic    $\bar{X} = 22.0$
    Normal           $\bar{X} = 22.2$

Age disregarding diagnosis:
    Young            $\bar{X} = 19.0$
    Old              $\bar{X} = 25.2$

---

all cells in the cross-classification table have equal frequencies. This is true whether one uses "frequency weighting" (Gocka, 1973) or "equal weighting" in restricting the
solution. If the differences in cell frequencies are more
or less a chance occurrence, or if it is reasonable to consider populations that have equal frequencies in nature, then
the least squares regression solutions are meaningful. If
on the other hand, differential cell frequencies are inherent
characteristics of the populations being compared, it may be
highly artificial to equate them statistically.

The analysis of variance and analysis of covariance in observational type research, be it longitudinal or cross-sectional, should be conceived as "correlational" techniques. Hypotheses concern the relationship of a quantitative (dependent) variable to a categorical variable or classification factor. In more complex designs that include control variables, the hypotheses concern "partial correlations." If one carries this analogy to the point of examining the behavior of partial correlations in the usual multivariate situation, it becomes obvious that great care must be exercised in the interpretation of results. It is common knowledge that a highly significant partial correlation can be obtained between two variables that have no zero-order correlation at all. This occurs when the variables relate highly to a suppressor variable that is partialled out. In the analysis of variance paradigm, a highly significant main effect can be observed in an artifically balanced design even though no true difference exists prior to equating the groups on other variables. Main effects and interaction effects in observational type research should be interpreted with correlations and partial correlations in mind, not as one would interpret "treatment effects" in experimental research.

In conclusion, the point to be emphasized is that statistical methods are available to equate effectively naturally occurring groups. Such statistical analysis can achieve essentially the same results as might be obtained by detailed stratified sampling or matching procedures. The question is not whether statistical control is possible; it is whether it is desirable. Observational research is at best correlational. It involves the fitting of rational models to data. Statistical analyses can determine whether the data are compatible with a particular model, but they cannot confirm that the model is a correct explanation of nature. Through an inductive process, one gradually gains confidence in an explanation if evidence cannot be found to refute it.

REFERENCES

Bock, R.D.  Multivariate analysis of variance of repeated measurements.  In C.W. Harris (Ed.), Problems in Measuring Change.  Madison: University of Wisconsin Press, 1963.

Bock, R.D., and Haggard, E.A.   The use of multivariate analysis of variance in behavioral research.   In D.K. Whitla (Eds.), Handbook of measurement and assessment in behavioral sciences.  Reading, Massachusetts: Addison-Wesley, 1968.

Campbell, D.T., and Erlebacher, A.   How regression artifacts in quasi-experimental evaluations can mistakenly make compensatory education look harmful.  Disadvantaged Child, 1970, 3, 185-210.

Cochran, W.G.   Analysis of covariance:  Its nature and uses.  Biometrics, 1957, 13, 261-281.

Davis, F.B.   The assessment of change.   In Marquette University, Reading Center, Tenth Yearbook, National Reading Conference. Milwaukee: Marquette University, 1961.

Evans, S.H., and Anastasio, E.J.   Misuse of analysis of covariance when treatment effect and covariate are confounded.  Psychological Bulletin, 1968, 69, 225-234.

Gaito, J., and Wiley, D.E.   Univariate analysis of variance procedures in the measurement of change.   In C.W. Harris (Ed.), Problems in measuring change.   Madison: University of Wisconsin Press, 1963.

Gocka, E.F.   Regression analysis of proportional cell data.  Psychological Bulletin, 1973, 80, 28-30.

Kahneman, D.   Control of spurious association and the reliability of controlled variables.  Psychological Bulletin, 1965, 64, 326-329.

Lord, F.G.   Elementary models for measuring change.   In C.W. Harris (Ed.), Problems in measuring change.  Madison: University of Wisconsin Press, 1963.

Morrison, D.F.   Multivariate statistical methods.  New York: McGraw Hill, 1967.

McNemar, Q.   On growth measurement.  Educational and Psychological Measurement, 1958, 18, 47-55.

O'Connor, E.F., Jr. Unraveling Lord's paraodx: The appro-
    priate use of multiple regression analysis in quasi-
    experimental research. Research Bulletin, Princeton:
    Educational Testing Service, 1973.

Overall, J.E. Multiple covariance analysis by the general
    least squares regression method. Behavioral Science,
    1972, 17, 313-320.

Overall, J.E. and Klett, C.J. Applied multivariate analysis.
    New York: McGraw-Hill, 1972.

Overall, J.E., Spiegel, D.K., and Cohen, J. Equivalence of
    orthogonal and nonorthogonal analysis of variance.
    Psychological Bulletin, 1975, 82, 182-186.

Overall, J.E., and Woodward, J.A. Unreliability of differ-
    ence scores: A paradox in the measurement of change.
    Psychological Bulletin, 1975, 82, 85-86.

Overall, J.E., and Woodward, J.A. Nonrandom assignment and
    the analysis of covariance. Psychological Bulletin,
    1977 (in press).

Roy, S.N. and Bargmann, R.E. Tests of multiple independence
    and the associated confidence bounds. Annals of
    Mathematical Statistics, 1958, 29, 491-503.

Webster, H., and Bereiter, C. The reliability of changes
    measured by mental test scores. In C.W. Harris (Ed.),
    Problems in measuring change. Madison: University of
    Wisconsin Press, 1963.

Woodward, J.A., and Overall, J.E. Nonorthogonal analysis
    of variance in repeated measures experimental designs.
    Journal of Educational and Psychological Measurement,
    1976, in press.

## DISCUSSION

Wooldridge: It seems to me that there is one point that you overlook in equating these techniques with the use of matching. In matching you essentially take out error variance by controlling the background variables. None of that variance would be associated with the independent variables since the matching would assure that the variables for which you are controlling would be uncorrelated with the independent variables. Whereas, if you fail to match, you may have a situation in which you have considerable multi-colinearity, and thus you may take out an awful lot of the variance to be studied and thus achieve a lower correlation.

Overall: It is true that in a highly non-orthodonal design the standard error of estimate is increased and the power of your tests is decreased. However, in a regression solution where you have a highly non-orthogonal design, the parameters that you estimate and the hypotheses that you test are the same as those you would estimate if you did do the selective sampling.

Wooldridge: I agree with that, but it seems to me that there is a major issue here in terms of efficiency of design, and that matching is certainly much more efficient than trying to correct in the data analysis for grossly unmatched cases.

Overall: That is a very good point. I think that it depends completely on the availability of subjects and material you are dealing with. You may have to wait 10 years to get six more in a subgroup, so for a given total N it is better to go ahead and leave all the subjects in rather than selectively throwing away subjects in' order to balance the design.

Greenhouse: The examples you use relate to subjective-type variables. I wonder whether designs like this should be used when you are investigating the efficacy of drugs or some other treatment. If you performed a naturalistic or observational study to compare the effectiveness of different treatments on schizophrenics or on diseased patients in general, I believe you would be faced with the possible bias that those who are getting the drugs are more severely ill

than those who are not.  You may then obviously arrive at a
conclusion opposite to that obtained from randomized, controlled trials.

Overall:  I think that it is not possible to use this
type of approach in quasi-experimental research where the
groups are not substantially overlapping, where essentially
subjects are all assigned to one group or another.  It has
not been my experience in looking at the current process of
drug treatment among schizophrenic patients, for example,
or among even patients in the general inpatient population,
that drugs are actually used with the degree of selectivity
that you suggest.  It seems to me that on all variables that
I have identified as relevant you can, with not too large a
sample, find patients of all types treated with all drugs.
This could be a pre-condition to using this approach.

A COMBINED THIRTY-FIVE YEAR FOLLOW-UP AND FAMILY STUDY OF
SCHIZOPHRENIA AND PRIMARY AFFECTIVE DISORDERS:  SAMPLE
SELECTION, METHODOLOGY OF FIELD FOLLOW-UP, AND PRELIMINARY
MORTALITY RATES*

Ming T. Tsuang and George Winokur
Department of Psychiatry
University of Iowa College of Medicine
Iowa City, Iowa

INTRODUCTION

In this discussion of controlled versus naturalistic
studies in psychiatric research, we will be presenting an
example of the controlled approach.

Our study is locally referred to as the "Iowa 500."  It
is a combined follow-up and family study of a total of 500
schizophrenic and primary affective disorder patients who
were discharged from the Iowa Psychopathic Hospital approximately 35 years ago.

No one chooses a particular epidemiological method in a
vacuum.  The method may be dictated largely by available monies,
personnel, facilities, and potential data sources, as well as
the purpose for which the study is intended.  Or it may be,
as it is in our case, that the method is suggested by an unexpected precipitant.

A series of amazingly comprehensive medical charts was
discovered in the basement of Iowa Psychopathic Hospital by
one of us (G.W.) when he moved to Iowa in 1971.  Included in
these charts, which covered Hospital admissions in the 1930's
and 1940's, were the verbatim transcripts of staff meetings
and interviews with the patients, often as many as five single-
spaced typewritten pages in length.  These pages reflect the

_____
*
This study was supported by National Institutes of Health
Grant MH 24 189-02.

vigorous debate, citation of facts from psychiatric literature, and minute examination of details of history or
mental status which characterized the meetings.

Because of this overwhelming detail, it was possible to
extract from these charts valuable information from a large
pool of patients. By starting with the patients clearly
fitting two general diagnostic groups and following-up these
cases after 35 years, we hope to provide comprehensive
objective data on the symptoms, course, and outcome of
schizophrenia and affective disorder.

A family study is being conducted as well.  The advantage in this case is that the siblings and children of the
probands are now -- 35 years later -- well distributed
throughout the risk periods for the disorders under study.
Because of this, it will be possible to measure family
morbidity risks, rather than having to estimate them.

Another feature of the study is the inclusion of a non-
psychiatric control group so that there will be a baseline
for comparison with the psychiatric cases.

This report will focus on the mortality data from the
study as an example of the kinds of results that can be
obtained from this methodological approach.

SUBJECTS AND METHODS

Three specific aspects of the subject selection and
methods will be described: (1) the selection and composition
of the study population; (2) the methodological principles
and the methods themselves used to follow up these people
and to study their families; and (3) the manner in which we
are extracting preliminary data to get an immediate idea of
trends and characteristics in the index population.

The Study Population

There are three distinct groups in the study population: psychiatric cases, control subjects, and first-degree
relatives of both cases and controls.  The psychiatric cases
were selected first using two chief criteria: dates of
admission had to provide for a mean follow-up period in

excess of 30 years; and subjects had to meet specific
diagnostic criteria that had been set before the selection
process began.

The controls were obtained from admissions to the
Department of Surgery at University General Hospital during
the same period.  The ratio of psychiatric cases to controls
is about 3 to 1, so the matching involved was proportional
rather than exact.

Although we are only interviewing living parents,
siblings, and children in the family study, each of these
people is asked in turn about all of his or her first-degree
relatives.  In this way, we are obtaining information on as
many as five generations of a single family.

Source and Selection of Psychiatric Cases.  In the
planning stages of this study, the appropriate sample sizes
were set at 200 unipolar depressive, 100 bipolar manics, and
200 schizophrenics.

The diagnostic criteria for use in psychiatric research
of Feighner, et al. (1972) were used in the selection
process.  These criteria were familiar to the original
investigators and were considered appropriate to the purposes of the study because of their emphasis on typical
illness. A disadvantage of these criteria is that their use
results in the exclusion of many cases that would undoubtedly be diagnosed clinically as schizophrenia or affective
disorder.  However, since the criteria are relatively
objective and specific, they have the advantage of maximizing
clinician agreement about assignment of patients to the
diagnostic groups.

In all, 3800 consecutive admissions were reviewed.
Eight hundred and seventy-four charts bearing the diagnosis
of manic-depressive disease, involutional melancholia or
schizophrenia were intially selected to be examined in
detail.  A number of charts indicating psychosis or other
diagnoses with potential for meeting the established criteria
were also selected at this time.

Approximately one third of all charts initially selected
had to be discarded for failure to meet the study diagnostic
criteria.  Our psychiatric samples were drawn from the

remainder. An extra 25 unipolar depressives were inadver-
tently collected at this time. After the fact, it was
decided to keep them in the sample as insurance against the
possibility that some of the depressives would subsequently
have episodes of mania.

Source and Selection of Controls. In order to obtain a
baseline for comparison of outcome among the psychiatric
patients, we selected a group of psychiatric symptom-free
control patients who would be followed-up in exactly the
same manner as the psychiatric patients. Studying equal
numbers of cases and controls was rejected from the outset
as being too costly; in the end, a 3 to 1 ratio was established. The control group was matched to the psychiatric
patients for time of admission, age, sex, area of residence,
and socio-economic status.

The records of the Department of Surgery carrying the
diagnosis of appendectomy and herniorrhaphy were sampled to
determine an appropriate population from which to draw the
controls. These two populations were stratified for sex
and hospitalization status, i.e. private or public payment.
Each of the strata in both diagnoses were then sampled
randomly to obtain the same proportions that existed in the
psychiatric group. A selection was excluded if the admission
age was less than 14 or greater than 61. Any evidence of a
psychiatric referral in the chart, or mention of current or
past psychiatric symptoms, likewise resulted in the exclusion of a selection.

Final Composition of Study Population. The final
composition of the study population consisted of: 525
psychiatric cases -- representing depression, mania, and
schizophrenia; 160 controls -- 80 each from the two surgical
diagnostic groups; and approximately 2000 first degree
relatives -- an average of three per case and control.

Characteristics of Index Population. In the final
index population there were: 45% males, 55% females; the
mean age at admission was 35 years; and 43% of the group had
never married (Table 1).

There is a definite trend for the unipolar depressives
to be older than the bipolar manics, and for the schizophrenics to be younger than both of the affective disorder

Table 1

Characteristics of Index Population

|  | Unipolar | Bipolar | Schizo-phrenia | Control |
|---|---|---|---|---|
| N | 225 | 100 | 200 | 160 |
| Male | 100 | 38 | 103 | 65 |
| Female | 125 | 62 | 97 | 95 |
| Admission Mean Age | 43.8 | 34.1 | 28.6 | 31.3 |
| Single at Admission | 39 | 42 | 151 | 62 |

groups. This age difference probably contributed to the percentage of those who had never married among the schizophrenics being about 4-1/2 times the percentage of never-married depressives.

Methodology of Field Follow-up

As a practical matter, we have divided the follow-up into two "phases." During the first phase, we concentrate on locating living index cases and relatives and personally interviewing them. During the second phase, we will be concentrating on gathering information on those index subjects who have died.

One chief consideration in all methodological decisions has been how best to maintain objectivity and blindness in the data. Our goal has been to ensure, as far as possible, that those workers actually involved in the gathering and evaluation of data should be blind to its source, whether it came from a psychiatric case, a control subject, or a relative.

To achieve this goal, the various steps in the process
are strictly classified, and conducted by non-overlapping
teams of personnel. The only group with direct access to
the original medical charts are those individuals who are
engaged in locating the current whereabouts of the study
population.

Our basic tool in locating subjects is the telephone
directory. Seventy-five percent of the people we have traced
so far have been located by means of looking for the family
name in local phone books. The first member of a family
contacted is asked to provide information on other members
of the family concerning births, deaths, current addresses
of the living, and course and outcome of the index subject
following hospitalization. These telephone interviews then
become the source documents for locating other family
members and for arranging appointments for personal interviews.

Personal interviews are conducted -- usually at the
place of work or residence of the interviewee -- by spec-
ially trained persons, using a form specifically designed
for the study, the "Iowa Structured Psychiatric Interview"
("I-SPI"). Our interviewers are given only a name, address,
time and date of the interview, and no information whatso-
ever that would indicate the interviewee's relationship to
the study.

The administration of the form requires only a knowledge of its mechanics, and a knowledge on the part of the
interviewer of the exact meaning of the language of each
question. The questions are direct and specific, and
require either a simple, direct response -- a "Yes" or
"No" -- or a quantifiable one -- ages, dates, or number of
times a symptom has occurred. Interviewers are instructed
to record the responses of the interviewee just as they are
given. The information on the form is then computerized and
stored, awaiting the completion of an entire family -- index
case, plus first-degree relatives.

Simultaneously with the above activities, a file of
validating data is completed on each index patient from a
variety of sources: original chart information covering the
index admission; previously gathered follow-up information
from the hospital's division on social services; and records
from other institutions to where many of our psychiatric

patients were sent or subsequently seen following discharge from the index admission.

Ultimately, the aggregate of follow-up data and family data on the index cases and their families will be comprised of: a completed ISPI interview form for the living, an approximated ISPI for each deceased index subject, telephone interview, death certificate, medical records information, and independent diagnostic assessments of the ISPI by the psychiatric investigators.

This body of data will be evaluated to arrive at a final assessment of outcome. Additionally, these data will be submitted to computer analysis in an attempt to identify clusters of data that may make possible the formulation of homogeneous subgroups within the population. We expect to be analyzing this information for years to come.

Prior to this final accumulation of data, and the subsequent clinical and computer evaluation, we want of course, to have the capacity for analyzing data as they are collected. Specifically, we are interested in preliminary answers to the basic questions of outcome: were symptoms chronic or remitting; was the person able to work and support himself; did he require further institutionalization; what was the general state of his physical and mental health; and what were the mortality and suicide rates? This capacity is made possible by a device called, simply enough, "The Master Card."

Organization of Preliminary Data -- The Master Card

In the development of the master card, the original documents were used to extract identifying demographic data. Criteria were developed for coding outcome data as they became available in the course of follow-up, and a system was devised for continually updating the master card file for both research and administrative planning.

Each index patient for whom we obtain any current follow-up information is immediately given a master card rating on five variables that we consider to be relevant to outcome: (1) marital status; (2) employment; (3) physical health; (4) mental health; and (5) residence. Ratings in each of these categories are based only on current field follow-up information, and represent either current status, if living, or status at the time of death if deceased. Thus, the basic item of information we are seeking in our initial tracing procedures is whether or not the index subject is still alive. If he is deceased, every attempt is made to pin down the exact date of death, and special note is made of suicide as a cause of death. It is this mortality data that we will present in this report.

## RESULTS

There are several different aspects of our results so far that we think will be useful to describe as examples of the scope and activities of the "IOWA 500." The first of these is an overview of field interviewing; the second is what we call "Office Status", which basically describes our current state of knowledge about an index subject; the third is information about the follow-up data, where they come from, how they are distributed among the study population; and lastly, the mortality and suicide rates for the various diagnostic categories.

### Overview of the Field Interviewing

Up to this time, the order in which an individual was interviewed depended almost exclusively upon where he or she lived. Those people living in Iowa City were interviewed first so that we could test our methods and give our workers some experience without having to worry about the logistics of transportation and travel arrangements.

We have been working outward gradually from Iowa City. We are operating throughout an area bounded on the north and east by Minneapolis and Chicago, and on the south and west by St. Louis and Omaha. This is approximately a 300-mile radius around Iowa City, and is about as far as we plan to go to find first-degree relatives, unless they happen to live in the near vicinity of an index case.

Since we began interviewing in the spring of last year, the number of interviews has ranged between 15 and 65 per week. The peak came during the summer months last year, and the low rate in the midst of Iowa's worst winter in years.

By the end of December, 1974, we completed approximately
1100 interviews: 150 with index cases, and 950 with family
members.


## Office Status of Index Cases

Our routine tracing procedures have been tried on all
685 index cases, and been successful for over 80% of the
population. We know that 44% are deceased, and 38% still
living. The remaining 18% are currently being traced
through other clues in their original hospital charts.

The 153 who have been personally interviewed represent
58% of the 262 cases known to be living. So far, only about
5-1/2 percent of the index population has refused to participate. Before the completion of the study, we plan to try
again to interview these initial refusals.

Some of living index subjects are known to reside
outside of our immediate interviewing area. The majority of
these is in California, Texas, and Florida. It is our
intention to follow-up personally every living index subject, whereever he or she happens to be living.


## Characteristics of Follow-up Data

In coding follow-up data on the master card, all
available sources of information are used, although preference is always given to information obtained in a personal
interview. In the case of people who have died in institutions, preference is given to the written records from
that institution. No attempt has ever been made to concentrate our follow-up efforts on a particular diagnostic
group. The 80% of the population for whom we have any
follow-up data is well distributed throughout the psychiatric cases and controls.

As previously mentioned, the basic information that we
are seeking about an index case is whether he or she is
still alive. However, approximately two-thirds of all the
index cases we have traced can be given a preliminary rating
on one or more outcome variables.

Mean Ages and Mortality Rates. The mean ages for living index subjects, and the mean ages at death for the deceased, are presented in Table 2 for each diagnostic group. Only those known deceased for whom we had an accurate date of death are included in this table.

Table 2 represents data for: 78% of the schizophrenics; 71% of the bipolars; 76% of the unipolars; and 69% of the controls. One-hundred three of the original 200 schizophrenics are known to be living still. This represents 51% of schizophrenics compared with 29% for the bipolars, 23% for unipolars, and 49% for the controls.

At the time of admission, the schizophrenics had the youngest mean age, followed by the controls. Among the presently living, these two groups have exchanged rankings. There is a sizeable difference between the mean ages of living unipolars and bipolars now similar to the difference between these groups of mean age at admission.


Table 2

Mean Ages of Known Living/Dead Index Cases by Diagnosis*

|  | #Living (%) | Mean Age | #Dead (%) | Mean Age | Total (%) | Mean Age |
|---|---|---|---|---|---|---|
| SCHIZOPHRENIA 200 = 100% | 103(51) | 62.3 | 53(27) | 52.0 | 156(78) | 58.5 |
| BIPOLAR AD 100 = 100% | 29(29) | 63.9 | 42(42) | 59.3 | 71(71) | 61.2 |
| UNIPOLAR AD 225 = 100% | 52(23) | 71.5 | 120(53) | 65.3 | 172(76) | 67.2 |
| CONTROL 160 = 100% | 78(49) | 60.3 | 32(20) | 61.3 | 110(69) | 60.5 |
| TOTAL 685 = 100% | 262(38) | 63.7 | 247(36) | 60.9 | 509(74) | 62.3 |

* Excluding 52(8%) cases known deceased for whom no date of death is available: 17 Schizophrenics; 8 Bipolars; 20 Unipolars; and 7 Controls.

The figures for the mean ages at death are the first indication that there may be some illness-associated factors in the mortality rates. The mean age at death for each of the psychiatric groups is from 5 to 10 years younger than the mean age of the living in the respective groups; whereas the mean age for deceased controls is older than for the living. The mean age for deceased schizophrenics is particulary low, especially considering the number of people involved.

In order to make these data comparable, we have adjusted the rates to eliminate the age factor. We have utilized two different methods (Fleiss, 1973) to standardize mortality rates in the index population: direct age-adjustment, and age-standardized mortality ratios.

In order to carry out direct age-adjustment, these 561 index cases were first arranged in 10-year intervals according to their ages in 1940 -- the mid-point of our index admission period. On the basis of current information, age-specific and diagnosis-specific mortality rates were calculated for each interval. Table 3 presents the raw mortality

Table 3

Distribution of Deceased Among 561 Index Patients,
According to Age in 1940

| Age (1940) | Unipolar | Bipolar | Schizo. | Control | Total per age |
|---|---|---|---|---|---|
| 0- 9 | 0/ 0* | 0/ 0 | 0/ 0 | 1/ 2 | 1/ 2 |
| 10-19 | 0/ 0 | 1/ 1 | 5/ 18 | 4/ 30 | 10/ 49 |
| 20-19 | 6/ 17 | 11/30 | 20/ 66 | 8/ 34 | 45/147 |
| 30-39 | 19/ 39 | 5/11 | 27/ 67 | 5/ 14 | 56/131 |
| 40-49 | 29/ 44 | 16/19 | 11/ 15 | 14/ 26 | 70/104 |
| 50-59 | 58/ 63 | 12/13 | 5/ 5 | 7/ 11 | 82/ 92 |
| 60-69 | 27/ 28 | 5/ 5 | 1/ 1 | 0/ 0 | 33/ 34 |
| 70-79 | 1/ 1 | 0/ 0 | 1/ 1 | 0/ 0 | 2/ 2 |
| Total per Diagnosis | 140/192 | 50/79 | 70/173 | 39/117 | 299/561 |
| Crude Rate | .729 | .633 | .405 | .333 | .533 |

* #Deceased/(#Deceased + #Still Alive)

data for each diagnosis and age group.

Table 4 presents the raw data for suicide among the index cases.

There were no suicides among the controls up to the cut-off date for these data. Since that time, however, we have found one control who committed suicide. Because the number of suicides is small relative to the whole population, it has not been considered advisable to attempt to standardize the suicide rates at this time.

For comparison purposes, we have standardized mortality rates on two different populations: the total index population with current follow-up data, and the population distribution of Iowa for 1940. Table 5 is an example of the standardized mortality rates for the unipolar patients. In this method, the age-specific mortality rates in the study group are multipled by the population distribution of Iowa -- the effect is to weight the specific mortality rates by population size. The direct age-adjusted mortality rate may be interpreted as the population crude mortality rate that would prevail if the members of the general population

Table 4

Distribution of 26 Suicides Among 561 Index
Patients, According to Age in 1940

| Age (1940) | Unipolar | Bipolar | Schizo. | Control | Total per age |
|---|---|---|---|---|---|
| 0- 9 | 0/ 0* | 0/ 0 | 0/ 0 | 0/ 2 | 0/ 0 |
| 10-19 | 0/ 0 | 0/ 1 | 0/ 18 | 0/ 30 | 0/ 49 |
| 20-29 | 0/ 17 | 0/30 | 2/ 66 | 0/ 34 | 2/147 |
| 30-39 | 3/ 39 | 0/11 | 4/ 67 | 0/ 14 | 7/131 |
| 40-49 | 3/ 44 | 3/19 | 0/ 15 | 0/ 26 | 6/104 |
| 50-59 | 8/ 63 | 0/13 | 0/ 5 | 0/ 11 | 8/ 92 |
| 60-69 | 1/ 28 | 1/ 5 | 1/ 1 | 0/ 0 | 3/ 34 |
| 70-79 | 0/ 1 | 0/ 0 | 0/ 1 | 0/ 0 | 0/ 2 |
| Total per Diagnosis | 15/192 | 4/79 | 7/173 | 0/117 | 26/561 |
| Crude rate | .0781 | .0506 | .0405 | .0000 | .0463 |

* #Suicides / (Age-Diagnosis specific population)

Table 5

An Example of Direct Age-Adjustment:
Unipolar Rates on 1940 Iowa White Population

| Age (1940) | Distribution for all of Iowa ($P_{2i}$) | Unipolar age-specific rates ($c_i$) | $P_{2i}c_i$ |
|---|---|---|---|
| 0- 9 | .162 | .000 | .000 |
| 10-19 | .179 | .000 | .000 |
| 20-29 | .162 | .353 | .057 |
| 30-39 | .139 | .487 | .068 |
| 40-49 | .130 | .659 | .086 |
| 50-59 | .108 | .921 | .099 |
| 60-69 | .077 | .964 | .074 |
| 70-79 | .043 | 1.000 | .043 |
| Sum = Direct adjusted rate: | | | .427 |

Table 6

Mortality Rates in 561 Index Patients

| Rates | Unipolar | Bipolar | Schizo. | Control |
|---|---|---|---|---|
| Crude | .729 | .633 | .405 | .333 |
| Age-adjusted on Index Population ± S.E. | .542 ±.038 | .658 ±.046 | .562 ±.030 | .363 ±.046 |
| Age-adjusted on Iowa Population ± S.E. | .427 ±.024 | .588 ±.028 | .478 ±.027 | .331 ±.065 |

were to share the mortality experience of the study group.

Table 6 is a summary of the various mortality rates
that we have calculated for the index patients. It is a
good example of what may be expected to happen when the
study population is highly heterogeneous for age. In 1940,
the age distribution of our unipolar patients was skewed to
the older age groups, and the Iowa Population was skewed
towards the younger ages. When the very high age-specific
mortality rates of the older unipolars are applied to the
small population distribution of older Iowans, the age-
adjusted rate drops considerably from the crude rates for
unipolars.

The adjusted mortality rates for the controls show only
slight differences from the crude rate on both the Index and
Iowa populations. We are hopeful that this is an indication
of the representativeness of our control group.

When the mortality rates are adjusted on the total
index population. there are no intra-psychiatric population
differences; and each of the psychiatric subgroups' rates is
significantly different from that for the controls (p $<$ .005).
When the rates are adjusted on the Iowa population, however,
a significant difference is shown between the unipolars and
the bipolars (p $<$ .001), and between the bipolars and the
schizophrenics (p $<$ .005); the significant difference between
the unipolars and the controls disappears.

The second method that we have employed to analyze
mortality in the index population is the determination of
age-standardization mortality ratios. For the probands and
controls whose mortality status was ascertained and whose
dates of death known, an analysis was performed on the
observed number of deaths in each cohort in comparison to
the Iowa population and the Iowa mortality statistics.
Mortality statistics for the state of Iowa were determined
for the years 1940, 1950, 1960 and 1970 and were applied to
cohort years of follow-up 1935-45, 1945-55, 1955-65, and
1965-75, respectively. These Iowa age-specific mortality
rates for each decade formed our standard set of rates to be
used as a comparison to the mortality experience of each
diagnostic cohort during the appropriate follow-up years.

To compute the expected age-specific number of deaths
for each 10 year period for a given cohort, the person-years

Table 7

Age Standardized Mortality Ratios+

| Cohort | 1935–1945 | 1945–1955 | 1955–1965 | 1965–1975 |
|---|---|---|---|---|
| Unipolars | 2.20** (1.97**) | 1.22 (1.07) | 1.45* (1.59) | 1.28 (1.61*) |
| Bipolars | 3.82** (3.40**) | 0.88 (0.75) | 1.17 (1.27) | 1.72 (2.09**) |
| Schizophrenics | 2.87** (2.68**) | 1.65 (1.89*) | 1.18 (1.44) | 0.87 (1.20) |
| Controls | 0.0 (0.0) | 0.87 (0.80 | 0.95 (0.87) | 1.10 (1.52) |

+ Top Number: excluding 52 deceased with unknown date of death; ( ): including proportional allocation of unknowns.

* Significance at .05 level; ** Significance at .01 level.

at risk contributed by the cohort was determined. The Iowa age-specific and decade-specific mortality rates were applied to these person-years at risk to obtain an expected number of deaths for the cohort. The person-years at risk is computed for each subject as the portion of this total risk experience for the appropriate ages. A person can, and usually did, contribute person-years to two age categories during a given 10-year period.

The expected number of deaths was summed across the ages for each decade and each cohort (only the ages 10-79 were used in the calculation); the ratio of the observed deaths during the decade to the expected number would be the age-standardized mortality ratio (S.M.R.) for the particular cohort during the appropriate decades. These figures are shown in Table 7 along with the chi-square test results for testing the hypotheses that the standardized mortality ratio is equal to one.

For each psychiatric cohort an excess of deaths is noted in the first decade after admission; in addition during the 60's an excess is found in the depressive cohort. It is noteworthy that no excesses are found in the control group. An additional analysis was performed on the data utilizing the deceased whose dates of death were unknown. These deaths were assigned dates of death proportionately to the Iowa Mortality rates and are in brackets in Table 7; addi tional significant excesses of deaths are found in the unipolar and bipolar cohorts during the 1965-75 decade and the schizophrenic cohort during the years 1945-55. Again no excess is noted in the control cohort. The effect of proportional allocation of the unknown dates of death to the Iowa population is to produce a greater number of deaths during the decades 1965-75; this could explain observed excesses found in the unipolar and bipolar population during these years.

Similar analysis will be performed on the suicide data when the causes and dates of death in the cohorts are ascertained more accurately and completely. The suicide data for the entire state of Iowa will be used as the standard of comparison.

Because of the obvious differences in mean age at admission among the four index groups, we considered it appropriate to employ techniques of age-adjustment to the mortality rates. We are aware that the practice of stan- dardizing rates is not without its critics. However, for the purposes of obtaining some kind of summary index from preliminary data, they serve quite adequately, so long as the specific rates in the study population are also reported.

REFERENCES

Feighner, J., Robins, E., Guze, S., Woodruff, R., Winokur, G., and Munoz, R. Diagnostic criteria for use in psychiatric research. Archives of General Psychiatry, 1972, 26, 57-63.

Fleiss, J.L. Statistical method for dates and proportions. New York: John Wiley and Sons, 1973.

OPEN DISCUSSION

Schulsinger: I have just one little specific question.
In your sample, unipolars were about 125 women and 100 men,
and the bipolars were sixty-some women and forty-some men.
That is quite opposite what is usually found with the age
group studied in your sample. It's usual that unipolars are
2-3 times as frequent in women, and there is no big difference in the frequency for bipolars between the two sexes.
That lends itself to three possible explanations: either
this whole sample is very peculiar and not representative;
second, the researchers are very peculiar in selecting and
diagnosing; or third, there is some other explanation, and
I ask what that is.

Tsuang: When we complete our study, I may have several
explanations. But the question you raise is very important.
This sample was selected basically according to the Feighner
criteria. We have called this group the Iowa 500. When I
got to Iowa one year after the study started, my suggestion
was, how about studying those excluded from the Iowa-500
(the Iowa non-500). I think it is very important to study
those excluded, to study them with those meeting the Feighner criteria, and to compare their age and sex distribution,
their diagnosis and outcome. So we are now also studying
those cases excluded, starting with schizophrenics. This
may help us understand possible bias in the selection of
Iowa 500.

Cowen: I was interested in the original selection of
subjects. As I understood it, you had about 500 subjects
that you selected from a sample in which there was a 50%
reduction, so that there would have been in all about 750 in
the unipolar, bipolar, and schizophrenic group, selected
out of the total group of 3800. Could you give us some kind
of read-out of what the remaining 3000 were like?

Tsuang: Most of them are personality disorders, neurosis,
and other kinds of non-psychotics and mental deficiencies.

Blumenthal: I just wanted to comment on what you think
about the Feighner diagnoses. I think we haven't talked quite
enough about the Feighner diagnoses as a mechanism for providing a rather homogeneous group. The needs for homogeneity
are not the same things as trying to identify a case for

epidemiological purposes. Those goals are quite different
and I think one of these days we ought to talk about what
the purpose of specific diagnostic mechanisms is; whether we
wish to shrink our groups to something homogeneous or whethe
we wish to include all possible cases including maybe the
subclinical ones.

Tsuang: Many studies have been done without specifying
diagnostic criteria. Our next project would be to use Feighner criteria to select patients not from the hospital, but
from the general population. I know there are a lot of disadvantages using Feighner criteria, but at least by using
them the diagnosticians' agreement will be very high, and
because the criteria have been specified, one can say
clearly this is the group one is studying.

Weissman: When you were calculating suicide rates, did
you adjust for age and sex?

Tsuang: Because the number is so small at this stage,
I think it will be misleading to present the data analysis
at this moment, though I have data adjusted for age. It
looks as though schizophrenia, mania, and depression have no
differences in terms of suicide rates, and our impression
is that schizophrenics seemed to commit suicide during the
first decade of the follow-up period, and those with depression and mania committing suicide were distributed evenly
throughout the four decades.

# GENERAL DISCUSSION OF SECTION I

Formal Discussant: Joseph Zubin

I'm afraid I'm here under false prctenses because to summarize these very highly developed methodological and statistical papers is beyond me. Of course it is true that by reputation I'm supposed to be a statistician, but statisticians think I'm a psychologist, and I quess I've pulled wool over both their eyes.

To make this discussion interesting, I will have to provide you with some kind of framework, some kind of a loom on which to weave my comments. The problem discussed this morning, the comparison of controlled vs. naturalistic studies, arises from the fact that most of our methodology, ANOVA, correlational analysis, etc., has been developed for studies with randomly generated samples, and the application of these methods to naturalistic studies has to be justified. This is really the essential problem before us.

It would have been nice of God to have so ordained the world that for every illness there would be a sufficiently large population of identical twins and non-identical twins with large proportions of discordant pairs who were readily accessible for examination. Then our troubles would be over. We could have both a naturalistic and a controlled experiment on natural groups. Since this is not the case, we have to examine the methods of controlled experimentation and see how they can be adapted.

My own inclination is to re-invoke a concept which has been dormant for a long while, actually since 1944 when Slater introduced it, namely the concept of vulnerability to mental disorder. A simple statement of this hypothesis is that the vulnerability becomes manifested depending upon the stressors (both internal and external) which impinge on the person. The person with low vulnerability would require a tremendous amount of stress before he would become ill; once he does so, he'll have an episode; that episode doesn't last forever and when he recovers, he's as well as he was before. The more vulnerable person requires less stress in order to get into an episode, but he, too, soon recovers and

returns to his baseline functioning. But you don't always
know that the episode is over in his case because he was so
poor to begin with; it looks as if he's still sick. Maybe
many of our chronics belong in this category; not that they'ı
still sick, they just were unable to cope before the illness
got them, and there's no reason to believe that after the
illness episode leaves them that they're any more capable of
coping with life than before. This essentially is a framewoı
in which some of the measures to determine vulnerability
and life events stressors might best be viewed. A longitudinal prospective would determine how vulnerability develops,
and how the sensitivity to life stressors can become greater
or less depending upon the variety of experiences to which
one is exposed.

Accepting this hypothesis, what implications do papers
in this group have for a vulnerability hypothesis? In general, longitudinal research takes on the role of following
the development and growth of vulnerability in individuals
with different levels of risk, and of determining the forces
in the ecological niches that they occupy, that either elicit
or inhibit the actualization of the risk. The same ecological niche will give rise to different outcomes depending on
the vulnerability of the individual in the niche, while the
same degree of vulnerability will lead to different outcomes,
depending on the niche's degree of noxiousness. Consequently
we must have measures of both the individual's vulnerability
and the parameters of the niche if we are to do significant
research. Let me remind you in passing that we have far
better measures of vulnerability, such as consanguinity,
psychophysiological, neurophysiological, and biochemical
measures, than we have measures of the parameters in the
ecological niche the person occupies, like stressors and life
events.

However, given that we have such measures regardless
of their reliability, what has Dr. Overall's panoramic view
had to say about the treatment of data? In longitudinal
studies difference scores over time with or without intervention loom very large, and the differences that are found
between contrasting groups, concordant vs. disconcordant
twins, for example, treated and untreated groups, etc.,
are an important criterion for measuring vulnerability,
stressors, and their impact. Thus it might be important
to compare the differences in growth and intelligence from

age 4 to age 8 in children who have experienced minimal
brain damage, with the growth in comparable normal controls.
The question raised by Dr. Overall is how reliable must the
differences between age 4 and age 8 be in order to yield
meaningful differentials between MBD's and controls? His
answer, paradoxically, is that if the reliabilities of the
differences in growth are zero, the likelihood of detecting
a differential between the MBD's and the controls will be
a maximum. It's hard to believe, but that's what he said.
If you accept this conclusion at its face value, you would
have the following incomprehensible conflict with common
sense. If you have a choice of several differences, different scores for comparing two contrasting groups, throw away
the reliable differences and pick those of zero reliability
so they will give you the maximum powers if you want to find
a differential between groups.

Dr. Joseph Fleiss, head of the biostatistics section
with Biometrics Research Unit, and I pondered over this
one for a long time, and it's a very important point. We
examined Overall's and Woodward's paper very carefully;
we believe we have found the basis for this paradox. They
assume that there is no interaction between subjects and
time in their repeated measurements. In other words, every
subject achieved the same difference from pre- to post-test
except for errors of measurement, i.e., that the difference
is constant between pre- and post-test, except for errors of
measurement. No matter what your score is initially, if
it's 50, then at post- it's 60; if it's 30, then at post-
it's 40. It's a constant difference, and that's what no
interaction means, except for the error of the measurement.
Hence, if you correlate two determinations of change for
each individual, you're correlating two constants, each
supplemented by error. Since errors are presumably independent, they correlate zero, and since constants do not correlate, the end result is a reliability correlation of zero.
As a matter of fact, if you took the repeated difference
scores many, many times, the error would wash out and you
would be left with a constant difference for each subject.

If you make such an unlikely assumption, you do indeed
emerge with Overall's conclusion. If, however, you make
the more realistic assumption of the presence of an interaction, that is, of the presence of subject-to-subject variation in the differences, you find that the most reliable

difference produces the highest differentiation between
groups. Thus, contrary to what Overall states, the reliability of difference scores has the highest relevance
for comparison of treatment effect or other group differences.

The following is the situation with respect to Overall'
view concerning the analysis of co-variance applied to unreliable covariates. The authors cited by Overall make a simpl
assumption that there is no treatment effect, that there is
no differential from pre- to post-test between the groups,
and proceed to demonstrate that because of the error of
measurement that's present, there may appear a significant
difference between groups which are in fact similar.
Overall, on the other hand, does not deal with this assumption; he assumes that there is a difference between groups
and proceeds to demonstrate that the presence of errors does
not matter. It is clear that an observed differential between the groups can be due either to the error of measurement following Kahneman (Control of Spurious Association)
and reliability of the the controlled variable (see Overall's
bibliography) or to the factors beyond errors of measurement, following Overall, to reach a conclusion that the two
approaches must be considered together, but unfortunately
Overall is unilateral in this treatment, neglecting the
Kahneman approach.

Another problem which Overall tackles is that of non-
parallel regression lines in analysis of covariance, which
is a problem we are often met with. Overall's suggested
remedy for non-parallel regression lines in analysis of covariance, namely to stratify on the covariate, is most
inefficient. Nonparallel lines necessarily imply treatment
effects; but of different magnitude and different direction,
depending on the value of the covariate. To stratify is to
ignore the quantitative nature of the covariate, to give
up too many degrees of freedom, and most seriously to fail
to apply an analysis method especially developed to handle
the situation, namely the Johnson-Neyman method. What this
method provides for the case of two groups is a partition
of the range of the covariate into three regions. In the
lowest region, one of the groups may be said to have a significantly lower mean than the other; in the highest region,
it may be said to have a definitely higher mean than the
other; in the middle region, generally corresponding to

those values of the covariate near to where the two lines
intersect, no significant difference between the groups
can be declared.  The algebra necessary to carry out the
Johnson-Neyman method is more complicated than the algebra
for Overall's suggested remedy, but the payoff is much more
precise and usable.

The cautions which Overall points to are well taken and
should be followed by all those who tilt with ANCOVA.  The
areas for legitimate use of ANCOVA to eliminate the initial
differences between naturally formed groups and covary differences are still very debatable.  As Meehl has pointed out
in his nuisance variables and ex post facto design, the
essential purpose of ANCOVA is to determine what the result would be if the groups were made comparable with respect
to the uncontrolled variables, and as Anderson points out,
one may well wonder what exactly it means to ask what the
data would be like if they weren't what they are.

Instead of resorting to ANCOVA, the earlier workers
turned to matching individuals in the two contrasting groups
on the covariate; but this led to selected samples, as Dr.
Overall pointed out, on the basis of the fortuitous presence
of matchable pairs and to restrictions on generalization from
unrepresentative samples as well as to differences due to regression effects in the two groups.

Fleiss and Tanur (1973) have provided another solution
which seems to avoid most of the difficulties of matching
and ANCOVA.  They base their method not on the performance
of individual subjects, but rather on the average performance
of many different groups of subjects.  Perhaps the classic
example of this is an article on the elements of generalized
or lawful relationships between height and weight by A.S.C.
Ehrenberg in 1968 in the Journal of the Royal Statistical
Society, in which he takes very distinct groups of children
with different ages and different other variables and by
taking the log weight against height, he points out that the
means that all fall in a straight line, and thus describe a
straight line which relates height and low weight across many
different kinds of groups.  The kind of groups he has are
13-year-olds from Birmingham, 7-year-olds from Ottawa, 5-
year olds from Birmingham again, and so on.  If you were to
find a group of children whose measures did not fall along

that line, then you can look further to see why they deviate
significantly.

What we have done in a similar situation is to apply
this method to behavioral data. It has been known for a
long time that schizophrenics have a slower reaction time
than normals, partly as a function of lack in motivation
and so on. Some work has actually been able to shorten the
reaction time in schizophrenics to normal, if they use metho
for increasing motivation. We presented in a group of schiz
phrenics and normals, light and sound in a variety of random
sequences, and then compared the response to light following
a light (ipsi modal) to the response to light following soun
(cross modal). In this way we randomized the effect of motivation. We discovered that the response to light following
a sound was longer than the response to light following a
light. Because of problems in the original diagnostic assign
ments, we reviewed the diagnostic status of the entire
group and discovered that there were some schizophrenics who
were not schizophrenic, and there were some normals who
weren't normal; so we had four groups: "pure normals,"
"impure normals," "pure schizophrenics," and "impure schizophrenics". We did a covariance analysis and there was no
difference among the groups. Then we applied the Fleiss-
Tanur method. We discovered with this method that the
schizophrenics were distinctly different. This is essentiall
not a new, but a different technique for getting away from
errors of measurement and getting away from intra-group
regression lines. We're not worried about intra-group relationships; all we're worried about is do the mean relationships between groups fall along a straight line?

This matter of reliability introduces a very interesting old classic problem, the placebo problem. Why is it
that you always get about 30% of the placebo group improved,
and furthermore, why are they not always the same people on
repeat trials? If you assume that the original reliability
of the classification measure is of the order of 57%, then
it follows mathematically that 30% will show improvement,
no matter what the treatment. And furthermore, if you look
at outcome data over the centuries, you usually find that
one-third of the patients get better, one-third get worse,
one-third remain unchanged, If you assume that the reliability of the diagnosis of normal/abnormal and for outcome is approximately .57, again you will come up with

one-third, one-third, one-third as a necessary statistical
result no matter what the treatment amounts to. So we have
this unreliability problem with us most of the time (Windle,
1962).

Let me say one or two words about Myrna Weissman's paper.
I think it's an excellent idea to bring back the old life
table method which has been neglected for so long in our
field. It's true, we have used it for mortality analysis
and for first-admission analysis, but until now we haven't
used it in the follow-up studies that have been done. Why
is it so important to have the life table approaches? Well,
for one reason, it includes all data. You don't have to stop
at a particular point in time, you don't have to throw away
the dead, the drop-outs - they're all included in the picture.
Dr. Fleiss and his colleagues have recently illustrated its
use in follow-up studies of manic-depressives (Fleiss, et al.,
1976).

Open Discussion

Overall: In response to your points about reliability,
the concept of reliability is concerned with the relative
magnitude of the components of variance due to true individual differences and the components of variance due to random measurement error. With regard to the power of tests
of significance of change, one way to maximize that power is
to minimize the experimental error, so we're concerned with
the magnitude of the experimental error. In terms of measurement models, experimental error is composed of two components:
a true component due to the true differences between the individuals in the sample, and in addition, a measurement error
component. The measurement error component is essentially
inherent in the measuring instrument, and it always pays to
get a more precise measuring instrument. But given a particular measuring instrument, then we should still be concerned
with the component of variance due to true differences between subjects, or what I'll call sampling error. Now reliability does depend on the magnitude of interaction in a
simple subjects by time design; however, it is not understandable to me how you could say that the more reliable your
difference scores, the more useful they are in assessing
change. If subtracting one score from another would remove
entirely the true component, the true differences between

subjects, and leave only the measurement error as a source
of variability of the difference scores, you will have
reduced your experimental error to a minimum insofar as it
is possible to do so with that measuring instrument. But at
the same time, if you achieve that you have zero reliability.
Thus, the closer our difference scores approach zero reliability for a given measuring instrument, the better they are
in terms of measuring significance of change. I won't
comment on the analysis of covariance problems, since we do
have a rather extensive treatment of that in another manu-
script. We have also in press a more technical reply to Dr.
Fleiss in Psychological Bulletin, 1976, where any interested
person can see your criticims of the change-score reliability issue debunked.

Zubin: Well, I'll hide behind my excuse of being a
psychologist. I think that if you have a yardstick that
contracts and expands, it is unreliable, as compared to the
yardstick that stands up rigidly and gives you the same
measure each time. Just on the basis of common sense, I
wouldn't take that rubber yardstick, I'd take the rigid
yardstick.

Overall: It is the reliability of difference scores,
though, Dr. Zubin, not the reliability of the rigid measuring instrument.

Zubin: Dr. Overall should be aware that we are not
stuck with the measurement error component of variance for
a given measuring instrument; we can make it as small as we
like by obtaining as many repeat determinations on each subject, as necessary. We are, however, stuck with the interaction component of variance. On every psychologically
meaningful variable different subjects change by different
amounts. I would be suspicious of a measuring instrument
for which this was not the case.


Formal Discussant: Fini Schulsinger

I'll start out by congratulating the people here in
Rochester with the Monroe County Register. That's a very
good thing and can be used for many, many things. As you
know, we have a register in Denmark and we have utilized it
for many purposes. I'll give you a little list of things we
have used this old register for. As you know, we have done

family studies using adopted schizophrenics. We have screened the adoptive population, and we have screened their parents in the psychiatric register. We have been doing studies of adoptees who have a biological parent who is alcoholic. One other question we are studying as well is an issue that has been discussed for years; namely, whether the hallucinogenic psychoses from LSD and amphetaimes are psychosis per se, or if they only happen in people who have a family disposition for schizophrenia. We are doing a study on that using the register where we can easily pick out 500 LSD and amphetamine psychoses over the last few years and do a family study. So that's very nice and to further tell how good it is, I'll mention the study by Tsuang and Winokur because that is a good illustration of how difficult it is to do studies when you have not got a psychiatric register. It's a big, big, big work to do studies like their study. If they had had a psychiatric register in Iowa City, they wouldn't have had to do all that work.

I conceive of the Iowa 500 study as a technically well-thought out repetition of many, many earlier studies using follow-up and family histories, and it might very well yield a relatively excat version of the natural history of schizophrenia and of affective disorder in a changing era during which ECT, insulin treatment, and neuroleptics were introduced. It would help out, though, I think, if the investigators structured their research to test a known hypothesis in this field and also some sociological hypothesis; I think the outcome would be more precise if the analyses were designed to test certain hypotheses over this long span of changing years.

What we are doing in Denmark is an aggregate of studies, and there is one common paradigm used. That is the paradigm of an old Danish geneticist, Johansson: the genotype plus the environment results in the phenotype. And most of the research which is going to be discussed later in this meeting can be viewed with this model as a background. Let me give you just a small example of how flexible it is and how nice it is. For instance, we did a family study using psychopathic children who were adopted away in early life, and we wanted to test a hypothesis that brain damage as a result of perinatal complication might be an etiological factor. We had the psychopaths, we had the birth histories, and the types and prevalence of mental illness in the biological

relatives.  The hypothesis then, was that if such complications are an etiological factor, you would expect less
character disorder in the biological relatives of those
psychopaths who had had complicated births.  You have the
genotype (a family score of mental illness) as the dependent
variable.  You have the environment, which is well defined
because it is a perinatal score.  And you have the phenotype
that is diagnosis, so it is under control, everyone is a
reliably-diagnosed psychopath.  If you try this model out
on other types of studies as well, you will find that any
of the three parts of the model can be either the dependent
variable, or deferred or be under control.


Open Discussion

   Thomas:  With regard to ethical issues in longitudinal
research, a point made by Dr. Weissman, I think that the
nature of longitudinal studies, at least certain of them,
is such that ethical issues of great importance inevitably
arise.  Even if you have a study such as we have in which
you gather data on a population over time, and then a certain number of the youngsters develop behavior problems,
you're faced with the question, do you intervene and ad-
vise the parents on the basis of the information you have?
If you don't intercede, what are the ethical issues concerned?
Many such ethical issues come up in long-term longitudinal
studies that don't come up in short-term studies.

   Regarding the difference between naturalistic and controlled studies, in many long-term longitudinal studies the
differences in care that some children get may provide a
blend of the naturalistic and experimental.  You may start
with a naturalistic study, in which you gather behavioral
data without controls, yet you may get differential outcomes
with differential life experiences occurring which provide
you essentially with the possibility of an experimental situation occurring naturally.  For the converse, in longitudinal
experimental or controlled studies, over time changes do occur
aside from the changes we think we're introducing by our own
variables that we control, so that these studies become more
naturalistic.

   Weissman:  Regarding ethical issues in longitudinal research, I think that in psychiatry we're not at the point

for example, where the Framingham longitudinal study of
heart disease is.  As a result of the Framingham study, we
know what the risk factors are for heart disease, and we can
define who has a high probability of developing heart disease
and who might be treated with preventive measures.  We
don't quite know this in psychiatry.  Hopefully in the future
we will be able to define which portion of the well population is at high risk for developing a psychiatric disorder.
In a longitudinal study in psychiatry, if you have a child
who develops a disease, then you would recommend treatment
for him, but we don't know enough about the risk factors for
psychiatric disorders and say who among the well persons we
should treat as a preventive measure.

 Zubin:   There's one more point, I believe that needs
to be said here.  It isn't so much a question of whether
naturalistic studies are good or not good.  The real issue
methodologically is do we have the techniques for examining
the data that we obtain on naturally formed groups?  For
example, the application of the covariance method to naturalistic groups has been questioned.  I would not be surprised
if some of the designs using analysis of variance might also
be criticized.  In other words, the question is how can we
translate from the randomization approach in experimentation
to observational studies, and I think that in itself is worthy
of a session sometime.

 Strauss:   I think it works the other way, too, that
sometimes the controlled study may eliminate a lot of the
variables that you don't yet know are important.  Carrying
out controlled studies without having a good mapping of a
large area using the naturalistic approach first can lead
to a lot of error and misunderstanding.  There may be
variables that are crucial determinants of results that you
have no idea of.  I think there is a reciprocity between
the naturalistic and controlled designs.  In the naturalistic study, you should collect a wide range of data, too.
Deciding to carry out controlled studies should usually
imply that you have an idea what the key variables are,
and that they are the ones you're looking at.

 Klein:   There are two kinds of study - a hypothesis-
generating study, and a hypothesis-testing study.  What
John Strauss has said is that you have to have some good
hypothesis generating studies before you get to the hypothesis testing stage, and I think that's scientific common

sense. The question is, to what degree can you test hypotheses on the basis of non-experimental designs. I think that the approach that John Overall has taken, is, that he has moved away from the idea of testing hypotheses to model fitting. What he's saying is that if he can generate models and show you that his model fits the naturalistic data, it may not be the right model, but at least it fits the data pretty well, so we ought to pay attention to that model. I think that's what he's doing, but that's not my idea of a way to test hypotheses, but rather of a way to generate them.

Fleiss, J.L., and Tanur, J.M. The analysis of covariance in psychopathology. In Hanuver, M., Salzinger, K., and Sutton, S. (Eds.), Psychopathology, contributions from the social, behavioral and biological sciences. John Wiley and Sons, 1973.

Windle, C. Prognosis of mental subnormals: a critical review of research. American Journal of Mental Disease, Supplement 5:180, 1962.

Fleiss, J.L., Dunner, D.L., Stallone, F., and Fieve, R.R. The life table: a method for analyzing longitudinal studies. Archives of General Psychiatry, 1976, 33, 107-112.

# Section II

# Life Events

THE CONCEPTUALIZATION AND MEASUREMENT OF STRESSFUL LIFE

EVENTS: AN OVERVIEW OF THE ISSUES

Bruce P. Dohrenwend
Department of Psychology
Columbia University

Barbara Snell Dohrenwend
Department of Psychology
City College of the City University of New York

Studies of the effects of natural and man-made disasters --especially the disaster of war--have provided the most unequivocal evidence for the proposition that stressful events can produce psychopathology in previously normal personalities (cf. Arthur, 1974; Cooper & Shepherd, 1970; Kinson & Rosser, 1974; Hocking, 1970). For example, when a systematic sample of the population in a rural section of Arkansas was interviewed shortly after the area was hit by a severe tornado, 90 per cent reported "...some form of acute emotional, physiological or psychosomatic after-effect" (Fritz & Marks, 1954, p. 34). Similarly, pervasive effects were implied by Star's (1949) finding, based on a series of studies during World War II using subscales from the Neuropsychiatric Screening Adjunct, that "...the fear and anxiety implicit in combat brought forth psychosomatic manifestations in so many men that these (symptom scales) served less and less to discriminate between men who were labeled psychiatric casualties and those who were not" (p. 455).

Although elevation in symptom levels was not necessarily accompanied by breakdown in performance, under some conditions such breakdowns became endemic. In a study of 2,630 soldiers who had broken down during combat in the Normandy campaign during World War II, Swank estimated that the onset of combat

*This work has been supported by Research Grant MH10328 and by Research Scientist Award K5 MH14663 from the National Institute of Mental Health, U.S. Public Health Service.

93

exhaustion occurred even in previously normal soldiers when
about 65 per cent of their companions had been killed,
wounded or had otherwise become casualties (1949, p. 501).
Swank emphasized that the men in this study had been highly
selected for health and ability to cope.  As he describes
them:  "They were of better than average stability and willingness by virtue of the fact that they had passed the various
training tests (induction, overseas assignment, battle simu-
lation exercises), had been selected for combat units, and had
proved their mettle by remaining in combat varying lengths of
time" (p. 476).  And while men who were stable prior to combat remained in combat longer without breaking down (p. 480
and p. 500), such prior stability did not prevent the eventual
onset of combat exhaustion (p. 507).

Nor are the symptoms caused by such situations of extreme
stress limited to those included under the heading of trau-
matic war neurosis, combat fatigue, and combat exhaustion.
There is evidence that psychotic symptoms can appear in the
form of what have been called "three day" psychoses (Kolb,
1973, p. 438).  It is possible, in fact, that such extreme
circumstances can play a major role in inducing outright psychotic disorder since, as Paster (1948) found, there is far
less evidence of individual predisposing factors in combat
soldiers who became psychotic than among soldiers who developed psychotic disorders in less stressful circumstances.  It
would seem that most of the varied signs and symptoms observed
in psychiatric patients in civilian settings have also been
observed as reactions to combat (e.g., Kolb, 1973, pp. 436-
438).  In this sense, war has been indeed "a laboratory which
manufactures psychological dysfunction: (Grinker & Spiegel,
1963, p. vii).

The extent to which symptomatology and disturbance of
functioning produced by such extreme situations in previously
normal persons are transient and self-limiting is a matter of
controversy (cf. Kinston & Rosser, 1974).  Most observers
have emphasized the transience of the symptoms (cf. Dohrenwend
& Dohrenwend, 1969, pp. 110-130).  At the same time, follow-
up studies of persons exposed to these extraordinary events
have repeatedly found some individuals with more or less severe pathology that apparently began at the time the stress-
full experience occurred (cf. Kinston & Rosser, 1974, pp.
445-448).  Certainly at the extreme of exposure to the brutal-
ities of Nazi concentration camps, there is strong evidence

that not only does severe stress-induced psychopathology persist in the survivors (Eitinger, 1964), but also that the
survivors are more prone to physical illness and early death
(Eitinger, 1973).

## THE PROBLEM

Natural and man-made disasters, fortunately, are rare
occurrences whose devastating effects are limited to relatively small populations of exposed persons. Most people live
their lives without experiencing any of these extraordinary
events. Yet psychopathology and somatic disturbances are far
from rare in peace-time populations relatively secure from war,
flood, famine and other disasters. If stressful situations
play an etiological role in these disorders, the events involved must be more ordinary, more frequent experiences in the
lives of most people. It is for this reason that we turn our
attention to things that happen to most people at one time or
another -- things such as marriage, birth of a first child,
and death of a loved one. These are not extraordinary events
in the sense of being rare occurrences in most populations.
But they are extraordinary occurrences in the lives of the
individuals who experience them. They are the life events
that most of us experience, in a greater or lesser number,
over our allotted years.

Most of these life events, taken singly, are far less extreme than natural or man-made disasters. One reason is that
a disaster is likely to entail as sequelae a number of events
all at the same time or closely spaced in sequence -- injury,
loss of home and other possessions, death of a loved one. It
seems reasonable to assume that life events must show a cumulative pattern, a clustering in the lives of some people in
otherwise more ordinary times if they are to have a similarly
stressful impact and similarly severe consequences. This is
the strongest reason, for seeking information about the occurrence of a wide variety of life events in relation to one another in investigations of the possible etiological significance of such events in physical and psychological disorders.
If this is so, the central question becomes: What kinds of
life events in what combination over what period of time, and
under what circumstances are causally implicated in various
types of physical and psychiatric disorders?

To date, the results of research on the influence of

these more ordinary life events on various types of physical
and psychiatric conditions are far more equivocal than the
results of research on the effects of natural and man-made
disasters.  We will, therefore, selectively review the results of this research over the past ten years and the controversies which these investigations have given rise as a
background in our attempt to set forth the major methodological issues that need to be resolved.


PREVIOUS RESEARCH ON STRESSFUL LIFE EVENTS


The Correlates of Such Events

The greatest variety of correlates of life events has
been described by Holmes and Masuda (1974).  In addition to
reporting that overall changes in health were related to life
events, they cited studies showing the following specific
correlates:  heart disease, fractures, childhood leukemia,
pregnancy, beginning of prison term, poor teacher performance,
low college grade point average, and football injuries.  Among
the specific somatic disorders, Hinkle (1974, p. 38) and
Theorell (1974) have focused attention on coronary heart disease both fatal and nonfatal.

Paykel (1974), Hudgens (1974), and Brown (1974) have
added evidence that various types of psychiatric disorder may
follow life events; specifically, acute schizophrenia, depression, suicide attempts and neurosis.  The range of correlates
has been expanded to include associations with symptom scales
that measure various types of psychological distress rather
than outright disorder.  Markush and Favero (1974) found that
relatively mild symptoms of depression as well as a symptom
scale of less specific psychological distress were related to
measures of life events.  Uhlenhuth, Lipman, Balter, and
Stern (1974) have reported similar findings. Myers, Lindenthal
and Pepper (1974) have shown with still another measure of
symptomatic distress that symptom scores will fluctuate over
time with fluctuations in the nature and number of life events
experienced.  And Gersten, Langner, Eisenberg and Orzek (1974)
have shown that the associations between various symptom measures and life events hold for children as well as for adults.
Such evidence from recent clinical and epidemiological investigations ·is consistent with Hinkle's conclusion "...that

there would probably be no aspect of human growth, development, or disease which would in theory be immune to the influence of the effect of a man's relation to his social and
interpersonal environment" (Hinkle, 1974, p. 10). It would
seem that almost any disease or disability may be associated
with these events.


## Controversy About Interpretation

But "may" is not "will;" the important questions become:
First, what is the probability, or risk that disorder will
actually follow life events? And second, if disorder does
follow, why is it of one type rather than another? On these
questions, we find ourselves in the realm of controversy.

Holmes and Masuda, for example, appear to assume that a
clustering in time of life events of sufficient magnitude
will have strong etiological implications for physical or
psychiatric health that are relatively independent of constitutional or other predisposing characteristics of the individual involved. They postulate that when more ordinary life
events accumulate to "crisis" proportions, these events will
evoke "adaptive efforts by the human organism that are faulty
in kind and duration, lower 'bodily resistance' and enhance
the probability of disease occurrence" (1974, p. 68). Such
a "crisis" will have "etiologic significance as a necessary,
but not sufficient, cause of illness and accounts in part for
the time of disease onset" (p. 48). By contrast, Hinkle (1974)
sees the role of predisposing factors as primary, with accumu-
lations of stressful life events playing a very secondary part.
Other investigators tend more or less explicitly to assign
varied weights to life events as a threat to health in general
or in the etiology of particular disorders (cf. Dohrenwend &
Dohrenwend, 1974). In general the consensus that has grown
up about the impact of extreme situations such as natural or
man-made disasters has not extended to more ordinary stressful
life events.


## SOURCES OF CONTROVERSY

The basic difficulty is that the evidence currently
available simply does not permit us to answer questions about
how important stressful life events are in the etiology of

the various types of symptomatology and disorder with which
such events have been found to be associated.  There are
three sets of reasons for the ambiguities:  The first has to
do with the designs of most of the research in which such
correlations have been found; the second with the ways the
populations of stressful life events have been defined and
sampled for purposes of these investigations; and the third
involves the procedures used to assess the stressfulness of
the life events independently of their relation to the symptoms, illnesses or disorders that are being investigated.


## Design Limitations

The majority of the studies of the effects of stressful
life events have involved case-control designs.  That is, the
investigators have started with a group or series of patients
and then compared these cases with a group or series of controls, usually healthy persons matched to the clinical cases
on some of the relevant background characteristics.

In the case-control studies, the frequent finding that,
compared to their controls, the clinical cases tend to have
an excess of stressful life events prior to illness onset suggests that such events are a factor in the etiology of the
disorder.  However, only studies of cohorts of persons who
differ with respect to the nature and number of stressful life
events experienced provide information about the magnitude of
the risk that illness will actually follow these events. While
a few such studies of general health changes in special groups
of non-patients have been published (cf. Holmes & Masuda,
1974), research on relations between diagnosed psychiatric
disorders and life events in non-patient populations is barely
beginning (e.g. Dohrenwend, 1974).  Most of the published literature on relations between life events and psychological
problems in general populations contains reports of results
for scales measuring psychological distress in general rather
than for cases of psychiatric disorders.  And only a few such
studies (e.g., Myers, Lindenthal, & Pepper, 1974) provide data
over time.  By and large, therefore, there is no satisfactory
way from the existing data to calculate the magnitude of risk
entailed in various types and numbers of life events for physical illnesses (Dohrenwend & Dohrenwend, 1974, especially
pages 315-316) much less for psychiatric disorders.

Problems in Defining and Sampling the Relevant
Population of Stressful Life Events

Especially where the role of life events in relation to
psychopathology is being examined, there is a problem not
only about how to estimate the magnitude of risk attached to
the life events but, even more basic, whether etiological inferences from the correlations of these events with psychopathology are even warranted.  This problem resides less in
the research designs used to investigate the events than in
how the events to be studied have been defined and sampled.

Consider some of the general definitions of stressful
life events by researchers who have investigated the relations
of various samples of such events to physical and psychological symptoms and disorders.  For Holmes and Rahe extrapolating
from the types of events that they extracted from "life
charts" recording case histories of patients admitted to
treatment for medical problems, stressful life events are
those "whose advent is either indicative of or requires a significant change in the ongoing life pattern of the individual"
(1967, p. 217).  Brown and Birley focus on "events which on
common sense grounds are likely to produce emotional disturbance in many people ...(and usually involve) either danger;
significant changes in health, status or way of life; the
promise of these; or important fulfillments or disappoint-
ments" (1968, p. 204).  Similarly, Myers and his colleagues
define "crises" or "events" as "experiences involving role
transformations, changes in status or environment, or imposi-
tions of pain" (1972, p. 399).  And Antonovsky and Kats refer
to "life crises" consisting of "objective situations which, on
the face of it, would seem to be universally stressful" and
involving "an experience which either imposed pain or necessitated a role transformation" (1967, p. 16).

These definitions indicate both broad agreement and some
differences in emphasis concerning what is important about
life events.  The agreement centers on the idea that stressful
life events include those that involve change in the usual
activities of most individuals who experience them.  The differences and the reasons for them are more varied.

Some of the differences are straightforward in the sense
that there are important events that are specific and meaning-

ful to some groups of subjects and not to others. For example, it is meaningful to include "court martial" on lists of
events to be investigated among military personnel (Rahe et
al., 1967) and experience in Nazi concentration camps in
studies done in Israel (Antonovsky & Kats, 1967). Other differences, however, reflect underlying issues of major theoretical and methodological importance that are barely suggested
by the contrasts in emphasis among the highly abstract and im-
precise general definitions of life events quoted above.

    The first of these issues is partly evident in the dis-
tinction between objective and subjective events made by some
investigators (e.g., Thurlow, 1970). Subjective events --
for example, "sexual difficulties," "major changes in number
of arguments with spouse," and "major changes in sleeping
habits" (Holmes & Masuda, 1974, pp. 48-49) are more likely to
be manifestations of or responses to underlying psychopathology than causes of such pathology. Moreover, the problem is
not limited to "subjective" events since many objective events
such as "divorce" or "being fired from work" (e.g., Holmes &
Masuda, 1974, pp. 48-49) contained on the lists of different
researchers are as likely to be consequences as causes of
psychopathology -- depending on the investigator's ability to
date their onset in relation to the onset of the pathology and
to learn something about whether the events are within or outside the control of the subject. By Hudgens' count, for example, 29 out of the 43 events on the list constructed by Holmes
and Rahe (1967) "are often the symptoms or consequences of
illness" (Hudgens, 1974, p. 131). As Brown (1974) and B.P.
Dohrenwend (1974) have pointed out, this kind of bias in a
sample of life events seriously limits the kinds of inferences
that can be drawn from a correlation between the number or
magnitude of events experienced and illness. The limitation
on causal inference in particular is especially severe in investigations of psychiatric disorders that are often of insidious onset and long duration.

    Most samples of events also include major physical illness
or injury -- understandably enough since these are negative
events and entail serious disruption of usual activities. However, it is a basic proposition of psychosomatic medicine that
physical disorders are accompanied by some degree of emotional
disturbance and emotional disorders by some degree of somatic
disturbance. There is no instance of which we are aware in
which investigations of relations between physical illness and

emotional disturbance have failed to report a strong positive
correlation between the two (cf. Lipowski, 1975). And, as
Hinkle points out with reference to various types of physical
illness, "the presence of one disease may imply the presence
of others and beget yet other disease" (1974, p. 39), a fact
that accounts in part for his findings that risk of disease
is not randomly distributed in groups of similar people who
share similar experiences over periods of from ten to twenty
years (Hinkle, 1974). Thus, once again, a sample of events
that includes physical illness and injury -- and most lists
do -- can lead to further problems of interpretation when the
events are summed to provide scores for the amount of stress
experienced by particular individuals. The additional problem
of interpretation centers on the extent to which a positive
correlation indicates the impact of amount of change and hence
amount of stress or, instead, the relation among physical illnesses or between physical and psychiatric symptomatology --
important problems in their own right.

We have argued, therefore, that there are at least three
distinct populations of life events that must be sampled and
kept distinct for purposes of analysis (B.P. Dohrenwend, 1974;
Dohrenwend & Dohrenwend , 1974). These are:

1.  A population of events that are confounded with the
    psychiatric condition of the subject.

2.  A population of events consisting of physical ill-
    nesses and injuries to the subject.

3.  A population of events whose occurrences are inde-
    pendent of either the subject's physical health or
    his psychiatric condition.

As a general principle, the more a sample of events in a
particular measure of stressful life events represents a sum-
mated mixture from these three event populations, the more
difficult it is to assess the etiological implications of a
relationship between such a measure and various types of psychopathology.

Nor is it likely that meaningful distinctions will end
with specification of these three main types of event populations. Paykel and his colleagues (1974), for example, have
found in case-control studies that events involving loss or

exit of significant others from the immediate environment are
conspicuous in the onset of depressive disorders. This is, of
course, a theoretically relevant finding and it raises the in-
triguing possibility that other theoretically dictated distinctions may sharpen the specificity with which particular
outcomes can be predicted for particular types of stressful
life events.

It would seem, then, that it will be necessary to refine
the largely common sense definitions of stressful life events
quoted above if we are to build on available theory and on
the research already done while avoiding some of the problems
and pitfalls involved in previous work. Such specification
would be a prerequisite to deciding on the relevant populations of events to be sampled -- for example, physical illnesses and accidents, loss events outside the individual's
control, and so on. Once the realms of events in which we are
interested have been designated, it is also useful to get nom-
inations by the subjects to be studied as to the composition
of these populations of events. We have found in our own previous research that the respondents we have interviewed mentioned quite a number of events that have been major ones in
their lives that we failed to include on our own "common
sense" checklist of events (e.g., B.P. Dohrenwend, 1974). Our
question to our respondents was: "What is the last major
event in your life that, for better or worse, interrupted or
changed your usual activities?" As our own definitions of
what constitutes stressful life events become more precise, we
should be able to put more and more precise questions to our
subjects as we enlist their help in delimiting the relevant
populations of life events to be sampled.

Once the realms of events to be sampled have been enumerated, the question becomes one of how to sample them in a particular study. There is no easy answer. Coverage of the
total population of events experienced by a particular individual over the course of his or her lifetime runs into major
practical obstacles; foremost among them is the problem of
imperfect recall of remote events (cf. Uhlenhuth, Balter, &
Lipman, 1974). It is for this reason that focus is often on
a recent time sample of events -- say during the past year.
We strongly suspect, however, that the factors of primacy,
frequency and recency would affect the impact of life events
as they do most things (cf. Horowitz, Schaefer, & Cooney,
1974). For example, if the loss reported in the past year

is one in a cumulative pattern of losses over the preceding
five years, it might be expected to have added weight, other
things constant.  On the other hand, it is possible that early
experience with some types of events may innoculate against
adverse effects of recent events of the same kind.  This appears to be the case in bereavement (Bornstein et al., 1973,
p. 565).  There is also evidence that early adversity may be
a factor leading to superior performance later in life -- at
least among highly educated males selected for health
(Vaillant, 1974, p. 19).

The problem is one of how to come to terms with the opposition between practicality and what is required on grounds
of theoretically relevant research operations.  There is never
an easy answer to such a question.  Our own suggestion is to
focus on contemporary events but to study their relation to
psychopathology prospectively as well as retrospectively.  In
addition, we believe it necessary to try as well to elicit
from our subjects by way of context a history of certain more
remote landmark events from the event populations in which we
are most interested (B.P. Dohrenwend, 1974).  Examples of the
latter would be deaths or other major separations from parents
or parent surrogates -- something few adults will fail to remember about their childhood; incapacitating physical injuries
and illnesses -- things likely to be remembered about one's
history of physical problems.

### Assessing the Stressfulness of Life Events

Let us assume for purposes of argument that the general
design limitations and the general problems of defining and
sampling the relevant population of stressful life events discussed above have been surmounted.  This would be a long step
toward being able to assess whether causal inferences from
correlations between life events and various types of disorder
and symptomatology were warranted.  It should also take us
part of the way to learning why different types of disorder
follow stressful life events.  Additional problems will have
to be resolved, however, if we are to be able to specify the
risk attached to life events for various types of disorders.

The magnitude of the events.  In laboratory stress experiments with animals, there is little difficulty in defining
the magnitude of the stressful event to which the subjects
are introduced.  The experimental animals receive shocks of

greater or lesser voltage; are exposed to heat or cold of
varying temperature; are deprived of food for greater or
lesser periods of time; and so on. Similarly, extreme situations appear to have self-evident indications of magnitude:
for example, duration of time in combat; number of wounded
in the soldier's company; and so on. For the more usual life
events with which we are concerned here, however, things are
by no means so clear cut. Is "marriage" more or less stressful than "divorce?" Is "birth of a first child" more or less
stressful than "being laid off a job?" Are "marriage" and
"divorce" together more or less stressful than "birth of a
first child" and "being laid off a job?"

Holmes and Rahe (1967) have offered a very attractive
simplification of this problem. As mentioned earlier, Holmes
and Rahe constructed a list of events that they found were
positively correlated with illness onset in large samples of
medical patients. Their method of scoring these events followed S. S. Stevens' proposal that direct estimation procedures which produce a consistent quantitative relationship
between physical stimuli and perceptual responses could also
be used to measure psychological dimensions related to social
stimuli.

A simple form of this procedure, magnitude estimation,
involves designating a modulus with an assigned value and asking judges to rate other stimuli in relation to the modulus.
Holmes and Rahe designated "marriage" as the modulus, assigned
it a value of 500, and obtained quantitative judgments about
the amount of change or "readjustment" in relation to it for
each of the other 42 events on their list. Life Change Unit
(LCU) scores based on these ratings have been presented as a
measure of the stressfulness of the rated events just as, in
psychophysical experiments, ratings of sounds provide a measure of their loudness. The argument of Holmes and his colleagues is that if we weight events in terms of their different LCU scores and pay attention to how these weights add up
when a series of events occurs, the risk of illness attached
to the life events will vary directly with the magnitude of
the LCU scores.

Holmes in particular has emphasized the high level of
consensus about the amount of change associated with each life
event. He refers to correlations in the .80's and .90's between the mean ratings for each event obtained from such di-

verse status groups as Blacks and Japanese as well as whites. His argument for the universalism of perceptions of the amount of change entailed by and hence the stressfulness of particular life events, however, has been sharply criticized.  Among others, two of Holmes' collaborators have pointed out that considerable group differences are masked by the reported correlations:  Specifically, Rahe (1969) found that ratings secured in Sweden were consistently higher than Holmes' West Coast American ratings.  And Masuda and Holmes (1967) pointed out that certain differences in ratings of events by Japanese and American judges seem to be related to differences between the two cultures.  Other researchers have also reported cultural contrasts.  Miller, Bentz, Aponte, and Brogan (1974) have found sharp differences in the way their sample of rural North Carolina judges and Holmes' and Rahe's urban West Coast sample ranked such events as "marriage" and "taking out a mortgage of greater than $10,000."  In the urban sample, for example, marriage is ranked fourth in terms of the amount of change involved whereas in the rural sample, it is ranked twentyfirst.  Miller et al. make a strong case that these differences are meaningful in terms of contrasts in the norms and customs of the two samples.  Hough, Fairbank and Garcia (1976) have reported differences in the judged magnitude of life events corresponding to differences in the cultural backgrounds of their college student subjects.  Still other critics such as Brown (1974) have pointed out large individual variability in the LCU ratings in Holmes' and Rahe's data.

Nevertheless, there are great virtues in the general procedure developed by Holmes and his colleagues.  It makes sense that some events are, objectively, of greater magnitude than others.  Who would argue, for example, that the "death of a pet" is inherently as large an event as "death of a spouse?"  Yet, it also seems that much further work on the scaling procedures themselves needs to be done (cf. Hough, Fairbank & Garcia, 1976).  Individual variability can probably be reduced by providing less ambiguous descriptions of events to be rated; for example, instead of the event "change in responsibilities at work" supply two events:  "change to more responsibility" and "change to less responsibility at work".  It may also be possible to simplify the rating task and thereby improve reliability of judgments by using categorization procedures rather than direct estimation of a value for each event in relation to a standard.  And the problem of cultural differences in judgments about the events is interesting in its own right as

Holmes is aware.  As he points out, the LCU ratings "offer a powerful tool for delineating quantitatively and qualitativel cross-cultural differences" (1974, p. 57).  If so, the procedure for dealing with such differences would be to secure ratings from members of each of the contrasting groups and compute LCU scores that are specific to each of the groups (cf. Hough, Fairbank, & Garcia, in press).

Moreover, it is possible to envision valuable extensions of the rating procedure.  To date, the judgments have focused on the amount of change associated with the events.  Yet the general definitions of stressful life events quoted earlier mention other properties that might also be scaled.  The desirability or undesirability of the events; the amount of loss or gain involved; and, where illness or injury or crime are involved, the seriousness or severity of the event.  Some important work of this kind has already been done on physical illness of various types by Wyler, Masuda and Holmes (1968). In general, the extension of ratings beyond the single dimension of the amount of change would probably yield improved measures of the stressfulness of life events.

By and large, however, critics of the scaling procedures developed by Holmes and his colleagues have taken other tacks Concern about individual variability in judgments of the magnitude of life events has led to two recent innovations in measurement.  The first is a Subjective Life Change Unit scaling system developed by Rahe (1974, pp. 76-77).  In this procedure, the same subjects who are asked about events that have occurred in their lives and about their illness experiences also rate the amount of change involved in the events they have experienced.  Rahe has found that the resulting subjective LCU scores are better predictors of illness than the objective LCU scores.  The second innovation has been developed by Brown (1974) and relies on interviewers to probe the circumstances surrounding each event experienced by the subject and rate them on a number of dimensions, of which he has found the most useful to be "contextual threat."

While both procedures have the virtue of being directed at real difficulties with the original LCU ratings, both innovations have problems of their own that are at least as severe.  It is difficult to see, for example, what we learn on the basis of Rahe's subjective rating procedure if we find that a person who has suffered a heart attack after a particlar event tends to rate that event as more stressful than a person who has not suffered such an attack. It seems highly likely that his experience with the heart attack would lead the subject to retrospectively place a negative halo around the event. Surely such a rating tells us nothing about the antecedents of the illness that will add to our knowledge of etiology or aid in prevention.

Brown (1974), in contrast with Rahe, argues that his procedure for securing ratings of contextual threat by the interviewer is measuring objective circumstances rather than subjective perceptions of an event. The problem is that his method, at least as it has been developed and described to date, asks that we accept a certain mystification of measurement. So much is left to the interviewer and to his training in this particular procedure that it is not explicit or readily replicable by others. While we think that Brown is right in arguing that the circumstances of an event influence its impact, it is difficult to see how his global rating procedure, as so far developed, advances our understanding of the nature of that influence. The problem, is to make explicit what is implicit in this approach so that its virtues and defects can be assessed.

Mediating factors. The most valuable part of Brown's approach is that it draws attention to the fact that the stressfulness of an event or combination of events may be as much or more a function of the context in which they occur as of the magnitude of the events themselves. Brown (1974) points to contextual threat examined especially in terms of the social circumstances of the subjects of his research on schizophrenia and depression. Antonovsky (1974) theorizes about a wide variety of social and psychological "resistance resources" that mediate the impact of life events. And Hinkle who, as we pointed out earlier, differs most sharply from Holmes on the importance of life events emphasizes "pre-existing illness or susceptibility to illness" (1974, p. 42).

Let us try to clarify this central controversy over the relative importance of stressful life events in contrast with the myriad factors that mediate their impact. To do so, we will make use of a general paradigm of the stress response based on Selye's (1956) formulations. The paradigm consists of four main elements: an antecedent stressor -- often a toxic agent or electric shock in Selye's experiments with animals; conditioning or mediating factors such as climate or

diet that increase or decrease the impact of the stressor; th
General Adaptation Syndrome of nonspecific physical and chemical changes, indicating the intervening state of stress in ɛ
organism over time; and consequent adaptive or, in cases wher
there is a "derailment" of the mechanism of adaptation, maladaptive responses in the form of what Selye calls "diseases
of adaptation."

By stripping these four kinds of elements of particular
examples, it is possible to arrive at the general paradigm of
the individual organism's stress response shown in Figure 1.
This general paradigm, in turn, can be translated into social
and psychological terms (Dohrenwend, 1961).  For example,
stressors can range from extreme situations such as natural
and man-made disasters to the more ordinary stressful life
events that we have been considering.  And mediating factors
can be expanded to include both inner resources (e.g., intellectual abilities, physical health) and external resources
(e.g., material wealth; social support in the form of family
and friends, etc.).

Whether there is a General Adaptation Syndrome of nonspecific physical and chemical changes has been questioned
(Mason, 1975).  Whether there is anything directly analogous
to it in social and psychological terms is an open issue.  We
have, therefore, left out the adjective "general" in Figure 1
Certainly, however, social psychological adaptation syndromes
must have affective elements of adaptation rooted in the
arousal responses of fear and anger; conative elements of adaptation involving change or re-emphasis in activities --
abandoning some activities, taking up others, increasing or de
creasing still other activities; finally, adaptation is also
likely to involve changes in orientation involving assimilation of new information, alteration of beliefs, and so on.
Finally, when the adaptation fails or the mechanisms underlying it become "derailed," we can look for maladaptive responses in the form of transient or persistent psychopathology

In the context of this paradigm, it is easy to see why
the results of research on extreme situations such as exposur
to combat in wartime have seemed so much clearer than the results of research on more ordinary stressful life events.  No
only are differentials in the severity of combat stressors
self evident (e.g., the casualty rate for a company; duration
of combat), but also, these stressors have been shown to be

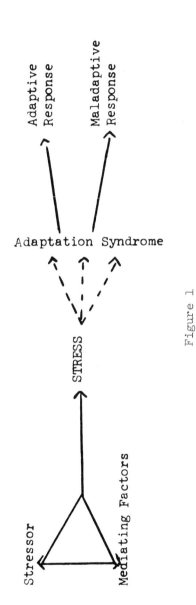

Figure 1

General Paradigm of the Stress Response

From: Bruce P. Dohrenwend, "The Social Psychological Nature of Stress," *Journal of Abnormal and Social Psychology*, 1961, *62*: 294-302.

more important than internal and external mediating factors.
Thus while such external mediating factors as leadership,
troop morale and such internal mediating factors as prior
psychiatric disorder are important in determining, for example, how much combat can be withstood before combat exhaustion occurs, the severity of the combat situations will
override such mediating factors (e.g., Swank, 1949).

Nothing of the sort has been shown to be the case with
more usual stressful life events in civilian populations in
times of peace.  Rather, it is in questions about the relativ
importance of the life events in contrast with the external
and internal factors that mediate their impact that the major
theoretical controversies occur -- for physical illness (cf.
Holmes & Masuda, 1974; Hinkle, 1974; Mechanic, 1974) as well
as for psychiatric disorders (cf. Hudgens, 1974; Brown, 1974;
B.P. Dohrenwend, 1974).  There are unanswered empirical questions underlying this controversy.  If we are to have better
answers, we shall have to be able to measure the magnitude of
the life events with something approaching the incisiveness
with which we measure the magnitude of electric shock or exposure to combat.

## CONCLUSION

Life events are eminently researchable.  They happen to
the people we study and are important to them.  Life events
are things that people know about, are interested in and can
tell us about.  If environmentally induced stress is an important factor in psychopathology, then life events are stra-
tegic phenomena on which to focus as possible major sources
of such stress.

The problem, however, is to ask the right questions about
life events and their effects under circumstances in which the
answers will provide clear demonstrations of whether and to
what extent they are causally related to psychopathology.  As
our analysis above suggests, it is by no means clear that research to date has demonstrated their importance either in the
etiology of psychiatric disorders or of physical illnesses --
though the fascinating tangle of correlations thus far reported virtually demands increased research effort toward
clarification (cf. Dohrenwend and Dohrenwend, 1974).  We have
described our views about some of the ingredients such efforts
should have if advances are to be made.

REFERENCES

1.  Antonovsky, A., & Kats, R.  The life crisis history as a
    tool in epidemiological research.  Journal of Health and
    Social Behavior, 1967, 8, 15-21.

2.  Antonovsky, A.  Conceptual and methodological problems in
    the study of resistance resources and stressful life
    events.  In B.P. Dohrenwend & B.S. Dohrenwend (Eds.),
    Stressful life events:  Their nature and effects.  New
    York:  Wiley, 1974. Pp. 245-255.

3.  Arthur, R.J.  Extreme stress in adult life and psychic and
    psychophysiological consequences.  In E.K.E. Gunderson &
    R.H. Rahe (Eds.), Life stress and illness.  Springfield,
    Ill.:  Charles C. Thomas, 1974.  Pp. 195-207.

4.  Bornstein, P.E., Clayton, P.J., Halikas, J.A., Maurice, W.
    L., & Robins, E.  The depression of widowhood after thir-
    teen months.  British Journal of Psychiatry, 1973, 122,
    561-566.

5.  Brown, G.W.  Meaning, measurement, and stress of life
    events.  In B.P. Dohrenwend & B.S. Dohrenwend (Eds.),
    Stressful life events:  Their nature and effects.  New
    York:  Wiley, 1974, Pp. 217-243.

6.  Cooper, B. & Shepherd, M.  Life change, stress and mental
    disorder:  The ecological approach.  In J.H. Price (Ed.),
    Modern trends in psychological medicine, Volume 2.  Lon-
    don:  Butterworths, 1970.  Pp. 102-130.

7.  Dohrenwend, B.P.  The social psychological nature of
    stress:  A framework for causal inquiry.  Journal of
    Abnormal and Social Psychology, 1961, 62, 294-302.

8.  Dohrenwend, B.P.  Problems in defining and sampling the
    relevant population of stressful life events.  In B.P.
    Dohrenwend & B.S. Dohrenwend (Eds.).  Stressful life
    events:  Their nature and effects.  New York:  Wiley, 1974.
    Pp. 275-310.

9.  Dohrenwend, B.P., & Dohrenwend, B.S.  Social status and
    psychological disorder.  New York:  Wiley, 1969.

10.  Dohrenwend, B.S., & Dohrenwend, B.P. (Eds.), Stressful
     life events: Their nature and effects. New York: Wile
     1974.

11.  Eitinger, L. Concentration camp survivors in Norway anc
     Israel. London: Allen & Unwin, 1964.

12.  Eitinger, L. A follow-up of the Norwegian concentratior
     camp survivors' mortality and morbidity. Israel Annals
     of Psychiatry and Related Disciplines, 1973, 11, 199-20S

13.  Fritz, C.E., & Marks, E.S. The NORC studies of human
     behavior in disaster. Journal of Social Issues, 1954,
     10, 26-41.

14.  Gersten, J.C., Langner, T.S., Eisenberg, J.G., & Orzek, I
     Child behavior and life events: Undesirable change or
     change per se? In B.P. Dohrenwend & B.S. Dohrenwend
     (Eds.), Stressful life events: Their nature and effects
     New York: Wiley, 1974. Pp. 159-170.

15.  Grinker, R.R., & Spiegel, J.P. Men under stress. New
     York: McGraw-Hill, 1963.

16.  Hinkle, L.E. The effect of exposure to culture change,
     social change, and changes in interpersonal relationship
     on health. In B.P. Dohrenwend & B.S. Dohrenwend (Eds.),
     Stressful life events: Their nature and effects. New Yo
     Wiley, 1974, Pp. 9-44.

17.  Hocking, F. Extreme environmental stress and its signif-
     icance for psychopathology. American Journal of Psycho-
     therapy, 1970, 24, 4-26.

18.  Holmes, T.H., & Masuda, M. Life change and illness sus-
     ceptibility. In B.P. Dohrenwend and B.S. Dohrenwend
     (Eds.), Stressful life events: Their nature and effects.
     New York: Wiley, Pp. 45-72.

19.  Holmes, T.H., & Rahe, R.H. The social readjustment
     rating scale. Journal of Psychosomatic Medicine, 1967,
     11, 213-218.

20.  Horowitz, M.J., Schaefer, C., & Cooney, P. Life event
     scaling for recency of experience. In E.K. Gunderson & F
     H. Rahe (Eds.), Life stress and illness. Springfield,

Ill.:   Charles C. Thomas, 1974.   Pp. 125-133.

21.  Hough, R.L., Fairbank, D.T., & Garcia, A.M.   Problems in
     the ratio measurement of life stress.   Journal of Health
     and Social Behavior, 1976, 17, 70-82.

22.  Hudgens, R.W.   Personal catastrophe and depression:   A
     consideration of the subject with respect to medically
     ill adolescents, and a requiem for retrospective life-
     event studies.   In B.P. Dohrenwend & B.S. Dohrenwend
     (Eds.), Stressful life events:   Their nature and effects.
     New York:   Wiley, 1974.   Pp. 119-134.

23.  Kinston, W., & Rosser, R.   Disaster:   Effects on mental
     and physical state.   Journal of Psychosomatic Research,
     1974, 18, 437-456.

24.  Kolb, L.C.   Modern Clinical Psychiatry.   Philadelphia:
     W.B. Saunders, 1973.

25.  Lipowski, Z.J.   Psychiatry of somatic diseases:   Epide-
     miology, pathogensis, classification.   Comprehensive
     Psychiatry, 1975, 16, 105-124.

26.  Markush, R.E., & Favero, R.V.   Epidemiologic assessment of
     stressful life events, depressed mood, and psychophysio-
     logical symptoms -- a preliminary report.   In B.P.
     Dohrenwend & B.S. Dohrenwend (Eds.).   Stressful life
     events:   Their nature and effects.   New York:   Wiley, 1974
     Pp. 171-190.

27.  Mason, J.W.   A historical view of the stress field.   Jour-
     nal of Human Stress, 1975, 1, 6-12.

28.  Mechanic, D.   Discussion of research programs on relations
     between stressful life events and episodes of physical
     illness.   In B.P. Dohrenwend & B.S. Dohrenwend (Eds.),
     Stressful life events:   Their nature and effects.   New
     York:   Wiley, 1974, Pp. 87-97.

29.  Miller, F.T., Bentz, W.K., Aponte, J.F., & Brogan, D.R.
     Perception of life crisis events.   In B.P. Dohrenwend &
     B.S. Dohrenwend (Eds.), Stressful life events:   Their
     nature and effects.   New York:   Wiley, 1974.   Pp. 259 -
     273.

30.  Myers, J.K., Lindenthal, J.J., Pepper, M.P., & Ostrander, D.K.  Life events and mental status:  A longitudinal study.  Journal of Health and Social Behavior,  1972, 1. 398-406.

31.  Myers, J.K., Lindenthal, J.J., & Pepper, M.P.  Social class, life events, and psychiatric symptoms:  A longitudinal study.  In B.P. Dohrenwend & B.S. Dohrenwend (Eds.),  Stressful life events: Their nature and effects. New York:  Wiley, 1974, Pp. 191-205.

32.  Paster, S.  Psychotic reactions among soldiers of World War II.  Journal of Nervous and Mental Disease, 1948, 1C 54-66.

33.  Paykel, E.S.  Life stress and psychiatric disorder:  Application of the clinical approach.  In B.P. Dohrenwend B.S. Dohrenwend (Eds.), Stressful life events:  Their nature and effects.  New York:  Wiley, 1974.  Pp. 135-1L

34.  Rahe, R.H., McKean, J.D., & Arthur, R.J.  A longitudinal study of life-change and illness patterns.  Journal of Psychosomatic Research, 1967, 10, 355-366.

35.  Rahe, R.H.  Multi-cultural correlations of life change scaling:  America, Japan, Denmark, and Sweden.  Journal Psychosomatic Research, 1969, 13, 191-195.

36.  Rahe, R.H.  The pathway between subjects' recent life changes and their near-future illness reports:  Represen tative results and methodological issues.  In B.P. Dohrenwend and B.S. Dohrenwend (Eds.), Stressful life events:  Their nature and effects.  New York:  Wiley, 19 Pp. 73-86.

37.  Selye, H.  The stress of life.  New York:  McGraw-Hill Book Company, 1956.

38.  Star, S.A.  Psychoneurotic symptoms in the army.  In S.A Stouffer, L. Guttman, E.A. Suchman, P.F. Lazarsfeld, S.A Star & J.A. Clausen (Eds.), Studies in social psychology World War II.  The American soldier:  Combat and its aftermath.  Princeton, N.H.:  Princeton University Press 1949.  Pp. 411-455.

39.  Swank, R.L.  Combat exhaustion.  Journal of Nervous and
     Mental Disease, 1949, 109, 475-508.

40.  Theorell, T.  Life events before and after the onset of
     a premature myocardial infarction.  In B.P. Dohrenwend &
     B.S. Dohrenwend (Eds.), Stressful life events:  Their
     nature and effects.  New York:  Wiley, 1974, Pp. 101-117.

41.  Thurlow, H.J.  Illness in relation to life situation and
     sick-role tendency.  Journal of Psychosomatic Research,
     1971, 15, 73-88.

42.  Uhlenhuth, E.H., Balter, M.D., & Lipman, R.S.  Remember-
     ing events.  Paper presented at Conference of the Society
     for Life History Research in Psychopathology, Department
     of Psychiatry, University of Rochester School of Medicine
     May 21-23, 1975.

43.  Uhlenhuth, E.D., Lipman, R.S., Balter, M.D., & Stern, M.
     Symptom intensity and life stress in the city.  Archives
     of General Psychiatry, 1974, 31, 759-764.

44.  Vaillant, G.E.  Natural history of male psychological
     health:  Some antecedents of healthy adult adjustment.
     Archives of General Psychiatry, 1974, 31, 15-22.

45.  Wyler, A.R., Masuda, M., & Holmes, T.H.  Seriousness of
     Illness Rating Scale.  Journal of Psychosomatic Research,
     1968, 11, 363-374.

## Open Discussion

Sells:  Just to make the issue more complicated, stress
can also be a positive factor.  In combat, there were men
who responded to the situation by developing initiative,
leadership, and other positive qualities, while others broke
down.  There is also the question of what is stressful to
different individuals.  I remember the case of a man who had
gone through World War II behind German lines as a Yugoslavian
partisan and was in constant danger of his life; he didn't
turn a hair, but when he came back home he had to face a
sadistic wife and very quickly had a severe anxiety state and
a bleeding ulcer.

Zubin:   In thinking about life events, we tend to think
in terms of macrochanges, e.g., getting married or divorced,
and so on, but that is hardly the totality.  There are also
microstructures, e.g., what getting married means, what chang
in habits it entails.  Now if we could study each life event
in terms not only of the macrostructure or major changes, but
also of the microstructure, the little changes in life, we
might be able to understand these processes much better than
we do now.

Robins:   Understanding the impact of life events is obviously difficult, but there is at least on thing, I think,
we have to do in addition to what's usually done.  What's
usually done is to try to show that people who have some sort
of psychopathology are more likely to have had some life even
for which they were not responsible in the period preceeding
it, than people who don't have the kind of psychopathology.
But one of the reasons that some people have more life events
for which they are not responsible than do other people is
that they come from very disturbed families that regularly
have a lot of crises.  Take death as an example.  If your
father is a drug pusher, the chances of his being killed are
a good deal better than if he isn't.  You certainly aren't
responsible for that.  If he is killed and if you then develop behavior problems, the question is whether you develop
them because he was killed or because he was a drug pusher
who perhaps half contributed a genetic component or set you
a bad example.  In addition to showing that people with psy-
copathology have more life events than other people, you also
have to demonstrate that these events are temporally related
to the onset of the psychopathology.  Thus the risk must be
increased as compared with  others during periods in their
own lives, as well as compared with rates in other people's
lives.  I think that is something that's seldom paid attention to.

REMEMBERING LIFE EVENTS

E.H. Uhlenhuth and Shelby J. Haberman
Departments of Psychiatry and Statistics
University of Chicago
Chicago, Illinois

Michael D. Balter and Ronald S. Lipman
Clinical Studies Section
National Institute of Mental Health
Rockville, Maryland

Most modern quantitative investigations of life stress depend upon cataloging the life experiences of individual subjects retrospectively over periods ranging from months to years (Dohrenwend & Dohrenwend, 1974; Gunderson & Rake, 1974). Although the unreliability of memory for important events in other contexts is well known (Anderson & Anderson, 1967; Haggard, Brekstad & Shard, 1960; Mechanic & Newton,

Note: This investigation was supported in part by National Institute of Mental Health Contract No. HSM 42-69-59.

West Coast Community Surveys collected the data, employing a sample drawn by William L. Nicholls II, Survey Research Center, University of California at Berkeley.

Dean I. Manheimer, MA, and Glen D. Mellinger, Ph.D. Institute for Research in Social Behavior, Berkeley; and Ira H. Cisin, Ph.D., Social Research Group, George Washington University, Washington, D.C. were consultants.

Computations were performed at the Computation Center, University of Chicago.

Michael Conley and Linda Sang provided technical assistance.

1965; Pany, Balter & Cisini, 1970-71; US National Health
Survey, 1961, 1963; Wenar & Coulter, 1962), little attention
has been paid the issue in relation to studies of life
stress (Casey, Masuda, & Holmes, 1967). This paper reports
decrements in recall over an 18 month period for stressful
events in general, 41 individual events, and various subgroups of events.


METHODS

The data were drawn from an urban health survey. The
survey employed a probability sample of all households in
the city of Oakland, California. One respondent between the
ages of 18 and 65 years was selected at random from each
household for interviewing. The interview required 1 to 1-
1/2 hours and ranged broadly over the respondent's life
situation, health problems (especially psychological), and
coping methods. A total of 735 interviews was held for a
response rate of 75 per cent.

Respondents completed a questionnaire inquiring about
the occurrence of 41 life events extracted from the list of
61 events developed and scaled by Paykel and his collaborators (1971). Events low in stress and frequency of occurrence were omitted from the survey list in order to conserve
respondents' time and effort. Respondents noted life
changes during the 18 months before the survey interview
together with the month of occurrence. Events that respondents could not date precisely, hereafter referred to as
"undated," were classified into the first, second, or third
half year period preceding the interview. Personal injury
or illness was omitted from all summary tabulations of life
events in this paper. The survey from which these data are
drawn aimed to study the relationship between life stress
and illness. Since the inclusion of illness in a tally of
life stress would spuriously inflate correlations between
illness and stress, we have consistently omitted injury or
illness from such tallies in all of our work.

Events that occurred during the month of the survey
interview presented a special problem. If the day of
interview was randomly distributed within the month of
interview, then this month, for purposes of tabulating events, was on the average only half as long as the preceding

months. Simply doubling the event count for the month of
interview would have implied an assumption that reports of
events have a linear relationship to time. Since the present purpose was to study the relationship of event reports
to time, such an assumption seemed unwarranted. Therefore,
events during the month of interview were omitted from summary tabulations.


## RESULTS

Table 1 shows the demographic distribution of the 735
respondents in the survey. Note the substantial representation of blacks (40%).

Table 2 shows the number of respondents who reported
different numbers of events in the month of interview and in
each of the 18 preceding months. The table also shows the
number of respondents who reported events, but not their
precise month of occurrence, in each of 3 6-month periods
preceding the survey interview (period 1 immediately preceded
the interview).

The percentage of respondents who reported one or more
events in a month declined progressively from about 17 per
cent in the latest quarter to about 7 percent in the earliest quarter. The number of respondents who reported 1, 2,
or 3 or more events each declined progressively. Figure 1
shows some of these trends in graphic form, with the data
converted to percent of all respondents who reported different numbers of events per month. The solid symbols reflect
twice the observed frequencies in the interview month for
rough comparison with preceding months.

One convenient measure of recall is the mean month
prior to interview in which respondents reported events. For
each subject who reported any events, the mean month of his
reports was computed. Mean report months then were computed
separately for respondents who reported 1, 2, 3 4, and 5 or
more events. Table 3 shows these statistics. Since events
over an 18 month period were included, the mean report month
would have been 9.5 if the events had been randomly distributed
over the 18 months. Respondents in every frequency group
reported events on the average substantially more recently
than 9.5 months. The mean report month did not vary signifi-

Table 1

Demographic Characteristics

| Characteristic | N |
|---|---|
| Sex | |
| Male | 361 |
| Female | 374 |
| Marital status | |
| Married | 380 |
| Divorced | 95 |
| Separated | 52 |
| Widowed | 49 |
| Single | 159 |
| Religion | |
| Protestant | 451 |
| Catholic | 169 |
| Jewish | 13 |
| None | 82 |
| Other | 19 |
| Unknown | 1 |
| Race | |
| White | 394 |
| Black | 290 |
| Other | 49 |
| Unknown | 2 |
| Age | |
| 18-19 | 47 |
| 20-29 | 219 |
| 30-39 | 140 |
| 40-49 | 112 |
| 50-59 | 148 |
| 60-64 | 66 |
| Social class | |
| I | 32 |
| II | 60 |
| III | 161 |
| IV | 265 |
| V | 215 |
| Household size | |
| 1 | 261 |
| 2 | 369 |
| 3 | 81 |
| 4 | 14 |
| 5 | 5 |
| 6 | 3 |
| 7 | 1 |

Table 2

Number of Respondents Who Reported Events in
Month of Interview and 18 Preceding Months (N=375)

| Month | Number of Events Reported | | | | | Tot No Events |
|---|---|---|---|---|---|---|
| | 0 | 1 | 2 | 3+ | 1+ | |
| Intvw | 661 | 59 | 14 | 1 | 7: | 91 |
| - 1 | 623 | 91 | 17 | 4 | 112 | 137 |
| - 2 | 595 | 101 | 31 | 8 | 140 | 189 |
| - 3 | 606 | 104 | 23 | 2 | 129 | 157 |
| - 4 | 635 | 88 | 11 | 1 | 100 | 113 |
| - 5 | 631 | 85 | 13 | 6 | 104 | 129 |
| - 6 | 641 | 70 | 21 | 3 | 94 | 121 |
| - 7 | 634 | 84 | 15 | 2 | 101 | 120 |
| - 8 | 637 | 77 | 19 | 2 | 98 | 122 |
| - 9 | 652 | 68 | 10 | 5 | 83 | 107 |
| -10 | 644 | 80 | 10 | 1 | 91 | 103 |
| -11 | 652 | 69 | 11 | 3 | 83 | 100 |
| -12 | 642 | 78 | 12 | 3 | 93 | 111 |
| -13 | 662 | 66 | 6 | 1 | 73 | 81 |
| -14 | 673 | 52 | 9 | 1 | 62 | 73 |
| -15 | 661 | 60 | 13 | 1 | 74 | 89 |
| -16 | 684 | 43 | 7 | 1 | 51 | 60 |
| -17 | 688 | 39 | 8 | 0 | 47 | 55 |
| -18 | 685 | 41 | 5 | 4 | 50 | 63 |
| Undated-1 | 704 | 24 | 4 | 3 | 31 | 49 |
| Undated-2 | 688 | 29 | 12 | 6 | 47 | 73 |
| Undated-3 | 679 | 41 | 8 | 7 | 56 | 86 |

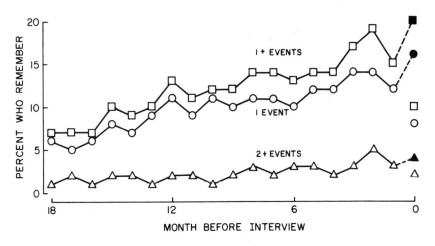

Figure 1

Percent of 735 respondents who reported 1 event,
2 or more events, and 1 or more event in each of
the 18 months before the survey interview.

cantly $(F=1.12, df=4/\infty, p < .05)$ among respondents who
reported different numbers of events. The mean report month
for all persons who reported any events $(N=587)$ was 7.89.

Table 2 and Figure 2 show the total number of events
reported in each month for the entire sample of 735 respondents. The filled point reflects twice the number of events
reported in the month of interview for rough comparison with
other data points. Under conditions of veridical recall and
reporting, we should expect the same number of events in
each month. The data clearly departed from this equiprobability model $(X^2=189.5, df=17, p < .005)$.

To estimate the rate at which reported events declined
with time, an exponential decay curve was fitted to the set
of 18 data points (excluding the month of interview). The
equation of this curve is: $P_j=ke-j\alpha$, where $P_j$ is the
probability that an event was reported specifically in month

Table 3

Mean Month of Report by Number of Events Reported

|  |  | Month of Report | | |
| No. of Events | No of Respondents | Mean | SD | SE |
| --- | --- | --- | --- | --- |
| 1 | 147 | 7.33 | 4.73 | 0.39 |
| 2 | 133 | 8.40 | 3.97 | 0.35 |
| 3 | 90 | 7.81 | 3.69 | 0.39 |
| 4 | 81 | 7.93 | 3.01 | 0.33 |
| 5+ | 136 | 8.02 | 2.54 | 0.22 |
| 1+ | 587 | 7.89 | 3.75 | 0.16 |

j.  The estimated value $\alpha$ =0.0557±0.0045.  Figure 2 shows the fitted curve.  This model also fails to fit the data ($x^2$=31.5, df=16, p $<$.05), but fits substantially better than the equiprobability model, with an 83 percent reduction in the chi square for deviation.  The points containing a dot are outliers (t $>$ 2.0).  The fitted curve indicates that the number of events reported fell off by about 5 percent each month.

The question arises whether this decline in reporting involved all 41 life events or only a limited subset.  Table 4 lists the 41 events in abbreviated form, their reported frequencies by 6-month periods prior to the survey interview (with the first being the most recent 6 months), and

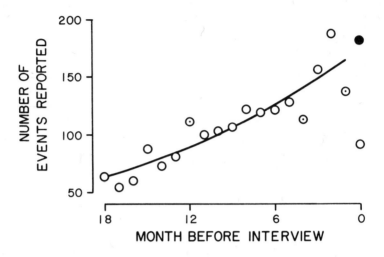

Figure 2

Total number of events reported by 735 respondents
in each of the 18 months before the survey interview.

their stress ratings as determined by Paykel, Pursoff, and
Uhlenhuth (1971). Inspection of the table reveals that
there was a very general tendency for events and their dates
to be reported more frequently in the more recent 6-
month periods. This was true particularly for events with
frequencies substantial enough to inspire confidence. There
was a corresponding tendency for events that could not be
dated to be reported more frequently in the more distant 6-
month periods. This tendency, however, was not sufficiently
strong to negate the overall tendency for higher frequencies
in more recent time periods.

     In another approach to evaluating the recall of specific
events, the mean month of report was computed for each of
the 41 events. These results also indicated that most

events were reported more frequently in recent months. Only 7 events, or 17 percent of the 41 different events, were reported on the average the expected 9.5 months or more before the interview. These 7 events were numbers 7, 8, 16, 21, 32, 36, and 40 in Table 4.

The frequencies of events grouped into certain important clusters also were examined. These included 12 exits from the social field as defined by Paykel, Myers, Dienelt, Klerman, Lindenthal, & Pepper (1969), 6 events beyond the respondent's control as defined by the Dohrenwends (1974), and dubbed "fateful" by S. Kellam (personal communication), and 16 events that might be regarded as salient on the basis that they generally are documented in the public record. These events are noted in Table 4. With veridical recall and reporting one would expect one third of the events in each group to be reported in each 6-month period. Table 5 shows the percentage of all (dated) events and events in each group that were reported during each 6-month period. In every group substantially more than 33 percent of the events were reported during the most recent 6-month period. Among fateful events, more than half were reported during the first period--almost 3 times as many as during the third period.

Fateful events also were tabulated by month of occurrence. Their distribution departed markedly from the equiprobability model ($x^2$=155.7, df=17, p <.005). An exponential decay curve was fitted to the 18 data points (excluding the month of interview). The estimated value $\alpha$ =0.0978+0.0099. This model also fails to fit the data ($x^2$=34.4, df=16, p <.01), but reduces the chi square for deviation by 78 percent. The fitted curve indicates that the reported number of fateful events fell off by about 9 percent each month--substantially faster than the reported number of other events ($x^2$=53.3, df=17, p <.005).

Another criterion of recall is the ability to locate an event precisely in time. For each group of events defined above, the percentage of reports dated by month of occurrence was computed. Table 6 shows that about 90 percent of reported events in most groups were dated. Only salient events were dated somewhat more often.

Casey, Masuda, and Holmes (1967) suggested that the retention of events in memory might be determined by their

Table 4

Frequencies and Stress Ratings of 41 Life Events
in the Oakland Health Survey

| | | Frequencies by Six Month Periods Prior to Interview | | | | | | |
| | | Dated Events | | | Undated Events | | | Stress |
| No. | Event | 1 | 2 | 3 | 1 | 2 | 3 | Rating |
|---|---|---|---|---|---|---|---|---|
| 1 | Move from another city. | 50 | 43 | 38 | 2 | 1 | 3 | 8.52 |
| 2 | Move within the city. | 67 | 71 | 34 | 3 | 6 | 5 | 5.14 |
| * 3 | Injury or illness in relative. | 97 | 59 | 37 | 8 | 5 | 12 | 15.30 |
| 4 | Personal injury or illness. | 40 | 43 | 21 | 1 | 0 | 1 | 14.61 |
| 5 | Loss or theft. | 67 | 48 | 19 | 4 | 11 | 5 | 14.07 |
| † 6 | Law suit. | 10 | 9 | 1 | 0 | 0 | 2 | 13.78 |
| † 7 | Marriage. | 14 | 17 | 13 | 0 | 0 | 0 | 5.61 |
| 8 | More arguments with spouse. | 5 | 16 | 16 | 4 | 3 | 5 | 13.02 |
| # 9 | Marital separation, circumstances. | 10 | 6 | 9 | 0 | 3 | 6 | 10.33 |
| # 10 | Marital separation, arguments. | 13 | 17 | 11 | 2 | 1 | 3 | 15.93 |
| 11 | Spouse unfaithful. | 5 | 5 | 4 | 1 | 1 | 2 | 16.78 |
| † # 12 | Divorce. | 17 | 6 | 7 | 0 | 1 | 1 | 16.18 |
| # 13 | Broken love relationship. | 30 | 24 | 9 | 1 | 1 | 3 | 13.23 |
| # 14 | Separation from friend or relative. | 34 | 29 | 17 | 2 | 2 | 2 | 10.68 |
| 15 | Miscarriage. | 9 | 8 | 3 | 0 | 1 | 0 | 15.82 |
| # 16 | Child left home. | 4 | 5 | 10 | 0 | 2 | 1 | 7.20 |
| † # 17 | Child joined Armed Forces. | 4 | 3 | 3 | 0 | 0 | 0 | 12.32 |
| † # 18 | Child married against your wishes. | 2 | 3 | 1 | 0 | 0 | 1 | 13.24 |
| 19 | Started affair. | 33 | 20 | 11 | 2 | 5 | 6 | 14.09 |
| 20 | Started work. | 40 | 21 | 24 | 1 | 1 | 1 | 8.84 |
| † 21 | Business failure. | 0 | 3 | 1 | 0 | 0 | 0 | 16.46 |
| 22 | Demotion on job. | 8 | 3 | 5 | 0 | 1 | 0 | 15.05 |
| 23 | Fired from job. | 11 | 7 | 5 | 1 | 0 | 3 | 16.45 |
| 24 | Major job change. | 71 | 49 | 31 | 4 | 2 | 4 | 9.23 |
| † 25 | Court appearance. | 12 | 8 | 5 | 1 | 0 | 1 | 15.79 |
| † 26 | Sent to jail. | 9 | 5 | 8 | 0 | 1 | 1 | 17.60 |
| † 27 | Dropped out of school. | 5 | 7 | 5 | 0 | 1 | 1 | 7.65 |
| *28 | Laid off work. | 19 | 14 | 3 | 1 | 2 | 1 | 15.26 |
| † 29 | New baby, wanted. | 15 | 23 | 14 | 0 | 1 | 0 | 5.52 |
| 30 | Pregnancy, wanted. | 10 | 7 | 1 | 0 | 1 | 0 | 4.62 |
| 31 | Major financial problems. | 5 | 4 | 1 | 0 | 0 | 2 | 16.57 |
| † # *32 | Death of spouse. | 4 | 1 | 5 | 0 | 0 | 0 | 18.76 |
| † # *33 | Death of child. | 1 | 0 | 0 | 0 | 0 | 0 | 19.33 |
| † # *34 | Death of other relative. | 58 | 46 | 26 | 3 | 4 | 4 | 17.21 |
| † # *35 | Death of friend. | 49 | 12 | 6 | 3 | 2 | 1 | 15.18 |
| 36 | Menopause. | 5 | 6 | 3 | 1 | 0 | 4 | 11.02 |
| † 37 | Graduated school. | 6 | 1 | 5 | 0 | 0 | 0 | 7.65 |
| 38 | Quit job. | 12 | 14 | 6 | 2 | 0 | 0 | 15.26 |
| † 39 | New baby, unwanted. | 1 | 1 | 1 | 0 | 0 | 0 | 5.52 |
| 40 | Pregnancy, unwanted. | 1 | 1 | 2 | 0 | 0 | 0 | 10.62 |
| 41 | Minor financial problems. | 31 | 41 | 21 | 3 | 14 | 6 | 10.96 |

*="Fateful" events      #=Exits from the social field      †=salient (publically documented) events

Table 5

Distribution of Dated Events in Major
Groups by 6 Month Period

| Event Group | N | Six Month Period | | | |
| | | 1 | 2 | 3 | Total |
| --- | --- | --- | --- | --- | --- |
| All events | 1930 | 44% | 34% | 22% | 100% |
| Exits from social field | 482 | 47 | 32 | 22 | 101 |
| Fateful events | 437 | 52 | 30 | 18 | 100 |
| Salient events | 453 | 46 | 32 | 22 | 100 |

salience as defined by their stress weights. They found a
correlation of 0.59 (p < .0005) between the consistency with
which events were recalled on 2 different occasions 9 months
apart and their stress weights. In Figure 3, the 41 events
of the present study are plotted to show the relationship
between their mean report months and their stress weights.
The correlation between report month and stress weight is
-0.24 (p > .10), and the slope of the fitted line is -0.10
(p > .10).

Table 6

Distribution of Events in Major Groups by Dated vs. Undated

| Event Group | N | Dated | Undated | Total |
| --- | --- | --- | --- | --- |
| All events | 2138 | 90.3% | 9.7 | 100% |
| Exits from social field | 531 | 90.8 | 9.2 | 100 |
| Fateful events | 483 | 90.5 | 9.5 | 100 |
| Salient events | 482 | 94.0 | 6.0 | 100 |

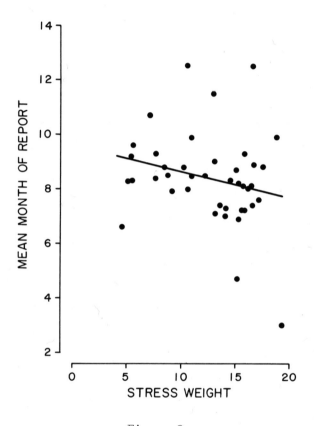

Figure 3

Relationship between mean month of report and
stress weight for each of the 41 life events in
the survey.

COMMENT

The data presented here indicate: (1) Respondents reported life events in general with decreasing frequency in successively more distant months. Reports fell off at a rate of about 5 percent per month. (2) The vast majority (83%) of different individual events participated in this trend. Subgroups of events including exits from the social field, fateful events, events of public record, and highly stressful events all participated in this trend. (3) Reports of fateful events fell off appreciably faster (9% per month) than reports of other events.

According to the rate of decline in reports estimated from the present data, only 54 percent of events in general and 34 percent of fateful events that occurred in the twelfth month prior to the survey interview were reported. An estimated 76 percent of events in general and 61 percent of fateful events that occurred in the sixth month before the interview were reported. These sixth-month figures can serve as reasonable estimates of recall, on the average, over the entire year prior to the interview. Interpreted in this way, they agree substantially with a recent validity study of recall for medication consumption (Parry, Balter, and Cisini, 1970, 1971), which showed that 65-70 percent of respondents known to have filled prescriptions some 9 months before the survey interview accurately reported this fact, unless special care was taken in the interview.

The present findings, however, disagree with the report by Casey, Masuda and Holmes (1967) in a number of important respects. First, although Casey found some decline in reports with time, it was quite slow, with mean stress levels (life change units, LCU) reported for 1957 about 50 percent of those reported for 1963. There was no appreciable difference in mean LCU scores for 1963 as estimated from reports by the same individuals on 2 different occasions 9 months apart. Second, whereas Casey found a strong positive relationship between consistency of reporting and the stress weights (interpreted as salience) of events, the present data showed no such relationship. Indeed, reports of fateful events, which have high stress weights, fell off more rapidly than reports of events in general.

These discrepancies between the 2 studies may depend upon a number of factors. The 2 approaches differed substantially. In the Casey study, "consistency of recall" appears to refer to 2 different phenomena: (1) the correlation of total LCU scores from events reported for 3 different years (1957, 1960, 1963) and (2) the consistency with which subjects reported specific events that occurred in 1957, 1960, and 1963 on 2 different reporting occasions 9 months apart. The present study does not deal with conventional measures of reliability, but rather estimates memory loss from data collected on a single occasion by comparing the observed distribution of reported events in time to the random distribution that would be expected theoretically with veridical recall and reporting.

The present study also differed from Casey's in some additional features. The event list itself was different. Unweighted event frequencies rather than total stress scores were employed. Stress weights for individual events were based on a modified scaling method (Paykel, Prusoff and Uhlenhuth, 1971) that takes some account of the social desirability of events. Respondents were asked to recall events over a shorter period (18 months) and to date them more precisely (by month rather than year of occurrence). Results were based on the full sample, rather than on respondents with "discrepant" reporting. The sample represented a non-institutionalized urban population rather than a medically trained, highly intelligent, homogeneous group of resident physicians. These sample differences probably account partly for the differing results: the U.S. National Health Survey (1963) and Parry, Balter & Cisini (1970-71) found that respondents with less education gave less valid responses. This issue raises the larger question, what characteristics of respondents (as contrasted with characteristics of events) are associated with differences in reporting events? Additional data from the present survey should help to answer this question.

The Casey study presents an unusually optimistic picture of the reliability of memory for events. It is difficult to evaluate their suggestion that "consistency" of recall is maintained over the same period in which recall substantially decreases. At any rate, the present results, together with those of other investigators noted above, seem to raise substantial question about recall,

especially over the longer term, as a reliable source of
data in studies of life stress. In light of these results,
the frequent practice of limiting retrospective data collection to about one year seems prudent.

Although the practical implications of the present study
agree with those of most earlier investigations, this study
provides no clear picture of the processes that were operating in the respondents' reporting. The most obvious hypothesis is that respondents forgot more events as time elapsed. All of the findings, however, could have followed
from a tendency merely to report events as more recent
than they actually were. Such a telescoping of events in
time could apply especially to more stressful events, such
as fateful events. The slight clustering of event reports
at 12 months (Figure 2) suggests a similar process.

The previous investigations providing for an external
check of respondents' reports offer some data relevant to a
choice between the processes suggested above. They indicate
clearly that respondents generally underreport the events
elicited by the survey interviewers. It seems likely that
actual omissions in reporting also accounted at least in
part for findings of the present study. Additional survey
studies specifically designed to investigate the nature of
the processes that distort reports would be of great theoretical and practical interest.

REFERENCES

Anderson, R., and Anderson, O.W. A decade of health services:
    Social survey trends in use and expenditure. Chicago:
    The University of Chicago Press, 1967, 177-183.

Casey, R.L., Masuda, M., and Holmes, T.H. Quantitative
    study of recall of life events. Journal of Psycho-
    somatic Research, 1971, 25, 300-347.

Dohrenwend, B.S., and Dohrenwend, B.P. (Eds.), Stressful
    life events: Their nature and effects. New York:
    John Wiley & Sons, 1974.

Gunderson, E.K.E., and Rahe, R.H. (Eds.), Life stress and
    illness. Springfield, Illinois: C.C. Thomas, 1974.

Haggard, E.A., Brekstad, A., and Skard, A.G.  On the relia-
    bility of the anammestic interview.  Journal of Abnormal
    and Social Psychology, 1960, 61, 311-318.

Mechanic, D., and Newton, M.  Some problems in the analysis
    of morbidity data.  Journal of Chronic Diseases, 1965,
    18, 569-580.

Parry, H.J., Balter, M.B., and Cisin, I.H.  Primary levels
    of under reporting psychotropic drug use (with and
    without the use of visual aids).  Public Opinion
    Quarterly, 1970-71, 34, 582-592.

Paykel, E.S., Myers, J.K., Dienelt, M.N., Klerman, G.L.,
    Lindenthal, J.J., and Pepper, M.P.  Life events and
    depression:  A controlled study.  Archives of General
    Psychiatry, 1969, 21, 753-760.

Paykel, E.S., Prusoff, B.A., and Uhlenhuth, E.H.  Scaling of
    life events.  Archives of General Psychiatry, 1971, 25,
    340-347.

U.S. National Health Survey.  Comparison of hospitalization
    reporting in three survey procedures.  Washington, D.C.:
    Public Health Service, 1963, Series D-8.

U.S. National Health Survey.  Health interview responses
    compared with medical records.  Washington, D.C.:
    Public Health Service, 1971, Series D-5.

Wenar, C., and Coulter, J.B.  A reliability study of develop-
    mental histories.  Child Development, 1962, 33, 453-
    462.

Open Discussion


Robins: In our follow-up, where we did have validity
measures, people who had been very mildly deviant tended to
push the dates and other deviance farther back than they
really occurred. They said, "Oh, it's been years since I
did that." One way of treating things that are embarrassing
to you you is to exaggerate their distance in the past.

Uhlenhuth: So that would be the converse of what we're
suggesting here...

Robins: You're assuming the dates are right and the
events are forgotten. I'm suggesting that the dates may be
forgotten and the events are right.

Zubin: I am concerned about your report not mention-
ing the fact that psychology has a rich literature on remembering, measured not only through recognition methods such
as you've been using, but through recall and through re-
learning, including such phenomena as familiarity, deja vu
and jamais vu.

Uhlenhuth: What I was trying to do was mainly to indicate that a procedure we have been relying on for studying
life events seems to have some quirks in it. This study in
fact was not specifically designed to investigate this particular issue. I just want to bring it up as a methodological question and indicate that there are certainly some peculiar things going on that we ought to look into further.

Blumenthal: I want to talk about Charles Cannel's
work in this regard. He has studied recording of health
events, hospitalizations, things like that. He started out
with people who were known to have been hospitalized, but
who didn't know that he knew. Cannel had access to that
information. His data are profoundly depressing in the
sense that he began to see a tremendous decline in the reporting of events after two weeks, let alone a year, to the
point where I think he would contend that asking someone
about an event like a hospitalization a year ago is utterly
useless. Moreover, Cannel finds that within the category
of being hospitalized there are a variety of other factors,
like what you were hospitalized for. You might imagine then

that people hospitalized for mental illnesses don't report
it, or if you've been hospitalized for carcinoma, for example, involving the genito-urinary tract you aren't going
to report that either.  Now I'm perfectly prepared to think
that if there is such variation within one category, hospitalization, there's going to be enormous variation in terms
of remembering other specific things, like marriages, divorce
and what have you.

Uhlenhuth:  I'm afraid that might be right.  In the stud
of prescriptions it also turns out that things are not the
way you would expect them.  You would expect that psycho-
tropic drug-taking would be less well recalled on the same
basis that you just mentioned than would let's say taking
antibiotics.  Well, that turns out not to be the case; it's
just the other way around.  So yes, it's very individualistic
and you can't guess at it.

Sells:  It gets to be more depressing.  We have found
that events may not only be forgotten, but may actually be
distorted over time, so that you may not just get things
left out, but wrong answers.

ANTICIPATION AND CONTROL OF STRESSFUL LIFE EVENTS:   AN

EXPLORATORY ANALYSIS*

Barbara Snell Dohrenwend
Department of Psychology
The City College of the
City University of New York
New York, New York

The most difficult problem to be solved before we can thoroughly understand the effects of stressful life events is the basis for the large individual differences observed in reactions to these events.  In general, we can look for explanation to two sources of variability.  The first is individual predispositions and vulnerabilities.  The second source of variability is the objective situation or context in which the stressful event or stimulus is experienced.  Ironically, this source of variability has largely been ignored by investigators concerned with stressful life events while being the focus of almost all experimental research on stress in the laboratory.

Recent reviews of this experimental literature point to two related situational variables as powerful determinants of the outcome of exposure to a stressful stimulus (Averill, 1973; Lefcourt, 1973).  One is anticipation of the stressful stimulus.  That is, when a subject is able to anticipate a noxious stimulus, either because a warning is provided or because of the regular timing of the stimulus, the effects of the stimulus are likely to be ameliorated.  One study showed, for example, that a fixed-interval noise produced less deterioration in performance on a subsequent proofreading task than did a random noise and that, in addition, this difference

*This work was supported in part by research Grant MH10328 from the National Institute of Mental Health.  I would like to thank Bruce Dohrenwend for his helpful criticism of earlier drafts of this paper.

135

in regularity had a far greater impact on subsequent performance than the loudness of the noise (Glass, Singer, &
Freidman, 1969).

The second, related situational determinant of the outcome of exposure to a stressful stimulus suggested by recent
experimental studies is control over the onset of the stimulus.  A generally consistent finding is that when a subject
either actually controls or believes that he controls the
administration of a noxious stimulus its effects are reduced
in intensity.  Thus, for example, when subjects were told
that they could turn off a loud, random noise if it became
unbearable, they performed better on a subsequent task when
they had no control over the stimulus (Glass, et al., 1969).

If we generalize these results to stressful life events
the implications are, first, that an unanticipated stressful
life event will have more serious effects than one that is
anticipated and, second, that a life event whose occurrence
is not controlled by the individual who experiences it will
have more serious effects than one that the individual does
control.  Unfortunately, these implications are not as
straightforward as we would like, mainly for two reasons.
First, the highly artificial settings typical of experimental studies, and of ethical necessity, the rather trivial
nature of the stressful experiences imposed on human subjects
raise the issue of whether their findings apply to naturally
occurring stressful experiences.  Some reassurance on this
point is provided, however, by the work of Schmale and his
colleagues (1972), who have reported a series of clinical
studies which suggest that people who feel helpless to anticipate or control events are particularly likely to suffer
serious illness or even death when stressful life events impinge on them.

The second reason for questioning the generalization of
experimental findings to naturally occurring stressful life
events is that inside the laboratory we can contrive settings
and procedures so that anticipation and control are independent of other factors that might influence the outcome of
exposure to a stressful stimulus.  However, in naturally
occurring life events this contrived independence is nowhere
to be found.  Therefore, before we can interpret anticipation
and control of the occurrence of stressful life events as
possible mediators of the impact of these events we must
answer two sets of questions:

First, are there characteristic differences between
the objective situations in which life events are anticipated and the objective situations in which they are unanticipated?  Likewise, are there characteristic differences between
the objective situations in which the occurrence of life
events is controlled by their participants and the objective
situations in which events are not thus controlled?  Second,
are there characteristic differences between people who do
and people who do not anticipate their life events, or between
those who do and do not control the occurrence of their life
events?

It is obvious that the answers to these questions might
lead to very different interpretations of anticipation and
control of stressful life events.  If we find that differences in degree of anticipation and control are related to
objective circumstances then studies of the effects of these
factors will expand our understanding of situational determinants of the impact of stressful life events.  In contrast,
if we find that differences in degree of anticipation and control are related to characteristics of the persons who experience stressful life events then these factors may help us
to understand predisposing personality determinants of the
impact of stressful life events rather than situational
mediators.  With this issue in mind, let me describe the results of analyses designed to explore the relation between
event characteristics, person characteristics, and the anticipation and control of stressful life events.


PROCEDURE

The data to be reported come from a methodological study
which was based on a stratified sub-sample of a representative sample of the population of New York City that had previously been interviewed in another study.  The stratified
sub-sample was designed to include males and females, married
or single, ranging in age from early 20's to 69.  The sub-
sample as drawn was 30 percent Black, 30 percent Puerto
Rican, and 40 percent non-Puerto Rican White.  Within each
of these three ethnic groupings we controlled social class
by sampling similar proportions at each of four levels of
years of formal education of the head of the household:
0 to 7 years, 8 to 11 years, 12 to 15 years, and 16 or more
years.

Interviews were completed with 52 percent of the available sample. The large loss resulted primarily from the
general increase in the proportion of urban respondents who
refuse to be interviewed and the fact that the interview of
which the life event questions were a part was administered
in two settings, one week apart, with 21 percent of the samp.
loss being due to refusal to cooperate the second time. The
distribution of the completed sample according to sex, ethnicity, and the three levels of education of head of househo.
used in most subsequent analyses is shown in Table 1.

Near the end of the interview the respondent was asked,
"What was the last major event that, for better or worse,
changed or interrupted your usual activities?" This question was followed by probes concerning the participants in

Table 1

Characteristics of Respondents Who Completed
Parts I and II of the Questionnaire (N=169)

SEX

| Male | 38.5% | (65) |
| Female | 61.5% | (104) |

ETHNICITY

| Black | 28.4% | (48) |
| Puerto Rican | 29.6% | (50) |
| Other White | 42.0% | (71) |

HEAD OF HOUSEHOLD EDUCATION

| Less than High School Grad. | 46.2% | (78) |
| High School Grad. | 33.7% | (57) |
| College Grad. | 20.1% | (34) |

the event and its date. After these questions, respondents
were told, "Now I'll ask you about a number of other experiences that people have. Some of these things happen to
most people at one time or another, while some of these
things happen to only a few people." Following this question, respondents were presented with ten lists of events
in various areas of activity, such as school, work, and
family, and asked, for each list, "During the last 12 months,
did any of these things happen to you, or to a member of
your family or to another person who is important to you?"
After each event was reported, probes were asked to determine the extent to which the respondent had anticipated the
occurrence of the event, the extent to which he had had
control over its occurrence, and the date of the event. The
questions concerning anticipation and control were designed
to measure these variables on a five point scale, with one
representing complete absence of anticipation or of control
and five representing complete certainty or total control.


### The Problem of Probes Appropriate to the Event

A basic canon of questionnaire construction is that one
should avoid the possibility of confounding variations in the
form or content of questions with variations in response.
To this end the rule is to standardize or hold constant the
question wherever responses are to be compared. Ordinarily
this rule means that a standard question is asked of all
respondents about each item of information (e.g., Richardson,
Dohrenwend, & Klein, 1965, p. 34 f).

In constructing questions about anticipation and control
of the occurrence of life events, however, we faced a dilemma.
We could ask the same question of all respondents about their
anticipation, or about their control of the occurrence of a
particular event, but we could not ask any respondent the
same questions about anticipation, or about control, of all
life events. Consider, for example, a respondent who had
been promoted and married. If we were to ask him whether he
had expected to be promoted he would probably tell us with
some precision how much he knew beforehand about the likelihood of his being promoted. But wouldn't he think us odd if
we asked him if he had expected to get married? He might be
able to provide an answer after recasting the question to
mean something like, "Have you always expected that some day
you would marry?" but this would not be the question we meant

to ask. Yet we should ask a question about his anticipation
of his marriage for we know that some people elope and
others marry after extended formal engagements.

The problem, therefore, was to find another way to ask
the question about anticipation so that it would be meaningful in relation to marriage. But then what happens when we
compare promotions and marriages or different categories of
events to which they belong, to determine whether one is more
likely than the other to be anticipated? We have confounded
variation in the question with possible variation in the response. Although, in practice, so long as we compare broad
categories of events the confounding will never be complete,
we see no way to avoid partial confounding. Every question
that we have been able to devise concerning either anticipation or control of occurrence is appropriate for some but
not for other life events.

Our solution to this problem was to use two questions
to inquire about anticipation and three questions to inquire
about control of the occurrence of life events. These
questions are shown in Appendix Table 1. The application
of these questions to specific life events is shown in
Appendix Table 2. After we carry out the main analysis we
will consider the effects of these variations in question
form on our results.

In some instances a question concerning anticipation or,
more often, control was not asked either because the answer
seemed too obvious or the question too threatening. For
example, if a respondent reported being fired we inquired
about his anticipation but not about his control over the
event, and if he reported being robbed, we asked about
neither. Where the inquiry was not made, because the answer
seemed obvious the assumed level of anticipation or control
is also indicated in Appendix Table 2. These assumed constants were not included in the analyses of group differences in anticipation and control of the occurrence of life
events.


RESULTS

In order to study the question of whether person characteristics are associated with degree of reported anticipation or control of the occurrence of life events, we examined

the relation of these variables to the sex, the ethnicity
and the social class of our respondents, the last as indicated by the education of the head of their household.

Anticipation of the Occurrence of Life Events

Table 2 describes the levels of anticipation of life
events reported by respondents classified according to
their sex, their ethnic background, and the education of the
head of their household, an indicator of social class. Levels
of anticipation did not differ significantly between sexes or
social class. In contrast, the comparison of the three ethnic
groups revealed a significant difference among them. Scheffe
post hoc tests of pairs of groups showed that the Puerto Ricans
differed significantly at the .01 level from each of the other
groups, who did not differ from each other.

Table 2

Relation of Respondent's Sex, Respondent's Ethnicity, and
    Education of the Head of the Respondent's Household
    to Reported Level of Anticipation of Life Events
(Unit of analysis is the respondent's mean anticipation score)

| Level of Anticipation | Sex | | Ethnicity | | | Years of education of head of household | | |
|---|---|---|---|---|---|---|---|---|
| | Male | Female | Black | Puerto Rican | Non-Puerto Rican White | 0-11 | 12-15 | 16+ |
| Mean | 2.95 | 2.88 | 3.18 | 2.38 | 3.06 | 2.78 | 2.89 | 3.21 |
| SD | 0.98 | 1.15 | 1.04 | 1.14 | 0.98 | 1.22 | 1.01 | 0.88 |
| Number of Respondents | 58 | 98 | 44 | 43 | 69 | 68 | 56 | 32 |
| F | 0.19 | | 7.71 | | | 1.69 | | |
| p | n.s. | | <.01 | | | n.s. | | |

Note: Where F is significant means connected by arrows do not
    differ significantly according to Scheffé post hoc test.

There is more than one possible explanation for this
ethnic difference.  Most simply, it might be due to the
Puerto Ricans having experienced life events that differed
from the other two groups or, alternatively, it might be due
to differences between groups in the extent to which they
anticipated the same life events.  This ambiguity in the
meaning of the observed differences arises in part from confounding that is inherent in the life events that people
experience, particularly if the experience spans a limited
time period.  That is, each person will experience a more
or less limited set of events and those sets will differ
from person to person.  Given this situation, data concerning recent life events take the general form schematized
in Table 3.  This schema indicates that person means,
symbolized at the bottom of the table by $\bar{P}$'s not only represent different persons, who may vary in predisposition
to anticipate events, but are based on different sets of
events, which may vary in predictability.  Furthermore, as
we have indicated by showing that only events A and B were
common to all three groups, group means as well as person
means are likely to be based on different events.  The actual
results in this respect are shown in Table 4, which indicates
which events were common to all ethnic, sex, or class groups.

Given the inherent confounding between persons and event
there is no way that we can completely separate their effects
However, some dissection is possible if we change the unit
of analysis.  The ethnic difference reported in Table 3 was
based on person means.  When we change the unit of analysis
to life event means calculated across persons, the statistic
indicated by $\bar{L}$ in Table 3, we can control certain event differences between groups that might account for the significan
ethnic differences in Table 3.  First, we can include means
only for those life events that were common to all three ethnic groups.  Second, with life event means as the unit of
analysis we give equal weight to each event, whereas with
person means we necessarily gave greater weight to events experienced by more persons.  Such unequal weighting could, as
suggested by events A and B in Table 3, produce spurious
group differences.  That is, suppose that event A was
inherently more predictable than event B.  Then, since A
was experienced by more persons in group Q than in groups
R and S while the reverse was true of event B, the inherent
difference in predictability between events A and B might
account for an observed difference in anticipation levels
when group Q is compared with groups R and S.

Table 3

Schematized Life Event Data Set

| LIFE EVENT | GROUP | | | | | | | | | | | |
|---|---|---|---|---|---|---|---|---|---|---|---|---|
| | Q | | | | R | | | | S | | | |
| | Person Number | | | | | | | | | | | |
| | 1 | 2 | 3 | | 4 | 5 | 6 | | 7 | 8 | 9 | |
| A | $X_{AI}$ | $X_{A2}$ | $X_{A3}$ | $\bar{L}_{AQ}$ | $X_{A4}$ | | | $\bar{L}_{AR}$ | $X_{A7}$ | | | $\bar{L}_{AS}$ |
| B | $X_{BI}$ | | | $\bar{L}_{BQ}$ | $X_{B4}$ | $X_{B5}$ | $X_{B6}$ | $\bar{L}_{BR}$ | $X_{B7}$ | $X_{B8}$ | $X_{B9}$ | $\bar{L}_{BS}$ |
| C | $X_{CI}$ | | | $\bar{L}_{CQ}$ | $X_{C4}$ | | | $\bar{L}_{CR}$ | | | | |
| D | | $X_{D2}$ | | $\bar{L}_{DQ}$ | | | | | $X_{D7}$ | | | $\bar{L}_{DS}$ |
| E | | | | | | $X_{E5}$ | | $\bar{L}_{ER}$ | | $X_{E8}$ | | $\bar{L}_{ES}$ |
| F | $X_{FI}$ | | | $\bar{L}_{FQ}$ | | | | | | | | |
| G | | | | | $X_{G4}$ | | | $\bar{L}_{GR}$ | | | | |
| H | | | | | | | | | $X_{H7}$ | | | $\bar{L}_{HS}$ |
| | $\bar{P}_{1}$ | $\bar{P}_{2}$ | $\bar{P}_{3}$ | | $\bar{P}_{4}$ | $\bar{P}_{5}$ | $\bar{P}_{6}$ | | $\bar{P}_{7}$ | $\bar{P}_{8}$ | $\bar{P}_{9}$ | |

$\bar{P}$: Person mean score    $\bar{L}$: Event mean score    X: Person–event score

Table 4

List of Life Events with Frequencies for Respondent as Central Figure
and Indications as to Which Respondent Events Were Common to Both
Sexes, to all Ethnic Groups, or to all Social Classes

| School | Frequency of respondent events in total sample for which anti-cipation or control was reported | Respondent events common to: | | |
|---|---|---|---|---|
| | | Both Sexes | All 3 Ethnic Groups | All 3 Social Classes |
| A. Started school or a training program after not going to school for a long time.... | 10 | − | + | + |
| B. Changed schools or training programs..... | 1 | − | − | − |
| C. Graduated from school or training program.... | 1 | − | − | − |
| D. Had problems in school or in training program.. | 1 | − | − | − |
| E. Failed school, training program | 2 | + | − | − |
| F. Did not graduate from school training program | | | | |

Table 4 (Con't.)

| Work | Frequency of respondent events in total sample for which anticipation or control was reported | Respondent events common to: Both Sexes | Respondent events common to: All 3 Ethnic Groups | Respondent events common to: All 3 Social Classes |
|---|---|---|---|---|
| N. Fired | 0 | – | – | – |
| O. Started a business or profession | 1 | – | – | – |
| P. Expanded business or professional practice | 1 | – | – | – |
| Q. Took on a greatly increased work load | 15 | + | + | + |
| R. Suffered a business loss or failure | 2 | + | – | – |
| S. Sharply reduced work load | 3 | – | – | – |
| T. Retired | 1 | – | – | – |
| U. Stopped working, not retirement, for an extended period | 5 | + | + | – |

Table 4 (Con't.)

| Love and Marriage | Frequency of respondent events in total sample for which anticipation or control was reported | Respondent events common to: | | |
|---|---|---|---|---|
| | | Both Sexes | All 3 Ethnic Groups | All 3 Social Classes |
| A. Becomes engaged | 0 | - | - | - |
| B. Engagement broken | 0 | - | - | - |
| C. Married | 6 | + | + | + |
| D. Started a love affair | 2 | + | - | - |
| E. Relations with spouse changed for the worse, without separation or divorce | 2 | - | - | - |
| F. Married couple separated | 4 | + | - | - |
| G. Divorce | 0 | - | - | - |
| H. Relations with spouse changed for the better | 6 | - | - | + |

Table 4 (Con't.)

| Love and Marriage (Con't.) | Frequency of respondent events in total sample for which anticipation or control was reported | Respondent events common to: | | |
|---|---|---|---|---|
| | | Both Sexes | All 3 Ethnic Groups | All 3 Social Classes |
| I. Married couple got together again after separation | 1 | — | — | — |
| J. Marital infidelity (Code for "wronged" partner) | 2 | + | — | — |
| K. Trouble with in-laws | 0 | — | — | — |
| L. Spouse died | 3 | + | — | + |
| Children | | | | |
| A. Became pregnant | 1 | — | — | — |
| B. Birth of a first child | 2 | — | — | — |

## Table 4 (Con't.)

Children (Con't.)

| | Frequency of respondent events in total sample for which anticipation or control was reported | Respondent events common to: Both Sexes | All 3 Ethnic Groups | All 3 Social Classes |
|---|---|---|---|---|
| C. Birth of a second or later child | 0 | – | – | – |
| D. Abortion | 1 | – | – | – |
| E. Miscarriage or still-birth | 1 | – | – | – |
| F. Found out that cannot have children | 0 | – | – | – |
| G. Child died | 2 | – | – | – |
| H. Adopted a child | 0 | – | – | – |
| I. Started menopause | 6 | – | – | + |

Table 4 (Con't.)

## Family Matters

| | Frequency of respondent events in total sample for which anticipation or control was reported | Respondent events common to: Both Sexes | All 3 Ethnic Groups | All 3 Social Classes |
|---|---|---|---|---|
| A. New person moved into the household (code for whose household moved into) | 4 | + | + | + |
| B. Person moved out of the household (code for whose household moved out of) | 8 | + | + | + |
| C. Someone stayed on in the household after he was expected to leave (code for whose household was affected) | 1 | − | − | − |
| D. Serious family argument other than with spouse | 5 | + | + | + |

## Table 4 (Con't.)

| Family Matters (Con't.) | Frequency of respondent events in total sample for which anticipation or control was reported | Respondent events common to: | | |
| --- | --- | --- | --- | --- |
| | | Both Sexes | All 3 Ethnic Groups | All 3 Social Classes |
| E. A change in the frequency of family get-togethers | 6 | + | + | + |
| F. Family member other than spouse or child died (code person most closely related to deceased) | 21 | + | + | + |
| **Residence** | | | | |
| A. Moved to better residence or neighborhood | 15 | + | + | + |
| B. Moved to a worse residence or neighborhood | 1 | − | − | − |

Table 4 (Con't.)

Residence (Con't.)

| | Frequency of respondent events in total sample for which anticipation or control was reported | Respondent events common to: | | |
| --- | --- | --- | --- | --- |
| | | Both Sexes | All 3 Ethnic Groups | All 3 Social Classes |
| C. Moved to a residence or neighborhood no better or no worse than the last one | 1 | – | – | – |
| D. Unable to move after expecting to be able to move | 5 | + | – | – |
| E. Built a home or had a home built | 0 | – | – | – |
| F. Remodeled a home | 1 | – | – | – |
| G. Lost a home through fire, flood or other disaster | 1 | – | – | – |

Table 4 (Con't.)

| Crime and Legal Matters | Frequency of respondent events in total sample for which anticipation or control was reported | Respondent events common to: Both Sexes | All 3 Ethnic Groups | All 3 Social Classes |
|---|---|---|---|---|
| A. Assaulted | 3 | + | − | − |
| B. Robbed | 8 | + | + | + |
| C. Accident in which there were no injuries | 8 | + | + | + |
| D. Involved in a law suit | 3 | + | − | + |
| E. Accused of something for which a person could be sent to jail | 1 | − | − | − |
| F. Lost drivers license | 0 | − | − | − |
| G. Arrested | 0 | − | − | − |

Table 4 (Con't.)

| Crime and Legal Matters (Con't.) | Frequency of respondent events in total sample for which anticipation or control was reported | Respondent events common to: Both Sexes | All 3 Ethnic Groups | All 3 Social Classes |
|---|---|---|---|---|
| H. Went to jail | 0 | – | – | – |
| I. Got involved in a court case | 1 | – | – | – |
| J. Convicted of a crime | 0 | – | – | – |
| K. Acquitted of a crime | 0 | – | – | – |
| L. Released from jail | 0 | – | – | – |
| M. Didn't get out of jail when expected | 0 | – | – | – |
| Financial Matters | | | | |
| A. Took out a mortgage | 9 | + | – | + |
| B. Started buying a car, furniture or other large purchase on the installment plan | 20 | + | + | + |

Table 4 (Con't.)

| Financial Matters (Con't.) | Frequency of respondent events in total sample for which anticipation or control was reported | Respondent events common to: | | |
| --- | --- | --- | --- | --- |
| | | Both Sexes | All 3 Ethnic Groups | All 3 Social Classes |
| C. Foreclosure of a mortgage or loan | 1 | – | – | – |
| D. Repossession of a car, furniture, or other items bought on the installment plan | 0 | – | – | – |
| E. Took a cut in wage or salary without a demotion | 0 | – | – | – |
| F. Suffered a financial loss or loss of property not related to work | 4 | + | + | – |
| G. Went on welfare | 3 | – | – | – |
| H. Went off welfare | 2 | – | – | – |
| I. Got a substantial increase in wage or salary without promotion | 8 | + | – | + |

Table 4 (Con't.)

| Financial Matters (Con't.) | Frequency of respondent events in total sample for which anticipation or control was reported | Respondent events common to: | | |
|---|---|---|---|---|
| | | Both Sexes | All 3 Ethnic Groups | All 3 Social Classes |
| J. Did not get an expected wage or salary increase | 2 | – | – | – |
| K. Had financial improvement not related to work | 3 | – | + | – |
| Social Life and Activities | | | | |
| A. Increased church or synagogue, club, neighborhood, or other organizational activities | 11 | + | + | + |
| B. Took a vacation | 71 | + | + | + |
| C. Was not able to take a planned vacation | 6 | + | – | + |

Table 4 (Con't.)

| Social Life and Activities (Con't.) | Frequency of respondent events in total sample for which anticipation or control was reported | Respondent events common to: | | |
|---|---|---|---|---|
| | | Both Sexes | All 3 Ethnic Groups | All 3 Social Classes |
| D. Took up a new hobby, sport, craft or recreational activity | 10 | + | + | + |
| E. Dropped a hobby, sport, craft or recreational activity | 1 | - | - | - |
| F. Acquired a pet | 11 | + | + | - |
| G. Pet died | 8 | + | + | + |
| H. Made new friends | 21 | + | - | - |
| I. Broke up with a friend | 7 | + | + | + |
| J. Close friend died | 8 | + | + | + |

Table 4 (Con't.)

| Respondent events | Frequency of respondent events in total sample for which anticipation or control was reported | Respondent events common to: | | |
|---|---|---|---|---|
| | | Both Sexes | All 3 Ethnic Groups | All 3 Social Classes |
| **Armed Forces** | | | | |
| A. Entered the Armed Services | 2 | − | − | − |
| B. Left the Armed Services | 1 | − | − | − |
| **Travel** | | | | |
| A. Took a trip other than a vacation | 13 | + | + | + |
| **Health** | | | | |
| A. Physical health improved | 11 | + | + | + |
| B. Physical illness | 14 | + | + | + |
| C. Injury | 7 | + | − | + |
| D. Unable to get treatment for an illness or injury | 2 | − | − | − |

Our argument, then, is that if the observed ethnic contrast in anticipation of life events was determined by differences in the particular events experienced by Puerto Ricans,
we should find that their anticipation scores do not differ
from those of other ethnic groups when only events that were
common to all groups are considered and these events are
weighted equally. However, if the ethnic contrast in anticipation scores was based on learned differences in predisposition to anticipate future events we should find that the contrast between Puerto Ricans on the one hand and non-Puerto
Ricans on the other hand holds even for equally weighted
events experienced by all groups.

Before we make this comparison, however, one further
possible source of ambiguity in the ethnic difference reported in Table 2 should be taken into account. Recall this
question concerning the events presented on the 10 lists:
"During the last 12 months, did any of these things happen
to you, or to a member of your family, or to another person
who is important to you?" The person means used in the
analyses reported in Table 2 summarized all events reported
by a given respondent regardless of whether he or someone
else had been the central figure in the event. To control
for this factor we would like to make separate comparisons
for each central figure. However, because the number of
events experienced by all ethnic groups with any central
figure other than the respondent, whether spouse, child, or
other relative or friend, was too small, we will limit compari
sons of event means to events in which the respondent was the
central figure.

Accordingly, Table 5 describes the levels of anticipation of events in which the respondent was the central figure
for common events, those experienced by at least one person
in each ethnic group, semi-common events, those experienced
by at least one person in two of the three groups, and by
non-common events, those experienced by one or more persons
in only one ethnic group. The significant F ratio for common
events implies that the difference previously reported is base
at least in part on learned predispositions that vary with
ethnicity rather than being due entirely to differences in
the predictability of events experienced by various ethnic
groups. Moreover, the results shown in Table 5 provide no
direct support for the alternative hypothesis, that the
observed ethnic difference reflected variation in events

Table 5

Relation of Respondent's Ethnicity to Reported Anticipation of Life Events in Which the Respondent was the Central Figure for Events Common to All Ethnic Groups, for Semi-Common Events Reported in Two of Three Groups and for Non-Common Events Reported in Only One Ethnic Group with Mean Event Score Within Each Ethnic Group as the Unit of Analysis

| | Category of event | | | | | | | | |
|---|---|---|---|---|---|---|---|---|---|
| | Common | | | Semi-common | | | Non-common | | |
| | Ethnic Group | | | | | | | | |
| Level of anticipation | Black | Puerto Rican | Non-Puerto Rican White | Black | Puerto Rican | Non-Puerto Rican White | Black | Puerto Rican | Non-Puerto Rican White |
| Mean | 3.25 | 2.27 | 2.95 | 2.47 | 2.22 | 2.48 | 2.20 | 1.57 | 3.50 |
| SD | 1.24 | 1.21 | 1.13 | 1.54 | 1.35 | 1.40 | 1.75 | 1.51 | 1.52 |
| Number of events | 27 | 27 | 27 | 18 | 10 | 18 | 10 | 7 | 6 |
| F | 4.82 | | | 0.19 | | | 2.35 | | |
| p | <.05 | | | n.s. | | | n.s. | | |

Note: Where F is significant means connected by arrows do not differ significantly according to Scheffé post hoc test.

experienced, since levels of anticipation did not differ
across groups for semi-common or for non-common events.

Note, however, that post hoc tests of the differences
for common events, between pairs of ethnic groups did not
yield the same pattern as previously observed.  Whereas the
analysis of person means based on respondents' total event
experiences indicated that Puerto Ricans differed from both
of the other groups, when we limited the analysis to events
in which the respondent was the central figure, and which were
were common to all three ethnic groups, only Blacks and
Puerto Ricans differed significantly in degree of anticipation.

However, further analysis of the same set of events
yielded a significant difference between Puerto Ricans and
non-Puerto Rican Whites.  That is, as shown in Table 6, when
we analyzed person-event scores for events in which the respon
dent was the central figure, rather than life event means
calculated across persons, we obtained a significant difference for events common to all ethnic groups between Puerto
Ricans and non-Puerto Rican Whites, as well as between Blacks
and Puerto Ricans.  In terms of the schema in Table 3, the
last analysis was based on the scores indicated by X's, whereas the previous one was based on the means designated by L's.
Therefore, the difference in anticipation levels between Puert
Ricans and non-Puerto Rican Whites depends, to a greater exten
than the difference between Puerto Ricans and Blacks, on frequencies of events and distributions of individual anticipatio
scores within the Puerto Rican and the non-Puerto Rican White
groups.  While further detailed analysis could be designed to
attempt to determine precisely what is involved in this differ
ence, we have not done so here, since this qualification of
the description of the ethnic difference does not modify the
general conclusion that anticipation of life events was
influenced by personal predispositions related to an individual's ethnicity.


Control of the Occurrence of Life Events

Table 7 describes the level of control of the occurrence
of life events reported by respondents classified according
to their sex, their ethnicity, and the education of the head
of their household.  As noted, the mean control level reported

Table 6

Relation of Respondent's Ethnicity to Reported Anticipation of Events in Which the Respondent was the Central Figure for Events Common to all Ethnic Groups, for Non-Common Events Reported in Only One Ethnic Group with Each Respondent's Score for Each Event as the Unit of Analysis

| Level of Anticipation | Category of Event | | | | | | | | |
|---|---|---|---|---|---|---|---|---|---|
| | Common | | | Semi-common | | | Non-Common | | |
| | Ethnic group | | | | | | | | |
| | Black | Puerto Rican | Non-Puerto Rican White | Black | Puerto Rican | Non-Puerto Rican White | Black | Puerto Rican | Non-Puerto Rican White |
| Mean | 3.53 | 2.48 | 3.35 | 2.29 | 2.29 | 2.45 | 2.09 | 1.57 | 3.38 |
| SD | 1.56 | 1.75 | 1.70 | 1.73 | 1.76 | 1.70 | 1.70 | 1.51 | 1.68 |
| Number of person-events | 93 | 71 | 155 | 34 | 17 | 53 | 11 | 7 | 8 |
| F | 9.00 | | | 0.11 | | | 2.46 | | |
| p | $<.01$ | | | n.s. | | | n.s. | | |

Note: Where F is significant means connected by arrows do not differ significantly according to Scheffé post hoc test.

Table 7

Relation of Respondent's Sex, Respondent's Ethnicity, and
Education of the head of the Respondent's Household to
Reported Level of Control Over the Occurrence of Life Events

(Unit of analysis is the respondent's mean control score.)

| Level of control | Sex | | Ethnicity | | | Years of education of head of household | | |
|---|---|---|---|---|---|---|---|---|
| | Male | Female | Black | Puerto Rican | Non-Puerto Rican White | 0 - 11 | 12 - 15 | 16 + |
| Mean | 2.52 | 2.15 | 2.60 | 2.06 | 2.24 | 2.13 | 2.51 | 2.28 |
| SD | 1.11 | 0.75 | 0.95 | 1.09 | 0.72 | 1.01 | 0.92 | 0.60 |
| Number of Respondents | 60 | 98 | 45 | 44 | 69 | 70 | 56 | 32 |
| F | | 6.15 | | 4.24 | | | 2.68 | |
| p | | $<.05$ | | $<.05$ | | | n.s. | |

Note: Where F is significant means connected by arrows do not
differ significantly according to Scheffé post hoc test.

by each respondent is the unit of analysis. In contrast to
the comparable results for degree of anticipation, males and
females as well as the three ethnic groups differed significantly in their reported control over the occurrence of their
life events. Scheffe post hoc tests of pairs of ethnic groups
showed that the only significant difference, at the .05 level,
was between Blacks and Puerto Ricans.

In order to clarify the meaning of these results we pro-
ceeded once more as we did in the analysis of anticipation
scores. We changed the unit of analysis to event means and
compared levels of control reported for events that were
common to both sexes, and for events common to all ethnic
groups, as well as for events that were not common across
sexes or across ethnic groups. To maximize the homogeneity
of experience for the common events, these analyses were
again limited to events in which the respondent was the central figure.

Table 8

Mean and Standard Deviation of the Levels of Control Over the
Occurrence of Life Events in Which the Respondent was the
Central Figure According to Sex for Events Common to Both
Sexes According to Ethnicity for Events Common to All
Three Ethnic Groups, Using Two Different Units of Analysis

| Unit of Analysis | | Sex | | Ethnicity | | |
|---|---|---|---|---|---|---|
| | | Male | Female | Black | Puerto Rican | Non-Puerto Rican White |
| Life Event Mean: | X̄ | 3.30 | 2.74 | 3.40 | 3.21 | 3.13 |
| | SD | 1.29 | 1.21 | 1.03 | 1.46 | 1.04 |
| Number of Events | | 24 | 24 | 16 | 16 | 16 |
| Person-Event Score: | X̄ | 3.40 | 3.28 | 3.71 | 3.76 | 3.32 |
| | SD | 1.34 | 1.35 | 1.30 | 1.46 | 1.18 |
| Number of person-events | | 106 | 135 | 63 | 43 | 107 |

We found no significant differences either between sexes or among ethnic groups in any of these analyses. Nor were any of the differences significant when the same analyses were carried out with person-event scores. Table 8 provides the descriptive statistics associated with these results. Thus, in contrast to anticipation, the evidence does not indicate that the observed variability in levels of control was due to learned group differences in predisposition to control the occurrence of life events, at least when the respondent is the central figure in the event.

It seems reasonable to hypothesize, however, that the differences in levels of control found with person means in Table 7, where all events were included, may depend on whether the respondent or someone else was the central figure. There are two ways in which differences in control related to the central figure involved in the event might account for group differences. First, there might be differences between groups in the level of control reported. Women, for example, might report having less control than men over the occurrence of events in which they were not the central figure. A group difference of this kind would be revealed in a significant interaction in a two way analysis of variance with respondent status as one factor and event central figure, that is respondent spouse, child or other relative or friend, as the other factor. However, these analyses yielded F ratios of less than one for the interaction between respondents sex or respondent ethnicity and central figure in the event.

Another possibility that we considered more likely on the basis of experience with other life event data (Dohrenwend & Dohrenwend, 1972; Dohrenwend, 1973), at least as an explanation of the sex difference in reported level of control over the occurrence of life events, involves two predictions: First respondents will generally report less control over the occurrence of events in which they were not the central figure than over events in which they were the central figure; second women's lower mean control score for all life events is accoun for by their reporting a higher proportion than men of life events in which they, the women, were not the central figure. The first prediction is supported by the finding that the main effect for central figure is significant at the .01 level in each of the two way analyses of variance described previously. Scheffe post hoc tests between pairs of means for the total sample show that the mean level of control for respondents' events differed from those for the other three central figures, which did not differ from each other. For all status groups pooled, the mean level of control reported for events in which the respondent was the central figure was 3.32; when the spouse was the central figure it was 1.91, for a child it was 1.96, and for another relative or friend it was 1.46.

The second part of our prediction is that women's overall control score is lower than men's because they reported more events in which they were not the central figure. One way to test this prediction is to divide the variance associated with the main effects in a two way analysis of respondent sex and event central figure into three components: the variance due to the relation between sex and central figure, the variance uniquely due to sex, and the variance uniquely due to central figure. We predict, then, that the main effect uniquely due to sex will not yield a significant F ratio, which, in an analysis using person-event scores, is what we found. Table 9 provides a description of the mean control scores and distribution of events associated with different central figures that underlie this result.

Table 9

Mean Levels of Control and Number of Events Reported by Males and by Females for Each of Four Central Figures

| Central Figure | Respondent Sex | | | |
| --- | --- | --- | --- | --- |
| | Male | | Female | |
| | Mean | % of events | Mean | % of events |
| Respondent | 3.33 | 74.2 | 3.31 | 54.2 |
| Spouse | 2.00 | 5.5 | 1.88 | 10.7 |
| Child | 1.75 | 14.7 | 2.02 | 25.1 |
| Other relative or friend | 1.67 | 5.5 | 1.41 | 10.0 |
| Number of person-events | (163) | | (319) | |

The same result was not obtained when we substituted
ethnic group for sex in the two way analysis of variance.
That is, the difference in levels of control between Blacks
and Puerto Ricans was not accounted for by an ethnic difference in the frequency of reporting life events associated
with different central figures.

Another possibility that we considered is that there
are group differences in the extent to which the people
feel that they control the occurrence of desirable and undesirable events. To test for this effect all events were
classified independently by two judges as being desirable
or undesirable by social consensus, or as ambiguous in this
respect. Disagreements between these two judges concerning eight of the 102 events were resolved by a third judge.
With events thus classified, two way analyses of variance
were done, using only events in which the respondent was
the central figure, with desirability as one factor and
respondent sex, ethnicity, or social class as the other
factor. Events that were judged ambiguous on social desirability were not included in these analyses.

In all three analyses of variance the main effect for
social desirability was significant, with p less than .01,
and the interaction was nonsignificant, with values of F
being approximately equal to or less than one. Thus, there
was no evidence that sex or ethnic differences in predisposition to control the occurrence of desirable or undesirable
life events contributed to the observed differences in control scores. Instead, all groups reported higher levels of
control for desirable events, with a mean score of 3.45 in
the total sample, than for undesirable events, for which the
sample mean was 1.90. The mean for ambiguous events fell
between these two values, at 3.13.

Given the difference between the control scores associated with desirable and with undesirable events in which the
respondent was the central figure, an excess of undesirable
events among women, or among Puerto Ricans compared to Blacks
would contribute to the observed overall group differences
in control scores. However, the difference between men and
women was slight. Among events in which they were the central
figure 30 percent reported by men and 35 percent reported by
women were socially undesirable, while 39 percent and 40 percent respectively were desirable. The remaining events were
classified as ambiguous.

The difference between Blacks and Puerto Ricans was the
opposite of the one that would explain the difference in
their control scores; 34 percent of Black respondents'
events and only 30 percent of Puerto Rican respondents'
events were undesirable, while 40 percent of each group's
events were socially desirable. The largest difference was
between these two groups and the relatively advantaged non-
Puerto Rican Whites; of the last group's events only 20 percent were socially undesirable and 49 percent were desirable.
Somewhat surprisingly, this contrast in proportion of undesirable and desirable events between relatively advantaged
and disadvantaged groups did not hold for social class.
The middle class reported the largest proportion, 30 percent
of undesirable events, while the lowest social class reported
25 percent and the highest 21 percent; the middle group also
reported the lowest proportion, 38 percent, of desirable
events while the lowest and highest classes reported 47 and
50 percent respectively.

In a further attempt to explain the observed ethnic
difference on control scores we divided the events into six
content areas and examined the mean control scores of the
three ethnic groups in each area. These means, as well as
means for other groups and for the total sample, are shown
in Table 10. We note that there are substantial differences
in mean scores among content areas with three of them,
school, work, and social events having means above the mid-
point of the scale and three, financial and legal, family,
and health events having means below this midpoint, the last
two far below. By comparison the ethnic differences within
areas are small, so that we cannot explain the observed
difference between Blacks and Puerto Ricans in terms of
differences related to varied life activities. This is
particularly clear since the pattern shown in Table 10 was
repeated for events in which the central figure was other
than the respondent, although, as we would expect, the absolute levels of control were lower than for respondent's
events.

The means for males and females and those for different
social classes also show relatively small variations within
categories of events compared to variations between categories. However, the social class means do indicate that
the relative advantage implied by differences in social
class is not irrelevant to level of control over the
occurrence of life events. That is, when we look at the

Table 10

Mean Control Scores for Events in Which the Respondent was the Central Figure
According to Contents of Events and Ethnicity, Sex and Social Class* of Respondents

(Based on person-event scores)

| Contents of events | All respondents | Ethnicity | | | Sex | | Years of education of head of household | | | |
|---|---|---|---|---|---|---|---|---|---|---|
| | | Black | Puerto Rican | Non-Puerto Rican White | Male | Female | 0-7 | 8-11 | 12-15 | 16+ |
| School | 4.42 | 4.60 | 4.33 | 4.25 | 4.00 | 4.46 | 5.00 | 4.40 | 4.20 | 5.00 |
| Work | 3.38 | 3.72 | 2.75 | 3.38 | 2.94 | 3.68 | 2.50 | 3.26 | 3.52 | 3.67 |
| Family | 1.63 | 1.56 | 1.79 | 1.59 | 1.94 | 1.50 | 1.33 | 1.12 | 1.85 | 2.14 |
| Financial & legal | 2.93 | 2.69 | 3.60 | 2.74 | 3.01 | 2.88 | 2.64 | 3.06 | 3.06 | 2.74 |
| Social | 3.29 | 3.44 | 3.33 | 3.18 | 3.57 | 3.10 | 3.61 | 3.30 | 3.43 | 2.91 |
| Health | 1.25 | 1.20 | 1.33 | 1.21 | 1.22 | 1.28 | 1.00 | 1.30 | 1.20 | 1.57 |

* The lowest group was divided into subgroups to clarify the results for
work and family events, as discussed in the text.

content area that we would expect to be most strongly affected
by an individual's social class, namely, work, we find a
direct relation between level of control and class level.
At the same time, the limited implication of social class for
control of the occurrence of life events is suggested by the
observation that there is no other area in which social
class was directly related to level of control.

Further Comparison of Anticipation and Control Scores

Our analyses of control scores indicates that they
were influenced by whether the respondent was the central
figure or not.  Levels of anticipation also differed significantly, at the .01 level, with the central figure in
the event.  However, in contrast to control scores, the
highest mean, 3.33, was associated with events in which a
child was the central figure and the lowest mean, 2.52, with
events in which another relative or friend was the central
figure.  Moreover, a Sheffe post hoc analysis of pairs of
means showed that, of the means for respondent, spouse,
child, and other relative or friend, only those for child
and for other relative or friend differed significantly,
at the .05 level, from each other.  In addition, unlike
levels of control, levels of reported anticipation were
significantly affected by the interaction of central figure
with one type of status, specifically, social class.  The
means involved in this interaction do not, however, show
any simple, easily interpretable pattern.  Thus, in contrast
to level of control, the extent to which an event is anticipated, while related to who is the central figure, was not
influenced in a straightforward way by this aspect of the
event.

Anticipation scores resembled control scores in relation
to the desirability of events.  That is, two way analyses
of variance of anticipation scores with desirable versus
undesirable events as one factor and sex, ethnicity, or
social class as the other factor yielded no significant
interaction terms and a significant main effect for desirability.  However, the difference in mean anticipation scores
was less marked than the difference in mean control scores
as a function of the desirability of events.  The mean anticipation score for desirable events was 2.93, for undesirable
events 2.34, and for ambiguous events was 2.86.

In contrast to mean control scores associated with
different content areas, which varied over almost the entire
range of the response scale, mean anticipation scores associated with different content areas, with the exception of
health events, varied over a relatively restricted range.
These means are shown in Table 11.


Relation to the Form of the Question to Observed
Differences in Anticipation and Control Scores

Table 12 shows mean anticipation and mean control scores
separately for each question form according to who was the
central figure, according to the social desirability of the
events, and according to the content of the events.  As
noted, these results are based on even means, thus simpli-
fying the comparison by controlling for variability between
groups in the frequencies of events.  We note that there were
large differences in the level of both anticipation and
control reported in response to different question forms.
As indicated in the first four rows of Table 12, this difference held not only for events in which the respondent was the
central figure but for events with other central figures as
well.

For the sake of discussion let us make the cautious
assumption that these differences were entirely a function
of the form of the questions rather than reflecting differences in the events that demanded these variations in probes.
On this assumption, and given the evidence that the varied
question forms did not yield equivalent means, the issue is
whether the observed differences between categories of events
were a spurious function of variability in responses to different questions.

Although the frequencies in Table 12 indicate some confounding of question form and event category, the patterns
of means within question forms argue against concluding that
differences between event categories were spurious.  On
the first point note, for example, that the first question
forms for anticipation and for control were used disproportionately with socially desirable events while the second
question form for anticipation and the third form for
control were used disproportionately for undesirable events.
However, as noted, we cannot account for the differences
between event categories in terms of partial confounding of

Table 11

Mean Anticipation Scores for Events in Which the Respondent was the Central Figure According to Contents of Events and Ethnicity, Sex, and Social Class of Respondents

(Based on person-event scores)

| Contents of events | All respondents | Ethnicity | | | Sex | | Years of education of head of household | | |
|---|---|---|---|---|---|---|---|---|---|
| | | Black | Puerto Rican | Non-Puerto Rican White | Male | Female | 0 - 11 | 12 - 15 | 16+ |
| School | 2.77 | 2.80 | 3.00 | 2.50 | 2.50 | 2.82 | 2.67 | 2.83 | 3.00 |
| Work | 3.23 | 3.21 | 2.17 | 3.67 | 2.59 | 3.78 | 3.51 | 3.07 | 3.09 |
| Family | 2.38 | 2.41 | 2.38 | 2.38 | 2.96 | 2.15 | 1.74 | 2.94 | 2.64 |
| Financial & legal | 2.94 | 2.80 | 1.90 | 3.51 | 2.98 | 2.91 | 2.38 | 3.01 | 3.76 |
| Social | 3.28 | 3.47 | 2.76 | 3.41 | 3.44 | 3.18 | 3.30 | 3.18 | 3.41 |
| Health | 1.68 | 1.60 | 2.33 | 1.35 | 1.92 | 1.50 | 1.71 | 1.73 | 1.50 |

Table 12

Mean Anticipation and Control Scores with Various
Categories of Events for Different Forms of
Anticipation Probes and Control Probes

(Based on event means)

| Event categories | Anticipation | | | | Control | | | | | |
|---|---|---|---|---|---|---|---|---|---|---|
| | | | | | Question form[a] | | | | | |
| | $n^b$ 1 | $\bar{x}$ | $n^b$ 2 | $\bar{x}$ | $n^b$ 1 | $\bar{x}$ | $n^b$ 2 | $\bar{x}$ | $n^b$ 3 | $\bar{x}$ |
| Central figure | | | | | | | | | | |
| Respondent | 20 | 3.45 | 52 | 2.23 | 22 | 3.68 | 20 | 2.41 | 11 | 1.56 |
| Spouse | 0 | | 34 | 2.58 | 1 | 3.00 | 16 | 1.75 | 2 | 1.00 |
| Child | 2 | 4.14 | 53 | 2.85 | 2 | 2.88 | 29 | 1.67 | 6 | 1.00 |
| Other relative or friend | | | 47 | 2.34 | 0 | | 19 | 1.42 | 4 | 1.25 |
| (Respondent central figure only) | | | | | | | | | | |
| Social desirability | | | | | | | | | | |
| Desirable events | 9 | 3.38 | 12 | 2.59 | 10 | 3.97 | 8 | 2.98 | 1 | 3.00 |
| Ambiguous events | 9 | 3.28 | 7 | 2.06 | 10 | 3.52 | 4 | 2.15 | 0 | |
| Undesirable events | 2 | 4.50 | 33 | 2.13 | 2 | 3.00 | 8 | 1.98 | 10 | 1.42 |
| Event content | | | | | | | | | | |
| School | 2 | 3.30 | 2 | 3.00 | 2 | 4.30 | 0 | | 1 | 3.00 |
| Work | 8 | 3.56 | 10 | 2.65 | 9 | 3.63 | 7 | 2.88 | 1 | 2.20 |
| Family | 4 | 3.00 | 20 | 2.22 | 4 | 4.25 | 6 | 2.40 | 4 | 1.50 |
| Financial and legal | 1 | 3.95 | 11 | 2.12 | 2 | 3.26 | 5 | 1.50 | 2 | 1.00 |
| Social | 5 | 3.58 | 5 | 1.90 | 5 | 3.23 | 1 | 3.50 | 2 | 1.50 |
| Health | 0 | | 4 | 1.52 | 0 | | 1 | 2.67 | 1 | 1.00 |

[a] See Appendix Table 1 for details

[b] Number of events

question form and event category since, the pattern of relatively high mean scores for desirable events and relatively low mean for undesirable events was repeated within each question form for control, and, for anticipation, was present in one and reversed in the other. As in the case of social desirability, in general the most striking effect of varying question form was to increase variability within event categories, thus suggesting that the differences between them were observed despite rather than because of the variation in the probes used to inquire about anticipation and control.


## DISCUSSION

We have found some interesting differences between factors associated with variation in level of anticipation of life events and factors associated with variation in level of control over the occurrence of these events. Briefly, these differences are as follows.

1.  When events were held constant and the central figure in the events was the respondent:

    a.  There was a significant ethnic difference in the anticipation of the occurrence of events.

    b.  There were no significant sex, class or ethnic differences in control over the occurrence of events.

2.  When the central figure in the events was varied:

    a.  Levels of anticipation did not differ among respondent, spouse, and child or among respondent, spouse, and other relative or friend, the only significant difference being between child and other relative or friend, a result which, in the context of the nonsignificant difference is without obvious substantive implications; levels of anticipation also differed for the interaction of central figure with respondent social class in a complex patterns that was not easily interpretable.

    b.  Levels of control over the occurrence of events differed significantly between events

in which the respondent was the central figure and events in which someone else, spouse,
child, or other relative or friend, was the
central figure, in a way that explained the
observed overall sex difference in control
scores.

3.  When events were grouped according to their conten-
    into school, work, family, financial and legal,
    social, and health events:

    a.  Mean anticipation scores varied within a rela-
        tively narrow range around the midpoint on a
        scale from one to five, with the exception
        of health events, for which the mean was
        relatively low.

    b.  Mean control scores varied over almost the
        entire range of the five point scale.

The greatest similarity between anticipation and control
was found when events were classified as socially desirable,
socially undesirable, or ambiguous. Both anticipation and
control scores were significantly higher for desirable than
for undesirable events, and intermediate for ambiguous events
However, the difference between anticipation means for desirable and undesirable events was about a third as large as
the difference between control means.

Our purpose in this analysis was to learn to what extent
intrapsychic as against immediate situational factors determined levels of anticipation and control of the occurrence of
life events. Although our findings do not provide unambiguou
answers on this issue, insofar as the immediate situational
determinants of anticipation and control can be defined in
terms of characteristics and circumstances of the events,
they do point to a relevant contrast. That is, anticipation
of the occurrence of events was more affected by characteristics of the respondents and less influenced by characteristics of the events than control. This difference suggests
that control over the occurrence of life events is more
strongly determined by the immediate situation than anticipation. However, this inference must be qualified by recognition of questions about respondent differences in control
left unanswered by our analysis.

The major unanswered question concerns the basis for
the large difference between Blacks and Puerto Rican in reported levels of control over the occurrence of their life
events. This ethnic difference could, for example, be based
on past learning of contrasting subcultural norms, on learned
differences reflecting varied histories of migration and
assimilation to the metropolitan setting of New York City,
or on some variation in the current social experience of
Black and Puerto Rican New Yorkers. However, the fact that
these two economically disadvantaged groups differed from
each other more than either differed from relatively advantaged White non-Puerto Rican New Yorkers suggests that we
will have to look beyond their current circumstances to
explain the sharp contrast between them.

Another question is raised by the large sex differences
in the proportion of events reported in which the respondent
was not the central figure: Are women more aware of the
life events of others because they are obliged to be by the
demands of the female role or does the relative failure of
men to report events that centered on others who are "important" to them reflect their greater egocentricity? In general, the question is whether this contrast reflects a sex
difference in personality or is largely imposed by different
environmental demands on men and women. Finer analysis of
the specific events involved may provide leads that will
help to answer this question.

These unanswered questions emphasize the methodological
contrast between the experimental research on which this work
is founded and the study of anticipation and control in
relation to naturally occurring life events. The experimenter creates but we must try to reconstruct the antecedents
of anticipation and control in order to learn, after the fact,
whether we are observing consequences of intrapsychic processes
or responses to the immediate situation, or some combination
of the two.

In the work reported here we have advanced this recon-
struction to the point where it seems clear that the distinction between anticipation and control is a useful one, something that was not entirely clear from experimental studies.
We base this conclusion on our finding that in their natural
life settings the antecedents of these two processes seem
to be different. Thus, the potential usefulness of studying
anticipation and control of the occurrence of life events

is now indicated not only by the results of previous experimental and clinical research but also by the apparent
difference in their genesis and, hence, in their possible
implications concerning the etiology of distress, disturbanc
or disability resulting from life events.


REFERENCES

Averill, J.R.   Personal control over aversive stimuli and its
    relationship to stress.  Psychological Bulletin, 1973,
    80, 286-303.

Dohrenwend, B.S.   Social status and stressful life events.
    Journal of Personality and Social Psychology, 1973, 28,
    225-235.

Dohrenwend, B.S., and Dohrenwend, B.P.   Social class and the
    relation of remote to recent stressors.  In M. Roff,
    L.N. Robins, and M. Pollack (Eds.), Life history researc
    in psychopathology, Volume 2.  Minneapolis, Minnesota:
    The University of Minnesota Press, 1972, pp. 170-185.

Glass, D.C., Singer, J.E., and Friedman, L.N.   Psychic cost
    of adaptation to an environmental stressor.  Journal
    of Personality and Social Psychology, 1969 , 12, 200-210

Lefcourt, H.M.   The function of the illusions of control and
    freedom.  American Psychologist, 1973, 28, 417-425.

Richardson, S.A., Dohrenwend, B.S., and Klein, D.   Inter-
    viewing:  Its forms and functions.  New York: Basic
    Books, Inc., 1965.

Schmale, A.H.   Giving up as a final common pathway to changes
    in health.  Advances in Psychosomatic Medicine, 1972, 8,
    20-40.

Appendix Table 1

Varied Forms of Probes Concerning Anticipation and
Control of Life Events

Form #                          Anticipation

1        Did you decide beforehand to (EVENT) or did you
         (EVENT) completely on the spur of the moment?
         (IF - Decided beforehand ask):
         After you had decided to (EVENT) were you abso-
         lutely positive that you would go through with it,
         quite sure, fairly sure or not very sure?


2        Did you have any idea beforehand that (EVENT), or
         was it completely unexpected by you?
         (If had idea beforehand ask):
         How sure were you that (EVENT)--would you say you
         were absolutely positive, quite sure, fairly sure,
         or, not very sure?


                                Control

1        Was the decision to (EVENT) entirely yours or was
         someone else involved in making the decision?
         (IF someone else involved ask):
         How much was (SOMEONE ELSE) involved in making the
         decision--would you say it was entirely (his/her/
         their) decision, mostly (his/her/their) decision,
         you shared about equally in making the decision, or
         was it mostly your decision?


2        (If had idea beforehand ask):
         Would you say that you had some responsibility for
         (EVENT) or would you say you had no responsibility
         at all for it?
         (IF some responsibility ask):
         Would you say it was entirely your responsibility,
         it was mostly your responsibility, you were re-
         sponsible to a moderate extent or shared responsi-
         bility equally with someone else, or you were re-
         sponsible to a small extent?


3        (IF had idea beforehand ask):
         Was there anything you could have done to prevent
         (EVENT)?
         (IF yes ask):
         How sure are you that you could have prevented
         (EVENT)--absolutely positive you could have pre-
         vented it, quite sure, fairly sure, or not sure
         at all?

Appendix Table 2

Life Event List with Associated Probing Procedure and Assumed Levels of Anticipation and Control

| Description of Event | Form of Probe[a] for: | | | | | | | | Assumed Level[b] of: | | | | | | | |
|---|---|---|---|---|---|---|---|---|---|---|---|---|---|---|---|---|
| | Anticipation | | | | Control | | | | Anticipation | | | | Control | | | |
| | R | Sp | Ch | O | R | Sp | Ch | O | R | Sp | Ch | O | R | Sp | Ch | O |
| **Schooling** | | | | | | | | | | | | | | | | |
| A. Started school or a training program after not going to school for a long time | 1 | 2 | c | 2 | 1 | 2 | c | 2 | | | | | | | | |
| B. Changed schools or training programs | 1 | 2 | c | 2 | 1 | .2 | c | 2 | | | | | | | | |
| C. Graduated from school or training program | - | 2 | 2 | 2 | - | 2 | 2 | 2 | 5 | | | | | | | |
| D. Had problems in school or in training program | 2 | 2 | 2 | 2 | 3 | 3 | 3 | 3 | | | | | | | | |
| E. Failed school, training program | 2 | 2 | 2 | 2 | 3 | 3 | 3 | 3 | | | | | | | | |
| F. Did not graduate from school, training program when expected | 2 | 2 | 2 | 2 | 3 | 3 | 3 | 3 | | | | | | | | |
| **Work** | | | | | | | | | | | | | | | | |
| A. Started work for the first time | 1 | 2 | 2 | 2 | 1 | 2 | 2 | 2 | | | | | | | | |
| B. Returned to work after not working for a long time | 1 | 2 | 2 | 2 | 1 | 2 | 2 | 2 | | | | | | | | |
| C. Changed jobs for a better one | 2 | 2 | 2 | 2 | 2 | 2 | 2 | 2 | | | | | | | | |
| D. Changed jobs for a worse one | 2 | 2 | 2 | 2 | 2 | 2 | 2 | 2 | | | | | | | | |
| E. Changed jobs for one that was no better and no worse than the last one | 2 | 2 | 2 | 2 | 2 | 2 | 2 | 2 | | | | | | | | |

## Appendix Table 2 (Con't.)

| Work (Con't.) | Form of Probe[a] for: | | | | | | | | Assumed Level[b] of: | | | | | | | |
|---|---|---|---|---|---|---|---|---|---|---|---|---|---|---|---|---|
| | Anticipation | | | | Control | | | | Anticipation | | | | Control | | | |
| | R | Sp | Ch | O | R | Sp | Ch | O | R | Sp | Ch | O | R | Sp | Ch | O |
| F. Had trouble with a boss | 2 | 2 | 2 | 2 | 3 | 3 | 3 | 3 | | | | | | 1 | 1 | 1 |
| G. Demoted at work | 2 | 2 | 2 | 2 | 3 | – | – | – | | | | | | 1 | 1 | 1 |
| H. Found out that was not going to be promoted at work | 2 | 2 | 2 | 2 | 3 | – | – | – | | | | | | | | |
| I. Conditions at work got worse, other than demotion or trouble with boss | 2 | 2 | 2 | 2 | 3 | 3 | 3 | 3 | | | | | | | | |
| J. Promoted | 2 | 2 | 2 | 2 | 2 | 2 | 2 | 2 | | | | | | | | |
| K. Had significant success at work | 2 | 2 | 2 | 2 | 2 | 2 | 2 | 2 | | | | | | 1 | 1 | 1 |
| L. Conditions at work improved not counting promotion or other personal success | 2 | 2 | 2 | 2 | 2 | 2 | 2 | 2 | | | | | | 1 | 1 | 1 |
| M. Laid off | 2 | 2 | 2 | 2 | 3 | – | – | – | | | | | | | | |
| N. Fired | 2 | 2 | 2 | 2 | 3 | – | – | – | | | | | | | | |
| O. Started business or professional | – | 2 | 2 | 2 | 1 | 2 | 2 | 2 | 5 | | | | | | | |
| P. Expanded business or professional practice | – | 2 | 2 | 2 | 1 | 2 | 2 | 2 | 5 | | | | | | | |
| Q. Took on a greatly increased work load | 1 | 2 | 2 | 2 | 1 | 2 | 2 | 2 | | | | | | | | |
| R. Suffered a business loss or failure | 2 | 2 | 2 | 2 | 3 | – | – | – | | | | | | 1 | 1 | 1 |
| S. Sharply reduced work load | 1 | 2 | 2 | 2 | 1 | 2 | 2 | 2 | | | | | | | | |

## Appendix Table 2 (Con't.)

| | Form of Probe[a] for: | | | | | | | | Assumed Level[b] of: | | | | | | | |
| | Anticipation | | | | Control | | | | Anticipation | | | | Control | | | |
| | R | Sp | Ch | O | R | Sp | Ch | O | R | Sp | Ch | O | R | Sp | Ch | O |
|---|---|---|---|---|---|---|---|---|---|---|---|---|---|---|---|---|
| **Work (Con't.)** | | | | | | | | | | | | | | | | |
| T. Retired | 1 | - | - | - | 1 | - | - | - | | | | | | | | |
| U. Stopped working, not retirement, for an extended period | 1 | 2 | 2 | 2 | 1 | 2 | 2 | 2 | | | | | | | | |
| **Love and Marriage** | | | | | | | | | | | | | | | | |
| A. Became engaged | 2[d] | | 2 | 2 | 2[d] | | 2 | 2 | | | | | | | | |
| B. Engagement was broken | 2 | | 2 | 2 | 3 | | 3 | 3 | | | | | | | | |
| C. Married | 1[e] | | 2 | 2 | - | | 2 | 2 | | | | | | | | |
| D. Started a love affair | 2 | | 2 | 2 | 3 | | 3 | 3 | | | | | | | | |
| E. Ended a love affair | 2 | | 2 | 2 | 3 | | 3 | 3 | | | | | | | | |
| F. Relations with spouse changed for the worse, without separation or divorce | 2 | | 2 | 2 | - | | 3 | 3 | | | | | 5 | | | |
| G. Married couple separated | 2 | | 2 | 2 | - | | 3 | 3 | | | | | | | | |
| H. Divorce | 2 | | 2 | 2 | - | | 3 | 3 | | | | | | | | |
| I. Relations with spouse changed for the better | 2 | | 2 | 2 | 2 | | 2 | 2 | | | | | | | | |
| J. Married couple got together again after separation | 2 | | 2 | 2 | 2 | | 2 | 2 | | | | | | | | |
| K. Marital infidelity (CODE FOR "WRONGED" PARTNER) | 2 | 2 | 2 | 2 | 2 | 2 | - | - | | | | | | | | |
| L. Trouble with in-laws | 2 | 2 | 2 | 2 | 3 | 3 | 3 | 3 | | | | | | | | |
| M. Spouse died | 2 | 2 | 2 | 2 | - | - | - | - | | | | | 1 | 1 | 1 | 1 |

## Appendix Table 2 (Con't.)

| | Form of Probe[a] for: | | | | | | | | Assumed Level[b] of: | | | | | | | |
|---|---|---|---|---|---|---|---|---|---|---|---|---|---|---|---|---|
| | Anticipation | | | | Control | | | | Anticipation | | | | Control | | | |
| | R | Sp | Ch | O | R | Sp | Ch | O | R | Sp | Ch | O | R | Sp | Ch | O |
| **Having Children** | | | | | | | | | | | | | | | | |
| A. Became pregnant | 1[e] | 1[e] | 2 | 2 | – | – | – | – | | | | | | | 1 | 1 |
| B. Birth of first child | 1[e] | – | – | – | – | – | – | – | | | | | | | | 1 |
| C. Birth of a second or later child | 1[e] | – | – | – | – | – | – | – | | | | | | | | |
| D. Abortion | 1 | 2 | 2 | 2 | 1 | 2 | 2 | 2 | | | | | | | | |
| E. Miscarriage or stillbirth | 2 | 2 | 2 | 2 | – | – | 2 | – | | | | | 1 | 1 | 1 | 1 |
| F. Found out that cannot have children | 2 | 2 | 2 | 2 | – | – | – | – | 5 | | | | 1 | 1 | 1 | 1 |
| G. Child died | 2 | 2 | 2 | 2 | – | – | – | – | | | | | 1 | 1 | 1 | 1 |
| H. Adopted a child | – | 2 | 2 | 2 | 1 | – | 2 | 2 | | | | | | | | |
| I. Started menopause | 2 | 2 | – | – | – | – | – | – | | | | | 1 | 1 | 1 | 1 |
| **Family Matters** | | | | | | | | | | | | | | | | |
| A. New person moved into the household (COD FOR WHOSE HOUSEHOLD MOVED INTO) | 2 | | 2 | 2 | 2 | | 2 | 2 | | | | | | | | |
| B. Person moved out of the household (CODE FOR WHOSE HOUSEHOLD MOVED OUT OF) | 2 | | 2 | 2 | 2 | | 2 | 2 | | | | | | | | |
| C. Someone stayed on in the household after he was expected to leave (CODE FOR WHOSE HOUSEHOLD WAS AFFECTED) | 2 | | 2 | 2 | 2 | | 2 | 2 | | | | | | | | |
| D. Serious family argument other than with spouse | 2 | | 2 | 2 | 3 | 3 | 3 | 3 | | | | | | | | |
| E. A change in the frequency of family get-togethers | 2 | | 2 | 2 | 2 | 2 | 2 | 2 | | | | | | | | |
| F. Family member other than spouse or child died (CODE CLOSELY RELATED TO DECEASED) | 2 | | 2 | 2 | – | – | – | – | | | | | 1 | 1 | 1 | 1 |

## Appendix Table 2 (Con't.)

| | Form of Probe[a] for: | | | | | | | | Assumed Level[b] of: | | | | | | | |
|---|---|---|---|---|---|---|---|---|---|---|---|---|---|---|---|---|
| | Anticipation | | | | Control | | | | Anticipation | | | | Control | | | |
| | R | Sp | Ch | O | R | Sp | Ch | O | R | Sp | Ch | O | R | Sp | Ch | O |
| **Residence** | | | | | | | | | | | | | | | | |
| A. Moved to a better residence or neighborhood | 2 | | 2 | 2 | 2 | • | 2 | 2 | | | | | | | | |
| B. Moved to a worse residence or neighborhood | 2 | | 2 | 2 | 3 | | 3 | 3 | | | | | | | | |
| C. Moved to a residence or neighborhood no better or no worse than the last one | 2 | | 2 | 2 | 2 | | 2 | 2 | | | | | | | | |
| D. Unable to move after expecting to be able to move | 2 | | 2 | 2 | 2 | | 2 | 2 | | | | | | | | |
| E. Built a home or had a home built | 2 | | 2 | 2 | 2 | | 2 | 2 | | | | | | | | |
| F. Remodeled a home | | | 2 | 2 | 1 | | 2 | 2 | | | | | | | | |
| G. Lost a home through fire, flood or other disaster | – | – | – | – | – | – | – | – | 1 | | 1 | 1 | 1 | | 1 | 1 |
| **Crime and legal** | | | | | | | | | | | | | | | | |
| A. Assaulted | – | – | – | – | – | – | – | – | 1 | | 1 | 1 | 1 | | 1 | 1 |
| B. Robbed | – | – | – | – | – | – | – | – | 1 | | 1 | 1 | 1 | | 1 | 1 |
| C. Accident in which there were no injuries | 2 | 2 | 2 | 2 | 3 | 3 | 3 | 3 | | | | | | | | |
| D. Involved in a law suit | 2 | 2 | 2 | 2 | 2 | 2 | 2 | 2 | | | | | | | | |
| E. Accused of something for which a person could be sent to jail | 2 | 2 | 2 | 2 | 3 | 3 | 3 | 3 | | | | | | | | |
| F. Lost drivers license | 2 | 2 | 2 | 2 | 3 | 3 | 3 | 3 | | | | | | | | |
| G. Arrested | 2 | 2 | 2 | 2 | 3 | 3 | 3 | 3 | | | | | | | | |
| H. Went to jail | 2 | 2 | 2 | 2 | 3 | 3 | 3 | 3 | | | | | | | | |

## Appendix Table 2 (Con't.)

| | Form of Probe[a] for: | | | | | | | | Assumed Level[b] of: | | | | | | | |
|---|---|---|---|---|---|---|---|---|---|---|---|---|---|---|---|---|
| | Anticipation | | | | Control | | | | Anticipation | | | | Control | | | |
| | R | Sp | Ch | O | R | Sp | Ch | O | R | Sp | Ch | O | R | Sp | Ch | O |
| **Crime and Legal (Con't.)** | | | | | | | | | | | | | | | | |
| I. Got involved in a court case | 2 | 2 | 2 | 2 | 2 | 2 | 2 | 2 | | | | | | | | |
| J. Convicted of a crime | 2 | 2 | 2 | 2 | 3 | 3 | 3 | 3 | | | | | | | 1 | 1 |
| K. Acquitted of a crime | 2 | 2 | 2 | 2 | 2 | 2 | 2 | 2 | | | | | | | | |
| L. Released from jail | 2 | 2 | 2 | 2 | 2 | 2 | 2 | 2 | | | | | | 1 | 1 | 1 |
| M. Didn't get out of jail when expected | 2 | 2 | 2 | 2 | 3 | 3 | 3 | 3 | | | | | | | 1 | 1 |
| **Financial** | | | | | | | | | | | | | | | | |
| A. Took out a mortgage | - | 2 | 2 | 2 | 1 | 1 | 2 | 2 | 5 | | | | | | | |
| B. Started buying a car, furniture or other large purchase on the installment plan | 1 | 2 | 2 | 2 | 1 | 1 | 2 | 2 | | | | | | | | |
| C. Foreclosure of a mortgage or loan | 2 | 2 | 2 | 2 | 3 | 3 | - | - | | | | | | | | |
| D. Repossession of a car, furniture or other items bought on the installment plan | 2 | 2 | 2 | 2 | 3 | 3 | - | - | | | | | | | | |
| E. Took a cut in wage or salary without a demotion | 2 | 2 | 2 | 2 | 3 | 3 | 3 | 3 | | | | | 1 | 1 | 1 | 1 |
| F. Suffered a financial loss or loss of property not related to work | 2 | 2 | 2 | 2 | 3 | 3 | 3 | 3 | | | | | | | | |
| G. Went on welfare | 2 | | 2 | 2 | 3 | 3 | 3 | 3 | | | | | | | | |
| H. Went off welfare | 2 | 2 | 2 | 2 | 3 | 3 | 3 | 3 | | | | | | | | |
| I. Got a substantial increase in wage or salary without a promotion | 2 | 2 | 2 | 2 | 2 | - | - | - | | | | | 1 | 1 | 1 | 1 |
| J. Did not get an expected wage or salary increase | 2 | 2 | 2 | 2 | 3 | - | - | - | | | | | 1 | 1 | 1 | 1 |

## Appendix Table 2 (Con't.)

| | Form of Probe for: | | | | | | | | Assumed Level of: | | | | | | | |
| | Anticipation | | | | Control | | | | Anticipation | | | | Level | | | |
| | R | Sp | Ch | O | R | Sp | Ch | O | R | Sp | Ch | O | R | Sp | Ch | O |
|---|---|---|---|---|---|---|---|---|---|---|---|---|---|---|---|---|
| **Financial (Con't.)** | | | | | | | | | | | | | | | | |
| K. Had financial improvement not related to work | 2 | 2 | 2 | 2 | 2 | 2 | 2 | 2 | | | | | | | | |
| **Social** | | | | | | | | | | | | | | | | |
| A. Increased church or synagogue, club, neighborhood, or other organizational activities | 1 | 2 | 2 | 2 | 1 | 2 | 2 | 2 | | | | | | | | |
| B. Took a vacation | 1 | 2 | 2 | 2 | 1 | 2 | 2 | 2 | | | | | | | | |
| C. Was not able to take a planned vacation | 2 | 2 | 2 | 2 | 3 | 2 | 2 | 2 | | | | | | | | |
| D. Took up a new hobby, sport, craft or recreational activity | 1 | 2 | 2 | 2 | 1 | 2 | 2 | 2 | | | | | | | | |
| E. Dropped a hobby, sport, craft or recreational activity | 1 | 2 | 2 | 2 | 1 | 2 | 2 | 2 | | | | | | | | |
| F. Acquired a pet | 1 | 2 | 2 | 2 | 1 | 2 | 2 | 2 | | | | | | | | |
| G. Pet died | 2 | 2 | 2 | 2 | 3 | – | – | – | | | | | | | | |
| H. Made new friends | 2 | 2 | 2 | 2 | – | 3 | 3 | 3 | | | | | | | | |
| I. Broke up with a friend | 2 | 2 | 2 | 2 | 2 | 2 | 2 | 2 | | | | | | | | |
| J. Close friend died | 2 | 2 | 2 | 2 | – | – | – | – | | | | | | | | |
| **Miscellaneous** | | | | | | | | | | | | | | | | |
| A. Entered the Armed Services | 1 | 2 | 2 | 2 | 1 | 2 | 2 | 2 | | | | | 5 | | | 1 |
| B. Left the Armed Services | 2 | 2 | 2 | 2 | 1 | 2 | 2 | 2 | | | | | | 1 | 1 | |
| C. Took a trip other than a vacation | 1 | 2 | 2 | 2 | 1 | 2 | 2 | 2 | | | | | 1 | 1 | 1 | 1 |

## Appendix Table 2 (Con't.)

| | Form of Probe[a] for: | | | | | | | | Assumed Level[b] of: | | | | | | | |
| | Anticipation | | | | Control | | | | Anticipation | | | | Control | | | |
| Health | R | Sp | Ch | O | R | Sp | Ch | O | R | Sp | Ch | O | R | Sp | Ch | O |
|---|---|---|---|---|---|---|---|---|---|---|---|---|---|---|---|---|
| A. Physical health improved | 2 | 2 | 2 | 2 | 2 | 2 | 2 | 2 | | | | | | | | |
| B. Physical illness | 2 | 2 | 2 | 2 | – | – | – | – | | | | | 1 | 1 | 1 | 1 |
| C. Injury | 2 | 2 | 2 | 2 | – | – | – | – | | | | | 1 | 1 | 1 | 1 |
| D. Unable to get treatment for an illness or injury | 2 | 2 | 2 | 2 | 3 | 3 | 3 | 3 | | | | | | | | |

Appendix Table 2 Footnotes


R - Respondent

Sp - Spouse

Ch - Child

O - Other relative or friend


a.  See Table 3 for contents of probes; blanks indicate that
    event was not possible; dash indicates that probes were
    not used.

b.  Blank indicates level was not assumed

c.  For minor child:  Anticipation and Control -1; for adult
                      child
                      Anticipation and Control -2

d.  For male respondents: Anticipation -1 without contingent
    question, no Control probe; for female respondent: Anti-
    cipation -2, no Control probe.

e.  Without contingent question

# GENERAL DISCUSSION OF SECTION II

Formal Discussant:  George Vaillant

I would like to express the view, perhaps more characteristic of a biologist/psychiatrist, that the importance of life events comes from factors within us as well as from events impinging upon the individual as emphasized by sociologists.  There are several such "internal" factors that need to be considered in understanding life events and their relationship to psychopathology.

The first is the individual's threshold for stress.  In following 100 individuals selected for health over 30 years, I found that people's subjective view of their physical health correlated only r=.22 with an objective view of their physical health.  Their subjective view of their physical health correlated very much higher than objective health measures, however, with an objective view of their psychopathology.  People who perceived their health as poor were very likely to be individuals that were chronically depressed, pessimistic, and psychiatrically ill.

A second "internal" factor is the possible existence of personal characteristics that may help cause life events.  For example, in the late '50's when Holmes first started his research, he studied life events as possible factors contributing to the cause of tuberculosis.  But a major factor in whether or not someone develops tuberculosis is whether or not he's alcoholic, and there's no better way to get a really high Holmes-Rahe life stress score than to be an alcoholic.

A third "internal" factor is the importance of other, perhaps unrecognized, personal traits best revealed by measuring whether the effects of stressful life events on psychopathology persist over a long period of time.  One example is the 3-day psychoses that occurred during wartime in people who seemed to have no premorbid disposition.  Many of the 3-day psychoses in World War II did remit rapidly as predicted which was considered as showing that they were almost entirely the effects of severe stress.  But when these individuals were followed up 10 or 20 years later, many of them were indeed actively schizophrenic.  The longitudinal perspective raised the question whether in many instances these really were pure stress reactions.

187

The fourth "internal" factor is the type of defense mechanisms used by an individual. For example, whether we use sublimation or projection under stress is going to make a difference whether we're called mentally ill or not. If Van Gogh under stress paints a transcendent picture or lops off his ear will determine whether a given life event is seen as precipitating mental illness or as producing a creative product. In looking at the defensive maneuvers in my study of 100 college men, I found that those who seemed to adapt best tended to use the adaptive style to stressful life events that is associated with Victorian morality plays, namely the stiff-upper-lip, altruism, humor, and affective anticipation. The 30 worst adjusted men were those who used the defenses of personality disorder like projection, turning against the self, and hypochondriasis, precisely those adaptive styles that are going to disrupt one's life and produce additional dislocations and life events.

A fifth "internal" factor is the meaning of the event for the individual. Stressful events generally are experiences involving role transformation, changes in status or environment, or unbearable pain. These are precisely the situations that elicit defensive maneuvers. Events that do not have such an impact even if apparently stressful may have a benign effect. For example, investigators went to Viet Nam where people were really under stress and studied the combat helicopter pilots to measure their urine steroid levels. These were perfectly normal. When questioned, the pilots said they weren't upset because they were not under stress in contrast to the poor guys down in the fire bases and in the jungle who were being shelled. When the investigators went down into the jungle and the fire bases and collected urines, these also were normal. When questioned, the soldiers said they weren't under as much stress as the helicopter pilots.

Formal Discussant:  Wells Goodrich

A point that has been implicit in these papers is that not all stressful situations are, strictly speaking, "life events." Developmental stages and the non-occurrence of certain anticipated events can also be stressful. Rausch and I, for example, noted in a pilot study of 50 newlywed couples several developmental processes and non-occurrences of events

that were very stressful. One such stressful developmental
process was the loss over the first 6 months after marriage
of what's been called the psychic honeymoon. Just after
marriage there is often a period of intense over-valuation
of the spouse. After a few months, or weeks in some cases,
there is a dropping of the rosy veil and by 6 months or so
the conflicts which had been swept under the rug begin to
appear. Those emerging conflicts are stresses we can predict
that are more a developmental process than an actual "event."
An example of a stressful non-event we noted occurred in certain couples who had not achieved an adequate sexual life in
the first few weeks of marriage. Several of those worked to
improve this situation and were planning for it to get better.
When improvement was not forthcoming, that non-event was a
major stress. The response to that and other non-events,
such as not becoming pregnant, can be considerable. It is
possible to anticipate these stressful stages and non-events
and study them and reactions to them in a way analogous to
the studies of the more commonly-considered stressful events.

# Section III

# Studies of Children at Risk

LONGITUDINAL VS. CROSS-SECTIONAL RESEARCH IN THE STUDY OF

CHILDREN AT RISK FOR PSYCHOPATHOLOGY

Norman Garmezy and Vernon T. Devine
Department of Psychology
University of Minnesota
Minneapolis, Minnesota

In the closing pages of his classic monograph on a Survey
of Objective Studies of Psychoanalytic Concepts, written
more than 30 years ago, Robert R. Sears (1943) sought an
answer to the critical question of what direction future
research should take to structure a science of personality --
a task Freud had set for psychoanalysis, but with empirical
roots that Sears had found wanting. He urged that a broad
data structure would be needed, based on a triumvirate of
forces that he identified as growth, learning, and the
social milieu. Learning, he indicated, would facilitate an
understanding of motivational processes, and the acquisition
of habit structures of coping and defense that could serve
the purposes of adaptation and of maladaptation as well.
The social milieu, he noted, contributed heavily to the
motivational and trait characteristics of the individual;
thus, a sampling of diverse social settings, through the
medium of cross-cultural comparisons of personality development, would provide evidence of the role played by different
cultural and learning contexts on basic personality structure.

Commenting on the critical significance of growth,
Sears wrote of a "crying need for the results of longitudinal
research on personality development" for the absence of
"reference to records obtained year after year from the same

Preparation of the paper was facilitated by the following
grants: Research Career Award (NG), MH-K6, 914, and the
Schizophrenic Research Program of the Supreme Council 33°
A.A. Scottish Rite, North Masonic Jurisdiction.

child" would insure serious lacunae in our knowledge of the
origins and sources of adult behavior.

Sears' focus was on the patterning of development as
the child merged into adolescence and then into adulthood.
For this task, the longitudinal, genetic, or repeated measurements design was essential for it could best provide the
substantive answers to those provocative questions posed by
psychoanalysis, a personality theory that had been welded
out of the study of individuals.

EARLY ORIGINS OF LONGITUDINAL STUDY

The 1920's saw the beginnings of a set of "growth
studies" conducted at Harvard, the Fels and the Merrill
Palmer Institutes, the University of California (Berkeley)
and other research settings.

Looking back on this period, Baldwin (1960) has written:

These long-range, longitudinal research programs were
not all alike by any means, but, as originally conceived,
they proposed to chart the physical, physiological, and
psychological growth of individual children over a
period of years...

Child development, as represented in the longitudinal studies, became more closely linked to biological
science than it had been formerly. Mental and psychological development viewed as one aspect of biological
growth led research in child development in a somewhat
different direction from the mainstream of psychological research (pp. 5-6).

The mainstream to which Baldwin made reference was
behavior therapy with its locus in learning. Separated from
this central concern of psychological researchers, the
longitudinal studies, too, stood apart -- a separatism that
was further reinforced by their early application to the
study of deviant children. Examining Stone and Onque's
(1959) volume on Longitudinal Studies of Child Development,
a survey of the psychological literature extending from the
1920s to 1955, one notes that the six earliest studies cited
are centered on the atypical child. Here are the titles of

the six references provided for the years 1924-1925:

1. The Problem Child (a comparison of 500 problem
children and 337 unselected controls, ages 4-16).

2. One Hundred Non-Conformed Boys (A study of 100
adolescent boys removed from school for disciplinary
reasons).

3. Dispensary Contacts with Delinquent Trends in
Children: Group 1. Forty-eight Cases of Stealing.
(48 delinquents were followed for 1-3 years and compared with 13 mentally defective and 35 normal children).

4. Dispensary Contacts with Delinquent Trends in
Children: Group 2. Abnormal Sex Trend. (A comparison
of 10 children with defective constitutional equipment
and 19 other children seen at the Phipps Clinic for
sexual misconduct).

5. The Psychology of Superior Children. (A follow-up
study of 70 children with I.Q.'s over 120).

6. How Foster Children Turn Out. (A follow-up study
through age 18 of 910 foster children).

Although early longitudinal studies were centered on
age changes in relation to physical growth and to motor,
cognitive, social, and personality development, the attachment to a repeated measurements design seems to reflect not
only the abiding interest of developmental psychologists in
the broad query, "What forms does development take?", but
for a subset of psychopathologists, interested in actual or
potential maladaptation, the equally significant inquiry,
"How did they turn out?"

It is, therefore, not at all surprising to find the
burgeoning field of risk research and its investigative
figures as the heirs apparent to a longitudinal tradition
that is designed to speak to the issue of growth, the facili-
tative forces that enhance it and the negative forces that
inhibit it.

The bridging tie proved to be the growing interest --
sparked intially by the Freudian influence -- in the effect

of early experience upon adult personality functioning.
Sears' concern with the validation of psychoanalytic con-
structs (a bog which has mired countless talents over time)
gradually gave way to the empirical restatements of others
linking childhood experience to adult behavior -- a more
general view which allowed for the introduction of the roles
played by social learning, trait and situational factors,
and their integration, within a biological context, with
attributes of temperament and constitution.

With this integrative effort, life grew more complex
for the designer of longitudinal programs.  Baldwin (1960)
comments:

> Longitudinal studies, as they were originally con-
> ceived, seemed to have gambled on the existence of
> clear developmental trends that would shine through the
> welter of influences of uncontrolled events.  In physi-
> cal growth, the gamble paid off quite well.  Many
> measures of physical growth are relatively uninfluenced
> by the disturbances found in the normal life of the
> child... The general shape of the growth curve is quite
> apparent, and the extrinsic disturbances do not affect
> the individual's growth pattern enough to destroy the
> predictability of early or late maturation, adolescent
> growth rate, adult height, etc. The organism's own
> growth pattern can be identified despite lack of
> control over many environmental factors (pp. 25-26).

The situation, however, with regard to a comparable
consistency in the growth pattern of an individual's personality development proved far less sanguine as has been
clearly demonstrated in psychology's major longitudinal
studies (cf. Jones, Bayley, McFarlane & Honzik, 1971).  The
problems of selecting relevant personality variables, the
inadequacy of measuring instruments, the range of variables
to be studied, all served to provide a justification for a
shot-gun approach, but one scarcely appropriate, given the
difficulties inherent in a longitudinal analysis of personality change.  Baldwin provided this admonition:

> It should be apparent that a longitudinal study of
> the effects of one, two, or three variables of childhood
> experience upon later personality is a big investment
> for relatively small return -- quantitatively speaking.

It behooves us, therefore, to precede such an under-
taking with careful pretesting, study of cross-sectional
differences, and cruder retrospective studies to establish the likelihood of major effects. A longitudinal
study is the last, not the first step in a research
program. It is an absolutely essential research method
if we are to get firm knowledge of psychological change,
but, paradoxically, it is to be avoided whenever possible
(p. 27).

In the sections that follow, we will evaluate the
utility of cross-sectional and longitudinal designs in
studying children who are at risk for severe psychopathology
in their lives.

Since both longitudinal and cross-sectional designs
each have their strengths and weaknesses, it may be helpful
to review these briefly to see their implications for risk
research. But first, a pause for definitions.

By the longitudinal method is meant the study of the
development of the same group of individuals over time,
through repeated measurements made on these individuals at
different temporal points. By contrast, a cross-sectional
design involves the study of independent groups of persons
at different points in time. Thus, the longitudinal design
can provide individual curves of development, whereas the
cross-sectional method only allows for measuring the average
development of a group.

## THE LONGITUDINAL DESIGN

McFarlane, in her introduction to the volume on the
Berkeley Growth Studies, The Course of Human Development
(Jones et al., 1971) quotes the observation of one advisory
committee to a foundation contemplating support of a longitudinal program:

> For longitudinal research a peculiar kind of
> selflessness is required...It is not obvious that such
> personality characteristics make a creative and pro-
> ductive scholar.

That for risk researchers! But there is more to longitudinal research than the selflessness of its advocates. The

power of the method lies in the more accurate extension it permits of the developmental process as represented by the group, and of equal importance of individuals within the group. The extraction of measures of central tendency and of dispersion at various age points reflects a power in the longitudinal method, but it is one shared as well by a cross-sectional strategy. But the former not only can help the researcher to become aware of the atypical cases represented at a given age level, but it can permit a tracing of the consequences of atypicality at one age level upon later development. In effect, this is what Mednick and Schulsinger (1973) did when they early identified groups of "sicks" and "wells" within their sample of risk children, and has also characterized Barbara Fish's (1975) contributions through her long-term follow-up studies of infants born to schizophrenic mothers, who early in their development show signs of an erratic and disorganized maturational pattern.

Group norms can, of course, be secured both by cross-sectional and longitudinal methods. But this should not obscure an observation made by Tuddenham (as quoted by Honzik in Jones et al., 1971) that:

> ...serial observations upon the same individuals offer fundamental advantages by rendering the sampling error constant from age to age, permitting much more efficient estimation of group changes (p. 451).

In risk studies, diversity of outcomes (as reflected in genetic probabilities) is a given. Such diversity, obscured by group averages, is markedly evident in the growth curves of individuals permitted by longitudinal analysis - a characteristic that is likely to hold for whichever domain, biological or psychological - may be tapped by a specific variable.

Measures repeated on the same indiviuals, too, permit an analysis of the interrelationships that obtain between growth, maturational, and experiential factors. In the study of risk factors, the child's age at the point at which the mother is hospitalized in the course of a psychotic episode, is viewed as a potentially significant stressor having long-term consequences. Often, however, these separation experiences have occurred prior to initiating the longitudinal study, a probability which increases as a function of the age of the proband group selected for study.

One can envision the significant observations to be made
were the offspring available for evaluation at the point of
loss of the parent through hospitalization for mental breakdown. Retrospective data have suggested the significance of
such losses early in the life of a child; ongoing analyses
of such stressful life history events would permit a more
fine-grained analysis of the consequences of imposing this
specific stress on the diathesis structure of a child at
risk for schizophrenia.

But despite these evident virtues, the longitudinal
design also generates some critical disadvantages. First,
there are the limitations imposed by the original sample
selection. Whatever the shortcomings of the sampling
procedure, its consequences will be manifest throughout the
length and breadth of the study. In research undertakings
involving uncommonly low base rates for the occurrence of
the phenomenon to be investigated (e.g., schizophrenia in
young adulthood), a major adjustment must be made in the
selection of a large initial sample in order to insure that
a sufficiently large number of cases will be available for
evaluating the outcome data.*

Related to this basic problem is the inevitable attrition of the subject pool that occurs in all longitudinal
studies. In risk studies, the loss of subjects or families
is an expensive and discouraging affair, for there is a
strong likelihood that dropouts from the study may well be
those very families with magnified risk potential. In all
repeated measurement designs, the disappearing cases should,
in some pattern, be evaluated against retainers in the study
in order to determine the types of losses that have occurred
and their significance for the interpretation of subsequent
results. This reality requires that in risk studies there
is need for an enlarged sample initially to insure that a
sufficinetly large N remains at the conclusion of the research
to evaluate the validity of outcome predictions.

*The problem of the availability of a sufficiently large N
in risk studies is accentuated by the moderately high refusal-
to-participate rates that a number of investigators have
encountered in recruiting parent-patients in hospital and
community psychiatric settings. A systematic analysis of the
attributes of such 'refusals' is necessary in order to
understand the cohort biases that may be present in samples
of cooperative participant families.

It is quite likely that the dropout rates for experimental and control families will differ in risk studies. Normal parents of normal offspring may well have higher levels of motivation for participation in a long-term study; they are more likely to share with investigators positive attitudes and values regarding developmental research; they are likely to place a higher valuation on social responsibility, on assisting others, and for contributing to the well-being of unknown others by joining in a major scientific effort. Values such as these serve to maintain a family in a long-term study. Vulnerable families that include parents who have known mental disorder may not possess these sustaining attributes. Superimpose the negative effects that accrue from fears of relevation of a prior hospitalization for psychiatric reasons, anxiety generated by the threat of recall of mental hospital experiences, guilt over an earlier mental disorder, and hostility that follows upon investigative intrusiveness and the cumulative factors that heighten drop-out rates will become evident.

An additional major problem characteristic of longitudinal research lies in the selection of those variables that warrant study. In the field of risk research it is not at all apparent to what extent a conceptual basis is used to select those tests, procedures, experiments, and behaviors now undergoing study. A recent review of risk projects (Garmezy, 1975) led to a catalogue of dependent variables as broad as the range of discplines involved in the mental health effort: clinical psychiatry is reflected in the structured instruments (e.g., the Present State Examination, ref. Wing et al., 1974; and Current and Past Psychopathology Scales, ref. Spitzer & Endicott, 1968) that are increasingly being used to measure mental status content and diagnosis; clinical psychology is represented by traditional child and adult assessment instruments of cognition and personality; social work, by home visits and case-history taking; developmental psychology is represented by Piagetian-type tasks, the analysis of children's play behavior, and studies of attachment, stranger-anxiety, mother-child interaction, referential communication, learning and conditioning tasks; educational psychology by school achievement measures, cumulative record analysis, and teacher evaluations; neurology by traditional neurological assessments; genetics by linkage studies; physiological psychology by measures of autonomic responsiveness, and electrophysiological measures; experimental psychology by perceptual studies, signal detectic

experiments, measures of vigilance, attention and information processing, and vestibular function; biochemistry by
studies of catecholamine metabolism assays; obstetrics by
the evaluation of pregnancy and birth complications; and
pediatrics by infant assessments including those of temperament and health history. Name the variable and even in the
newly emerging field somewhere a risk researcher is likely to
be using it or, at least, contemplating its utility with
vulnerable children. Is there a conceptual base, an hypothesis, a theoretical justification for the inclusion of such a
multitudinous array? In some cases the answer is in the
affirmative, but more often the justification for testing
the power of the variable is based upon a fallback to traditional procedures and an empiricism whose symbol is a blun-
derbuss.

Commenting earlier on the catholicity of tastes of risk
researchers, one of us wrote:

> With regard to the issue of the selection of
> variables, trends toward stereotype are also beginning
> to become apparent, not in the replication of the
> procedures used by others, because that obviously will
> prove advantageous, but rather, in an experimental
> approach that I would liken to One-Day-(or Two)-in-The-
> Life-of-The-Risk Child--in which a schedule of sequen-
> tial programming is set forth to provide the child with
> a brief exposure to many different testing procedures,
> with the expectation that by casting as wide a net as
> possible one will be more likely to capture the signifi-
> cant attributes of vulnerability. At the same time,
> insufficient attention is being paid to a whole range
> of problems extending from a prosaic concern about
> order effects or fatigue in the youngster to the profound
> issue of the ecological validity of such procedures.
> The possibility of a Type 1 (false rejection of the
> tested hypothesis) or a Type II (failure to reject a
> hypothesis that is false) error remains high when
> programming follows such a format. What is needed is a
> respite from the pervasive emphasis on longitudinal
> studies with some time out for cross-sectional research
> in which the focus will be on multiple investigations
> of a single construct in the hope of establishing an
> integrated network of correlations  (Garmezy, 1974, p.
> 97).

Obviously, the early development of a research area, a broad-gauged approach to the selection of variables, serves the important function (assembling reliability of measurement), of providing evaluations of numerous facets of the subjects' functioning. Unfortunately, the longitudinal method places severe constraints on the investigator to modify his study as data begin to indicate the potential utility of some variables, the uselessness of others. It is expensive to change the format of a longitudinal study, and yet a design using repeated measures lends itself to the uncovering of new leads and the formulation of new hypotheses that were not considered initially. When this occurs, procedural shifts in the design are required. Even more important as a warrant for change is Kessen's (1960) observation:

> There is another compelling reason for the occur-
> rence of procedural shifts in repeated measurements
> study--the absence of a single observational technique
> that is applicable across the developmental span...
> Particularly in the observation of the child from birth
> to school age, it is necessary to change techniques
> used to gather data as the child grows older. This
> consideration poses a serious problem for the under-
> standing of development--how are we to translate from
> one observational technique to another? To put the
> question in another way, what constitues the 'same'
> behavior at different ages?... An irreducible problem
> of developmental research is that we must modify our
> data-gathering techniques as the child and his environ-
> ment change. Moreover, it is no solution merely to
> give the same name to the results of different observa-
> tional procedures (p. 64).

The important point emphasizes the need for more adequate knowledge of developmental processes and the types of procedures by which to assess change. Kessen also urges the "overlapping of different techniques" to assess the relationship among procedures presumed to tap similar dimensions and to be age appropriate. Here is a cell for construct validity to assess the extent to which such procedures can effectively assess the same variable or related ones. Until such relationships have been mapped, the researcher, asserts Kessen, "would seem well advised... against assuming the equivalence of different procedures" (p. 65).

What Can Risk Researchers Learn From the
Classic Longitudinal Studies?

Risk researchers have much to learn from those whose
paths they follow. Although the populations from which these
investigators draw their samples have very special properties centered in predisposition to disorder, the findings of
the major longitudinal studies with regard to adult outcomes
warrant reflection.

Consider first the question posed by a study of a
somewhat comparable population presumed to be at risk.
Robins' classic study of Deviant Children Grown Up employed
a control group of children whose potential vulnerability
could have been ascribed to their early (economic) disadvantaged state. These children were viewed as controls for
clinical children on the basis of rather minimal criteria:
(1) they had never been seen in a psychiatric clinic; (2)
they had never had to repeat a full year (grade) in elementary
school; (3) they had never been expelled from school, nor
had they spend time in a correctional institution.

Seen on follow-up, 30 years later, these children, now
grown to adulthood, proved to be remarkably resistant to
psychopathology.  Commenting on the results of this important finding Robins (1966) wrote:

Despite a life beginning in the city slums for
most of them, the control subjects as adults have moved
to the suburbs in 60% of cases, have good jobs, no more
divorces than the American average, a high rate of
stability and home ownership, no current incarcera-
tions, only one past conviction for a felony for which
no prison term was served, no current mental hospitalization...and a very low rate of indigence (p.69).

Nor were the control children the only ones who managed
to achieve successful adulthoods.  Variability in outcomes
was also present within the samples of clinic children:
anti-social children, more typically, became maladaptive
acting-out adults, whereas the prognosis for neurotic problem cases proved to be relatively favorable.

What meaning do these observations of variability among
children, drawn from comparably deprived environments, have
for the risk researcher?  Currently, there is a lack of

consistent, reliable, hard data available to us on children
at risk for severe psychopathology in adulthood. Consider
in this context some recent findings from the pioneering
research program of Mednick and Schulsinger (1968) in
Denmark. When these investigators initially categorized
their first wave of adolescents born to schizophrenic mothers
they derived smaller subsamples of adaptive and maladaptive
children who were identified as the "well" and the "sick"
groups. The more recent reappraisals of the status of the
Danish risk children, based upon intensive re-interviewing
of them as adults over the past two years, also reflect
outcome variations and significant status shifts. Some
"sicks" have become well; some "wells" appear to have taken
a more pathological turn.

Next, consider the observations of Manfred Bleuler
based upon his life work of engaging 208 of his schizophrenic
patients in a major follow-through study of their adaptations
over a span of two decades. Observing the occupational and
marital lives of the 184 offspring of these patients,
Bleuler noted the quality of competence and adaptation they
demonstrated despite the stresses they had endured in childhood. The task of discovering causative factors in psychopathology is well served by Bleuler's (1974) words:

> But despite the miserable childhoods described
> above, and despite their presumably "tainted" genes,
> most offspring of schizophrenics manage to lead produc-
> tive lives. Indeed, after studying a number of family
> histories, one is left with the impression that pain
> and suffering can have a steeling--a hardening--effect
> on some children, rendering them capable of mastering
> life with all its obstacles, just to spite their
> inherent disadvantages. Perhaps it would be instruc-
> tive for future investigators to keep as careful a
> watch on the favorable development of the majority of
> these children as they do on the progressive deteriora-
> tion of the sick minority (p. 106).

Reference to these longitudinal and follow-up accounts
of children who are normal, disturbed or predisposed-to-
disturbance suggests that complexity and mystery so occupy
the development of personality over time that efforts at
prediction seem doomed from the very outset. Block (1971)
in a superb scholarly volume Lives Through Time reasons

otherwise.  Developmental psychology he argues, has been
hampered by the assumption of uniformities in development
across people and across time:

> Across people, the presumption in its pure form
> asserts that all people develop in essentially the same
> way.  There may be differences in initial or terminal
> status and in the rate or timing of development, but
> these differences pose no conceptual problems so long
> as the sequence or direction of development remains
> constant.  Across time, the hypothesis  of uniformity
> suggests that relationships or qualities observed at
> one time may be expected to apply later as well.  There
> may be changes over time in the specification of an
> individual or group, but, in the main, temporal corr-
> espondence or stability is to be expected if measure-
> ment has been adequate and important, central variables
> are considered (p. 10).

Longitudinally-inclined researchers can appreciate, if
not wholly accept, Block's observations that change over
time is a "disappointing" affair since it seems to insure a
failure to predict the future--a failure that will subsequently be attributed to measurement shortcomings, random factors,
or a reappraisal and down grading of the ill-behaving variable to which significance was originally attached.

For Block, however, such changes over time are to be
anticipated in individuals who take different developmental
paths, some of whom may show behavioral continuity, while
others may reveal a predictable instability in life patterns
in a manner equally revealing and significant.

To appreciate this observation a chronology of published commentary regarding the most famed of our longitudinal
projects, the Berkeley Guidance Study and the Oakland Growth
Study is necessary.  If we turn to the results of the longitudinal appraisal of the participants in those projects
the skein of evaluation from infancy to adulthood is broken.
These children were followed from infancy through childhood
and adolescence to age 18 and then were seen again at age 30
when their adaptation to the problems of adulthood were
again evaluated.

The ubiquitous variability of outcomes, already comment-
ed upon was again evident, at least from the viewpoint of a

clinical analysis of the data obtained on the subjects. It
led MacFarlane (1971), one of the founders of the Berkeley
Project when it was first initiated in 1929, to sound a
somewhat discouraging note four decades later:

> When we see the varieties of learning tasks with
> which they are confronted, the many incoherencies and th
> pressure put upon these differing organisms at different
> developmental periods, we still are not sure why so many
> of them turned out to be coherent adults. We were so awa
> of their uncertainties and dilemmas (and those of their
> parents and teachers) as they were growing up that seein
> them as adults some twelve years later occasioned dramat
> shock after shock.  Close to 50 percent turned out to be
> more stable and effective adults than any of us with our
> differing theoretical biases had predicted, some 20 per-
> cent were less substantial than we had predicted, and
> slightly less than a third turned out as predicted (p. 4

The last third, according to MacFarlane was made up
primarily of three groups: (1) "Over controlled, constricted
compulsives" who presented an encapsulated defense system;
(2) the mentally retarded; and (3) youngsters subjected
to such variable treatment at the hands of their parents,
ranging from overindulgence to harshness, that they failed
to learn "stable and integrated patterns" and appeared in
adulthood to have become, in large part, "compulsive adult
drinkers."

What of the failures of prediction?  In MacFarlane's
report, there was a more extreme group, representing 10% of
the sample, for whom disorganized adult lives had been
predicted, but who at age 30 had "turned out far better than
predicted and became mature, effective and understanding
adults or exceptionally creative ones."  These were individuals some of whom had known turmoil, others who had used
"their energies in defiance of regulations." still others
who were social isolates or "oddballs" or pedestrian in act
or outlook.

The usual question of 'Where did they do wrong?' would
appear to be better converted to the more basic inquiry
'Where did the researchers go wrong?'

McFarlane attempts to answer this vexing question of
the disparity between prediction and outcome in noting six

factors to which she ascribes the prediction errors.

1.  The Berkeley researchers "overweighted the trouble-
    some and pathogenic aspects and underweighted
    elements that were maturity-inducing;"

2.  They also "overestimated the durability of those
    well-learned behaviors and attitudes that were
    characteristic and habitual response patterns over
    a substantial period of time." What the Berkeley
    researchers failed to note was the capability of
    their subjects to discard outmoded coping devices
    and to acquire, however painfully, new ones;

3.  By contrast there was underestimation of the
    extent to which the traumas to which all lives are
    subject, the stresses of existence, "the pains and
    confusions of maturing experiences" could be
    growth-inducing rather than stultifying;

4.  New roles in marriage and parenthood provided
    opportunities that brought a sense of worth and
    responsibility that had not earlier been present
    in the lives of these children;

5.  The complementary theory of needs proved to be
    shibboleth. "Long-continuous patterns were modified
    and converted into almost the opposite character-
    istics." Dependent males did not elect to marry
    symbolically younger representations of their
    dominant mothers. More typically, they married
    less confident women and took on the new demands
    to be supportive and nurturant;

6.  And then there were the "late bloomers" who came
    to maturity more slowly and finally gained release
    from a less rewarding past.

But Block, not content with this more superficial
clinical analysis, has mustered case data (including apprais-
als of family and environment). clinical judges, and the Q-
sort methodology (to which he has contributed significantly,
cf. Block, 1961) to derive through factor analysis a typology of 46 male and female participants. In his volume he
compares the trend lines of personality development of his
different types from their junior high school and senior

high school years to adulthood finding correspondences and
discrepancies for these more homogeneous groupings of individuals. Block's methodology is complex and one can only
do a disservice to his scholarship by a scanty review of his
major analytic effort. What can be said is that his study of
Lives Through Time represents critical reading for risk
researchers on several grounds: (1) as an orientation to the
longitudinal appraisal of personality change in normal
individuals, and (2) in his demonstration that for some
personality types there is indeed evidence for behavioral
consistency over time, while for other types, personality
changes may be quite marked as the individual traverses the
years from adolescence to adulthood.  Thus, prediction does
not demand behavioral consistency and regularity in persons
over time; there may exist comparable predictability in the
irregular patterns of development characteristics of other
types of individuals. A comparable analysis of the type generated by Block, were the available data to be equally complete might render comprehensible the conversions in adaptation noted by Mednick and Schulsinger as they analyze their
findings for an age span not too dissimilar to the one tapped
by the Berkeley researchers.

     As noted, MacFarlane had written of the more stable
predictions that were derived for 'over controlled' and
'under controlled' individuals.  But, Block demonstrates the
stability that also inheres in other groups as well, citing
data on ego resilient males, protoypical females, cognitive
coping females; similarly, shifts seem to characterize other
types (e.g., 'belated adjusters' and 'anomic extraverts' in
males).  Block's utilization of the theoretical framework of
ego development advanced by Loevinger to place his types on
a continuum of maturity (1966), and his analysis of the
mediating role played by the family and diverse parental
personalities in fostering or inhibiting the growth of
offspring adds further significance of this project for risk
reseachers.

     Block's research would appear to provide for caution in
extrapolating by clinical analysis alone the determination
of changes over time without regard to potential "character-
iological syndromes" of personality that may accompany
different trends in development.  The search for such syndromes is an important future task for students of vulnerability research.

The Longitudinal Design:  A Summing-Up

We have been so beholden to Block for providing an enriched evaluation of the nature of perceived stability or inconsistency in behavioral functioning from adolescence to adulthood that we hesitate to borrow further from his writings.  And, yet we have encountered no more eloquent summary of the pros and cons of the longitudinal design than he has provided when he writes:

> The investigator who would embark upon a longitudinal study of human development must be imbued with a rare sense of dedication and selflessness.  The motivations for not initiating a longitudinal research program are many.  The inertial (sic) problems of locating and maintaining a proper project sample are oppressive; the would-be longitudinal researcher must make fundamental procedural decisions in the Now that are only gambles into the future; he knows that, despite his contemporary sophistication, retrospective wisdom a generation later will make him appear outdated; quick, neat research possibilities that are not longitudinal seductively compete for his attention and promise more immediate professional rewards; and finally, inescapably, there is a recognition that much of the harvest of one's efforts may be realized in another's lifetime these are some of the reasons why longitudinal studies are few, rarely prolonged, and of fluctuating quality over time.

> And yet, magnetically, psychologists are now increasingly drawn toward longitudinal studies for the ineluctable reason that there simply is no other way by which certain questions regarding development, cause and effect may be approached.  Correlational, cross-sectional, or experimental methods have great and suggestive contributions to make toward an understanding of the bases of behavior. But, these approaches do not encompass time and the trajectory of individual lives.  It would be pleasant if the world were differently arranged; it is not, and so the burdens of longitudinal study must, albeit perhaps reluctantly, be accepted and endured by psychology. When the long season of waiting has been survived and the data are in, then the excitement of the longitudinal approach begins.  Time is surmounted; in a richly-detailed

longitudinal study, belated or unanticipated questions
can be asked and their answers found, quickly in data
collected many years before. The payment, in patience
and barrenness during the beginning or middle of the
longitudinal study, can be justified at its end when a
flood of questions finds answers not otherwise pro-
vidable (Block, 1972, p. 30).


THE CROSS-SECTIONAL DESIGN

The cross-sectional design generates neither the en-
comiums nor the dispraise that has been visited upon the
longitudinal study. By contrast, with the richness of
longitudinal study, the cross-sectional design is simplistic,
almost drab in its unpretentiousness. The approach is a
multi-group one. Individuals of various ages, grades, or
comparable statuses are provided with similar situations,
tests, or experimental procedures with two objectives in
mind: (a) to plot information on the growth process for a
specific variable or set of variables, and (b) to secure
measures of central tendency or dispersion against which the
performance of individuals can be plotted (Anderson, 1954).
It is typically assumed in such cross-sectional analyses
that adulthood represents some asymptotic level, although a
curve of descending performance may be reflected at older
ages for certain types of variables.

The classic example of such a cross-sectional strategy
is in evidence in the norming of intelligence tests, and the
classic type of error is seen in Wechsler's initial assumptio
based on cross-sectional data, that specific intellective
functions decline at different rates--a decline that is
manifested at different points in the aging cycle (Wechsler,
1944). The original Wechsler data, it will be recalled, revealed marked age differences on subtests of the Wechsler-
Bellevue Intelligence Scale. Intelligence, as indexed by
the test and the performance of the different (by age)
normative groups, showed a steep rise from age 7 through the
mid-teens, a leveling off in the late teens and a falling
off at about age 25, followed by an accelerating decline
from age 35 to age 65. Fortunately, this pattern is not an
accurate representation of many current oldsters.

Before proceeding to the root of the error, however, it
is necessary to re-examine some assumptions underlying the

cross-sectional method.  First, it is required that the
samples of subjects at different age levels be comparable--
that cohorts be drawn from the same population of individuals
and that for each age the sample be a representative one.
Second, there should be evidence to indicate that measures
at different age levels have the same meaning, that they
reflect the same construct.  While the first is technically
feasible (but in actuality, quite difficult with regard to
such a factor as predisposition to psychopathology), the
second poses problems of considerable theoretical and practical complexity, as can be readily adduced from a literature
that seeks to evaluate the patterns of behavioral continuities
and discontinuities of development.

If these assumptions are violated, deforming conclusions
can be drawn about the developmental emergence of specific
processes.  Consider the first assumption--that of representative samples drawn from the same population albeit at
different ages.  In cross-sectional research the chronological
age variable can be confounded by the cohort variable.  If
significant changes have occurred across the generations
represented in the design with regard to the behavioral
process being evaluated, errors of interpretation can have
profound consequences as witness the early conclusions
drawn from Wechsler's standardization data.  In the original
sampling of the Wechsler-Bellevue Intelligence Scale, there
was a failure to note that a profound revolution had taken
place in the forty year period that separated the ascendent
20 year olds and the seemingly flagging 60 year olds.
Historical events had stamped the differences between the
two groups.  Two wars and a depression had intervened for
the older group.  Cultural stability had been irrevocably
modified (recalling the ancient Chinese curse, "May you live
in a period of social change."), but the older group had
come to their maturity under circumstances in which differences in education, technology and information diffusion
patterns had rendered noncomparable the test performance of
the two groups.  Indeed, subsequent modifications in the
Wechsler and the use of new normative samples over a three
decade span have markedly modified the picture of intellectual decline over time (Matarazzo, 1972).  Writing about
this general phenomenon, Wohlwil (1970) has stated:

The repeated finding of substantial discrepancies
between longitudinal and cross-sectional data, both for
biological variables such as height and vital capacity

and of psychological variables such as performance on
various cognitive and psychomotor tasks points to the
important role which the cohort factor may play. While
the examples...come from studies of changes over the
years of adulthood and old age, equally convincing
evidence comes from comparisons of the growth of children, sometimes over a very narrow span of cohorts (pp.
170-171).

Returning to the Wechsler data, Matarazzo (1972) has
carefully evaluated numerous studies that point to the issue
of cohort variations that are, in part, determined by shifts
in the "social-cultural-educational milieu." Matarazzo
illuminates this criticism with a telling example:

> Is years of education a variable with identical
> meaning across generations and, even if it is (which
> can be debated), is the number of years of formal
> schooling an individual completes an adequate measure
> of his "education" when making comparisons across
> generations in studies utilizing any of the available
> intelligence tests? There is no evidence, for example,
> that a 65-year-old with 12 years of education is "equal"
> in formal education, as this might be reflected in the
> items in such tests, to a 25-year-old with a similar
> number of years of schooling...an argument could be
> made that a 65-year-old who in his youth, completed 12
> years of education while his age peers, on the average,
> were completing only 6, would probably have earned at
> age 25...a higher intelligence test (standard) score tha
> would be earned today by his grandson, aged 25, who
> also completed 12 years of education (when his age
> peers also were completing an average of 12) (pp 115-
> 116).

Applying some of these problems of cross-sectional
analysis to the field of risk research generates some additional comments about cohorts and continuities. In a recentl
published article on the quality of premorbid adjustment and
the recovery of the mothering function in acutely ill
schizophrenic women who had been treated briefly in a community mental health center and then released to their homes,
Rodnick and Goldstein (1974) have compared the patterns of
child care shown by good and poor premorbid mothers (Phillips
1953) over a span of one year following discharge. Were

chronicity to have been allowed to vary randomly, obtained differences could have been attributed to such factors as the long-term effects of chronic disorder, length of institutionalization, maternal age, etc. To negate such an interaction, the investigators studied only an acute schizophrenic sample. Follow-up data were obtained at 30 days, 6 months, and at 1 year and included patient's self-report, informant reports, staff observations, and, in some cases, home visits. Their data indicate that the poor premorbid mothers were on the average seven years younger than were the good premorbids, that their children were younger (they had a least one infant child), whereas by contrast the children of the latter were primarily to be found in the range of middle childhood.

With regard to the mothering function the poor premorbid mothers lagged significantly behind the good premorbid mothers in recovery, requiring almost a year to achieve a status of good care-giving that the good premorbid mother achieved over a span of six months.

The differential patterns observed were these: (1) The poor premorbid mother tended to break down at an earlier age, had young children at home who were at an age where more intimate mothering over a more prolonged period of time was required; (2) by contrast, the good premorbid mother was older as were her children and her recovery was faster.

If we add to these data the findings of other investigators implying a genetic base for process schizophrenia and a reduced likelihood of genetic involvement in reactive schizophrenia (Gottesman & Shields, 1972; Kety et al., 1975), two factors became apparent. First, samples reflecting such differences in the ages of index children may reflect parental attributes characteristic of different populations; second, the offspring of process patients may have a heightened predisposition to psychopathology on the basis of both genetic and experiential factors. This interaction between vulnerabilities founded on both a genetic and an environmental basis thus heightens the probability for subsequent schizophrenia in the one group relative to the other. Birgitte Mednick's data (1973) on breakdown in the Mednick-Schulsinger sample of children who were younger at the time of their mother's psychotic break serves to reinforce this view, as does a recent comprehensive review of the area (Garmezy & Streitman, 1974).

The implications for cross-sectional studies of children at risk may now become apparent:  Efforts to adduce developmental trends from infancy to adolescence on the basis of the age groupings used by various risk investigative groups may prove to be spurious if factors such as premorbid status, age of maternal illness, age of child at time of mother's psychosis, social class of parents, type of admitting psychiatric institution, and length of time of separation of mother and child are not considered. Here the problem of differences in generational cohorts is a very real one, although as any risk researcher will testify the magnitude of the problems seems to be inversely proportional to the size of the solutions available to investigators through the combination of small Ns, and variations in settings needed to acquire even a limited number of cases. What this may well suggest is a necessity to narrow the age band in cross-sectional research with risk samples with appropriate caution in inferring subsequently the developmen tal processes suggested by findings with such a restricting sampling.

This suggested narrowing of the age band relates too to the problem of inferring continuity of behavior over time. As has been noted elsewhere (Garmezy, 1974) we must first determine which types of continuity we refer to in discussin this issue.  There is complete continuity in which manifest behavior and underlying process reveal stability, but such complete continuity is more typical of the post puberty years when the organization of psychological structures has neared completion.

Heterotypic continuity has reference to a common underlying process which can service two quite disparate response modalities and thus demands a level of ingenuity, inferentia reasoning, and a unifying theoretical structure to integrate seemingly different behaviors that command a common pathway. Homotypic continuity refers to stability in the same respons modality but such similarities may obscure the variable need states and expectancies that generate behavioral phenocopies and render interpretations of similarities difficult.

Nevertheless, many behaviors show stability over time, particularly those measured in later childhood and adolescence.  Since these are the years that anticipate the emergence of severe psychopathology, cross-sectional data based upon a narrowed range of ages rather than a broad span of

the years from infancy to adolescence would not be inappro-
priate for investigating developmental variations in vulnerable children.

Another factor that of secular time enters to modify
the picture of developmental change. Schaie (1965) has
included in the variables that require consideration in
evaluating such changes the factor of time of measurement.
An example drawn from the Minnesota studies points up this
issue rather dramatically. In studying attentional processes
of children at risk in the natural setting of the classroom
and the laboratory, we found ourselves last year in the
midst of a profound educational revolution. In part to
facilitate integration on grounds not solely determined by
race, and in greater part because of exciting administrative
leadership, the parents of Minnespolis elementary school
children (after community meetings that extended over months
and broad-gauged efforts by school officials to provide
parents with information) were given their choice of three
forms of educational philosophy and practice under which
their children could be taught--contemporary (or the traditional one room-one teacher classroom but with modifications
that would take into account individual variations in skills
acquisition), continuous progress with an emphasis on team
teaching and rotation to classrooms akin to the junior high
school format and the open school.

The effects on such variables as competence as indexed
by sociometric devices and attentional behaviors within
classrooms made freer by educational revision has within a
span of one year created a profoundly revised testing
milieu for our investigative team--one we had neither anticipated nor, in all honesty, welcomed. Neverthless the change
is here and since it is quite dramatic at the elementary
school grades, but less so at the junior high school level,
our former cross-sectional data on laboratory and classroom
attentional studies, all of which are conducted in the
schools, may be modified in ways not yet known to us.

It is apparent that cross-sectional studies have certain marked disadvantages. But in the area of risk studies
where one remains uncertain of the nature of the developmental processes involved, where uncertainty exists as to
behavioral manifestations of a particular variable or class
of variables either because: (1) developmental data based
upon "normal" children are lacking; (2) a suggestion exists

that the potential for early deviance may be modifying such
developmental factors; or (3) there exists the possibility
that the variable may reflect a dispositional quality that
differs markedly in its manifestation in normal as opposed
to deviant children, then the cross-sectional method may
provide a far more rapid answer as to the predictive validity
of a specific variable than is available to the longitudinal
design advocate.

A final point, the cross-sectional method, despite its
limitations, is withal the most economical method for ex-
ploring the relevance of specific variables. To launch a
long-term longitudinal project in an area where one is
uncertain as to the appropriate variables to study invites
failure and expensive failure at that. As Baldwin noted
(1960) one precedes longitudinal analysis with the pretesting
of procedures, a search for cross-sectional differences, and
even the use of the much maligned retrospective method in
order to heighten the likelihood that differences will be
found. Here it seems the cross-sectional method can make a
major impact on the current scene and serve to enlarge the
sophistication of risk investigation regarding those variable
which may have maximum payoff for the longitudinal studies
that will inevitably follow.


A COMPROMISE DESIGN:  CONVERGENCE

The strengths and weaknesses inherent in both longitudinal and cross-sectional designs dictates the development
of a research strategy that can take advantage of the assets
of each method while reducing their liabilities. This
requires that such a procedure permit study of the stability
and the predictive power of specific behaviors, traits, or
events in the same individual over time, while facilitating
as rapidly as possible, a determination of the nature of
age-related changes in the relevant variables under evaluatic

In 1953, Bell suggested such a strategy employing a
convergence technique (subsequently identified as the short-
term longitudinal or accelerated longitudinal design) -- a
procedure which makes use of independent groups of subjects
varying in age (the cross-sectional component), who are then
tested recurrently over relatively short periods of time
(the longitudinal component) so that data acquired on retesti

within each group can bridge into the age of the next
older group of the original cross-sectional sample.

The strategy can be clarified with an example. To
return to the problem of the assessment of intellective
performance over time, Schaie and Strother (1968) utilized
such a convergence design to demonstrate the shortcomings
of a simple cross-sectional analysis of intellectual changes
in aging. Initially these researchers took a stratified
sample of 500 individuals consisting of 25 males and 25
females at each five year age level from ages 20 through 70.
Their measure of intellectual functioning was the Primary
Mental Abilities Test. The results of an initial administration of this test revealed the predicted decline in scores
over age beginning at about age 35 and rapidly decelerating
to age 70. Seven years later, however, the investigators
relocated and again tested 302 subjects of the original
group of 500 and examined age changes for these different
age groups over a seven year span. Plotting these results
in a fashion comparable to the previous cross-sectional
analysis revealed that the anticipated decrements in performance over the entire age span used in the study did not
occur. Rather, scores on the test were found to "increase
modestly up to age 50 or so, and (to) show only a very
miniscule decline after that age level" (Matarazzo, 1972, p.
114). Thus, within a seven year span Schaie and Strother
were able to infer the developmental progression of intellectual functioning for a fifty year age span.

There is, however, one powerful caution to be observed
and this relates to the cohort problem discussed earlier in
this paper. Schaie and Strother lost 40% of their original
group by attrition prior to restesting. Their account suggests that the loss did not appear to markedly bias their
data:

> The retested subjects were distributed approximately
> equally by age, with a slight preponderance of female
> subjects. Comparison of socio-economic data for the
> original and final sample suggested that the attri-
> tion was fairly random and not significantly biased
> with respect to socioeconomic factors (p. 673).

But since locatability was a factor in successfully
contacting the original participants, socio-economic criteria

at the time of original testing may not be the sole element
determining comparability between the cohorts of returnees
and dropouts. Factors influencing retention in a prepaid
medical plan (the original source for obtaining participants)
migration and mobility patterns (outward, upward, downward,
over a seven year period), and unresponsiveness to inquiry
may eliminate from the retest sample individuals distinctivel
different from those who willingly return to the experimental task. The necessity for evaluating the dropout group on
criteria in addition to the original subject attributes
used in selection is a difficult, but necessary, requirement
in evaluating the generality of data derived through the use
of the convergence method.

The application of the convergence procedure to risk
research is exemplified by the coordinated program of
research that has been underway in the Department of Psychiatry of the School of Medicine of the University of Roch
ester (Cromwell and Wynne, 1974). This represents, we
believe, the first effort to apply this type of design in
the study of the potential development of psychopathology.

The project selects risk and control children on the
basis of defined psychiatric status of the biological parents at ages 4, 7, and 10. Testing of the risk children and
other family members is very extensive and involves approximately 40 hours devoted to various experimental and clinical
procedures.

It is hoped that these participants will return three
years hence when the cohorts are at ages 7, 10 and 13. If
there is comparability of performance on the central variable
under evaluation of the two 7 year old and the two 10 year
old groups (i.e., the original age and the retested age
samples), then it could suggest the nature of the development
course from ages 4 to 13 in these risk children. Thus, the
Rochester program, through convergence design, may permit
inferences of a probable nine year span of development from
the period of early childhood to the onset of adolescence,
and do so within a time span of three to four years.

Can this strategy be successfully exploited? That will
depend upon the problem of retention of the cohort and this,
in turn, will be dependent upon the continued cooperation of
the project's participants, their retention in the community,

and the stability and intactness of these families over time.

## SUMMARY

The search for etiological factors in mental disorders has recently taken a turn away from the retrospective accounts of the childhood experiences of mentally disordered adults toward the use of ongoing developmental studies of children who may be vulnerable to the later onset of psychopathology.

Such developmental studies now make use of both longitudinal and cross-sectional designs, the strengths and weaknesses of which are traced in this paper. The compromise strategy of a convergence design which takes advantage of the strengths of the two basic methods may be one that the investigators will use increasingly in the future if it can be demonstrated that cohort variations can be minimized and the retention of research participants maximized in the study of children at risk.

## REFERENCES

Baldwin, A.L.  The study of child behavior and development. In P.H. Mussen (Ed.), Handbook of research methods in child development. New York:  John Wiley & Sons, 1960, pp. 3-35.

Bell, R.Q.  Convergence;  An accelerated longitudinal approach. Child Development, 1953, 24, 142-145.

Bleuler, M.  The offspring of schizophrenics.  Schizophrenia Bulletin, 1974, 8, 93-107.

Block, J.  The Q-sort method in personality assessment and psychiatric research.  Springfield, Illinois: Charles C. Thomas, 1961.

Block, J.  Lives through time.  Berkeley: Bancroft Books, 1971.

Bryson, C.Q., and Hingtgen, J.N.  Early childhood psychosis. Annotated bibliography, NIMH, Rockville, Maryland, 1971.

Cromwell, R.L. and Wynne, L.C.  The University of Rochester
    Child and Family Study:  Development of competence and
    vulnerability in families at high-risk for schizophrenia
    Department of Psychiatry, University of Rochester,
    Mimeographed, 1974.

Fish, B.  Biologic antecedents of psychosis in children.  In
    D. Freedman (Ed.), The biology of the major psychoses:
    A comparative analysis.  Association Research Nervous
    and Mental Diseases Publication #54.  New York: Raven
    Press, 1975, pp. 49-80.

Garmezy, N.  Children at risk:  The search for the antece-
    dents to schizophrenia.  Part II:  Ongoing research pro-
    grams, issues and intervention.  Schizophrenia Bulletin,
    1974, 9, 55-125.

Garmezy, N. and Steitman, S.  Children at risk:  The search
    for the antecedents of schizophrenia.  Part I.  Concep-
    tual models and research methods.  Schizophrenia
    Bulletin, 1974, 8, 14-90.

Garmezy, N.  The experimental study of chidren vulnerable to
    psychopathology.  In:  A. Davids (Ed.), Child personali
    and psychopathology:  Current topics.  Vol. II.  New Yor
    John Wiley & Sons, 1975, pp. 171-216.

Gottesman, I.I., and Shields, J.  Schizophrenia and genetics
    New York: Academic Press, 1972.

Jones, M.C., Bayley, N., MacFarlane, J.W., and Honzik, M.P.
    The course of human development.  Waltham, Mass.:  Xerox
    College Publishing, 1971.

Kagan, J.  Change and continuity in infancy.  New York: John
    Wiley and Sons, 1971.

Kessen, W.  Research design in the study of developmental
    children.  In P.H. Mussen (Ed.), Handbook of research
    methods in child development.  New York: John Wiley
    and Sons, 1960, pp 36-70.

Kety, S.S., Rosenthal, D., Wender, P.H., Schulsinger, F., and Jacobsen, B. Mental illness in the biological and adoptive families of adopted individuals who have become schizophrenic: A preliminary report based on psychiatric interviews. In: R.R. Fieve, D. Rosenthal, H. Brill, (Eds.), Genetic research in psychiatry. Baltimore: The Johns Hopkins University Press, 1975, pp. 147-165.

MacFarlane, J.W. From infancy to adulthood. In: M.C. Jones, N. Bayley, J.W. MacFarlane, M.P. Honzik (Eds.), The course of human development. Waltham, Mass.: Xerox College Publishing, 1971, pp. 406-410.

Matarazzo, J.D. Wechler's measurement and appraisal of adult intelligence, 5th and enlarged edition. Baltimore: Williams & Wilkins, 1972.

Mednick, B.R. Breakdown in high-risk subjects: familial and early environmental factors. Journal of Abnormal Psychology, 1973, 82, 469-475.

Mednick, S., and Schulsinger, F. Studies of children at high risk for schizophrenia. In: S.R. Dean (Ed.), Schizophrenia: The first ten Dean Award lectures. New York: MSS Information Corporation, 1973, pp. 247-293.

Nunnally, J.C. Research strategies and measurement methods for investigating human development. In J.R. Nesselraode and H.W. Reese (Eds.), Life span developmental psychology. New York: Academic Press, 1973, pp. 87-109.

Phillips, L. Case history data and prognosis in schizophrenia. Journal of Nervous and Mental Disease, 1953, 117, 515-525.

Robins, L.N. Deviant children grow-up. Baltimore: Williams and Wilkins, 1966.

Rodnick, E.H., and Goldstein, M.J. Premorbid adjustment and the recovery of mothering function in acute schizophrenic women. Journal of Abnormal Psychology, 1974, 83, 623-628.

Schaie, K.W. A general model for the study of developmental problems. Psychological Bulletin, 1965, 64, 92-107.

Schaie, K.W., and Strother, C.R.  A cross-sequential study
    of age changes in cognitive behavior.  Psychological
    Bulletin, 1968, 70, 671-680.

Sears, R.R.  Survey of objective studies of psychoanalytic
    concepts.  New York:  Social Science Research Council,
    Bulletin 51, 1943.

Spitzer, R., and Endicott, J.  Current and past psychopatholc
    scales (CAPPS).  Evaluation Unit, Biometrics Research.
    New York State Department of Mental Hygiene.  New York,
    1968.

Stone, A.A., and Onque, G.C.  Longitudinal studies of child
    personality.  Cambridge:  Harvard University Press, 1959.

Wechsler, D.  The measurement of adult intelligence, 3rd ed.
    Baltimore:  The Williams & Wilkins Company, 1944.

Wing, J.K., Cooper, J.E., and Sartorius, N.  The measurement
    and classification of psychiatric symptoms.  Cambridge:
    Cambridge University Press, 1974.

Wohlwill, J.F.  Methodology and research strategy in the stud
    of developmental change.  In:  L.R. Goulet and P.R.
    Baltes (Eds.), Life span developmental psychology.
    New York: Academic Press, 1970, pp. 149-191.

PROSPECTIVE STUDIES TO INVESTIGATE BEHAVIORAL CHANGE

Michael Rutter
Department of Child and Adolescent Psychiatry
Institute of Psychiatry
DeCrespigny Park
Denmark Hill
London, England

Prospective or longitudinal studies are time consuming
and expensive to undertake, they are subject to a variety
of sampling hazards and the data obtained are difficult to
analyze. Individuals for longitudinal study are often chosen
in terms of their accessibility and cooperativeness; this fact
and the sample attrition over time render many longitudinal
samples biased and unrepresentative. The varying sample size
at different stages during the study and the hazards of data
linkage have meant that most longitudinal studies have used
only cross-sectional methods of analysis. That is to say,
most analyses have consisted of group associations or correlations between a variable at point B or point C, but only
rarely has there been an attempt to examine individual changes
in behavior over time. These and other criticisms of the
longitudinal approach are fair and valid but for certain types
of research questions longitudinal data are essential. Wall
and Williams (1970), in their review of longitudinal studies
and the social sciences argued that the first two indications
for a longitudinal approach are: (a) the objectives demand
measurement of change in individuals over time, and (b) some
'causal' relation can be postulated between an early and
a subsequent event. Undoubtedly in these circumstances longitudinal studies, for all their difficulties, have major advantages over cross-sectional investigations. In this
paper, some of these advantages and also some of the limitations will be considered using data from several recent
studies as illustration.

NON-RESPONSE BIAS

It is a feature of most studies, longitudinal and cross-
sectional, that a proportion of subjects refuse to cooperate
or are not traced. However, surprisingly little attention
has been paid to the biases created by non-response. For the
most part, investigators have been content to show that the
people missed did not differ from the main sample in terms of
variables such as age, sex and social class. Of course, in a
cross-sectional study it is never possible to determine whethe
the missed subjects differed on the variables studied, because
their non-response means that information is lacking on these
variables. But longitudinal studies may sometimes circumvent
this difficulty by examining the variable in non-responders at
an earlier point in time. For example, this was the case with
a study of London school children recently undertaken by my
colleagues and myself (Rutter, 1973; Rutter et al., 1975). In
brief, behavioral and educational data were obtained on a total sample of 10 year old children attending primary schools
in one inner London borough. Three years later the same child
ren were studied in the same way at age 13 years when they wer
in their second year of secondary school. Amongst other thing
the children took a group administered test of reading. Even
after repeated testings to pick up absentees, 8.6 per cent of
children had still not taken the test. Some findings on the
absentees in terms of their behavior and reading three years
earlier (at age 10 years) are shown in Table 1.

The rates of behavioral deviance and of poor reading
attainment were nearly twice as high among the absentees. It
has been a consistent finding in all our studies (e.g., Rutter
Tizard & Whitmore, 1970) and those of other investigators (e.g
West & Farrington, 1973) that children or adults who are not
tested or not interviewed are much more likely than other people to be deviant or disturbed in some way. The moral is clea;
Non-responders do create a bias and this must be taken into account in all studies.


INPUT BIAS

This same study also provided the opportunity to investigate another source of bias or distortion - that is selective
intake or input bias. Several studies have shown marked variations between secondary schools in rates of behavioral disturbance, delinquency and psychiatric referral (e.g., Gath

TABLE 1

CHILD CHARACTERISTICS IN PRIMARY SCHOOL AND ABSENTEEISM
AT SECONDARY SCHOOL

| Characteristics at age 10 years | Presence/Absence for Reading Test at age 13 years | | | |
|---|---|---|---|---|
| | Absent | | Present | |
| Teachers Question- naire Score | N | (%) | N | (%) |
| Non-deviant | 85 | | 1147 | |
| Deviant | 51 | (37.5)** | 301 | (20.8) |
| Total | 136 | | 1448 | |
| Reading Score | | | | |
| Normal range | 104 | | 1246 | |
| Very poor | 32 | (23.5)** | 202 | (14.0) |
| Total | 136 | | 1448 | |

** $p < 0.01$

et al., 1972). The same studies have shown that these between-school differences are not explicable in terms of factors such as social class or where the children live, and it has been concluded that the variation represents an effect of school life on children's behavior - sometimes for the better and sometimes for the worse. However, it has not been possible from cross-sectional studies to differentiate between selective intake (i.e., variations between schools in the proportion of disturbed children who are admitted) and school influences (i.e., differences in the proportion of children who become disturbed as a result of their school experiences). However,

we had available data on what the children's behavior and
attainments were like <u>before</u> they transferred to secondary
school that made it possible to differentiate between these
two situations.

Table 2 summarizes the findings on the characteristics
of the children prior to transfer.  The data refer only to
non-selective schools and in theory all the schools take the
same mixture of children.  In fact, some schools admit less
than 10 per cent of children who are very poor readers and
less than 10 per cent who are behaviorally deviant.  At the
other extreme, several schools have an intake in which nearly
half the children are either behaviorally deviant or poor
readers or both.  In short, there is a very substantial selec
tive bias in intake.  The cross-sectional data on social clas
and area of residence were quite misleading in its implicatio
that this did not occur.

TABLE 2

INTAKE TO NON-SELECTIVE SCHOOLS ACCORDING TO
CHARACTERISTICS PRIOR TO TRANSFER

| % Children Deviant | Number of Schools with that Percentage Deviant | |
|---|---|---|
|  | Reading | Behavior |
| 0 - 9 | 6 | 1 |
| 10 - 19 | 8 | 8 |
| 20 - 29 | 4 | 6 |
| 30 - 39 | 2 | 4 |
| 40 + | 1 | 2 |
|  | 21 | 21 |

Nevertheless, the fact that there was a selective intake to supposedly non-selective schools does not necessarily mean that this explains the variation between schools some years later. To examine that issue, it was first necessary to determine the strength of the association between children's behavior at age 10 and at age 14 years.* This was first examined in correlational terms, as shown in Table 3.

The correlations between children's behavior scale scores at 10 and at 14 years were low but highly significant in statistical terms - 0.22 for boys and 0.31 for girls. The mean scores for girls on the two occasions were fairly similar but for boys the mean was substantially lower during adolescence. On the basis of these findings it was possible to devise a regression equation to predict the 14 year old scores on the basis of the 10 year old scores. This constitutes the basis of the more familiar analysis of covariance which is the usual statistical technique used to examine end-product differences

TABLE 3

REGRESSION DATA FOR BEHAVIOR SCALE B

|  | Boys | Girls |
|---|---|---|
| Mean Score 'B' age 10 yrs. | 6.57 | 4.47 |
| S.D.          "   "   " | 7.14 | 5.56 |
| Mean Score 'B' age 14 yrs. | 4.61 | 4.84 |
| S.D.          "   "   " | 5.84 | 6.42 |
| Intercorrelation (10-14 yrs.) | 0.22 | 0.31 |

Regression equation for predicting $B_{14}$ =      $3.43 + 0.18B_{10}$      $3.24 + 0.36B_{10}$

* In order to reduce the non-response rate the survey was repeated at age 14 years as well as at age 13 years. Since the data were more complete on the second occasion, they are used here in preference.

after taking into account differences in initial level.  That
procedure was not suitable for our purposes since it did not
provide a measure of the degree of behavioral change in individual schools.  However, the regression equation involves
the same statistical procedure and has the advantage that it
may be applied to individual schools.  This is illustrated
in Table 4.

School A and school B are two schools with a rather simi
lar intake of behaviorally deviant boys - about average for
the part of inner London we studied.  Applying the regression
equations shown in Table 3, the expected mean score at age 14
years can be predicted on the basis of the findings for the
total population of boys in the borough.  As would be expecte
the prediction in each case is for a similar - about average
score.  But the actual mean scores in the two schools were
widely different.  In school A the mean was well below prediction whereas in school B it was far above prediction.  It

TABLE  4

REGRESSION FINDINGS FOR BEHAVIOR SCALE

|  | Behavior Scale Age 10 years | | Predicted Score at 14 years | |
| --- | --- | --- | --- | --- |
|  | Mean | S.D. | Mean | S.D. |
| School A Boys(n=65) | 6.59 | 6.67 | 4.62 | 1.20 |
| School B Boys(n=50) | 7.06 | 8.12 | 4.70 | 1.46 |

|  | Actual Score at 14 years | | Mean Difference |
| --- | --- | --- | --- |
|  | Mean | S.D. |  |
| School A Boys(n=65) | 2.59 | 4.15 | −2.03 |
| School B Boys(n=50) | 9.78 | 7.98 | + 5.08 |

may be inferred that school A had had a good influence on the boys' behavior whereas school B had had a bad influence.

This technique, however, involves a number of mathematical assumptions not met by the behavior scale which was devised to pick out deviant children rather than to make distinctions within the normal range (Rutter, 1967; Rutter, Tizard & Whitmore, 1970). Accordingly, it might be thought preferable to use the scale in this much simpler way. Table 5 shows how well the scale findings predict behavioral deviance from age 10 to age 14 years.

Boys who were deviant at age 10 years were twice as likely as other children to be deviant at 14 years and they were nearly three times as likely to be delinquent in adolescence. The differences for girls were even greater. Similarly, children who were poor readers at age 10 years were many times more likely than other children to be poor readers at age 14 years. Thus, the findings at 10 years of age provided a reasonable prediction of what the youngsters would be like four years later.

TABLE  5

PREDICTIVE INDICATORS

| 10 Years | GIRLS | BOYS |
|---|---|---|
| Behavior Scale | Deviant 14 years | Deviant 14 years |
| | | |
| Non-deviant | 15.3% | 15.3% |
| Deviant | 36.0% | 29.5% |
| | | |
| Behavior Scale | Delinquent 14 yrs | Delinquent 14 yrs |
| | | |
| Normal/Neurotic | 1.1% | 11.2% |
| Antisocial/Mixed | 12.8% | 27.1% |
| | | |
| Reading | Poor readers 14 yrs | Poor readers 14 yrs |
| | | |
| Adequate reader | 1.0% | 1.0% |
| Poor reader | 11.7% | 19.7% |

TABLE 6

STANDARDIZATION FINDINGS FOR BEHAVIOR SCALE

| SCHOOL A BOYS | (a) N | (b) % Deviancy Expected at 14 yrs | (c = a x b) No. Deviant Expected at 14 yrs |
|---|---|---|---|
| Non-Deviant at 10 yrs | 45 | 0.153 | 6.89 |
| Teachers Scale Deviant at 10 yrs | 20 | 0.295 | 5.90 |
| Total | 65 | ----- | 12.79 |

Actual No. Deviant at age 14 years = 6

| SCHOOL B BOYS | N | % Deviancy Expected at 14 yrs | No. Deviant Expected at 14 yrs |
|---|---|---|---|
| Non-Deviant at 10 yrs | 33 | 0.153 | 5.05 |
| Teachers Scale Deviant at 10 yrs | 17 | 0.295 | 5.01 |
| Total | 50 | ----- | 10.06 |

Actual No. Deviant at age 14 years = 24

These results may then be used to give the proportions
of deviant 14 year old children expected at each school on the
basis of the 10 year old findings. Table 6 shows how this is
done for school A using a straightforward standardization procedure. Column 'a' gives the numbers of children at the school
who were non-deviant and who were deviant when at primary
school. Column 'b' gives the proportion expected to be deviant at 14 years using the results for the total population
of children. Thus, 15.3 per cent of boys non-deviant at 10
years are deviant at 14 years, but 29.5 per cent of boys deviant at 10 are still so at 14 years. By multiplying column
'a' by column 'b' the expected number of deviant boys in the
school can be derived - in this case 12.79 boys. In fact,
only 6 boys in the school were actually deviant at 14 years.
School A had many fewer deviant boys than expected.

The same analysis for school B showed that about the
same number of deviant boys (10.06) is predicted as for
school A. However, there were actually 24 deviant boys at
the school. School B had produced over twice as many deviant
boys as expected on the basis of their intake. Again, as from
the regression findings, it may be inferred that school A had
had a good influence on the boys' behavior whereas school B
had had a bad influence. For these two schools, the two statistical methods have given rise to closely similar results.
Table 7 shows how far the two agree in the total group of
schools.

The agreement is remarkably close. Indeed, in most cases
the agreement on rank ordering of the schools is almost perfect. As so often happens, the difference in statistical
method has mattered hardly at all. Using either technique,
there are still huge differences between schools even after
having taken into account selective biases in intake. The
behavioral difference between the school that did best and
the one that did worst is equivalent to about one and a fifth
standard deviations in terms of the individual child findings.
This points to the likelihood of a considerable influence of
the school milieu on children's behavior - an effect which
could only have been shown by means of longitudinal data.
Research is now in progress to identify what factors in school
may be important in this connection.

TABLE 7

COMPARISON OF TWO TECHNIQUES TO ASSESS THE DIFFERENCES
BETWEEN OBSERVED AND EXPECTED LEVELS OF BEHAVIORAL DEVIANCE

| BOYS' SCHOOLS | STANDARDIZATION PROCEDURE | | REGRESSION PROCEDURE | |
|---|---|---|---|---|
| | Differences in Proportion of Deviant Children | Rank | Mean Difference in Scores | Rank |
| C | -19% | 1 | -3.34 | 1 |
| A | -10% | 2 | -2.03 | 2 |
| F | -10% | 3 | -1.03 | 4 |
| K | - 9% | 4 | -1.82 | 3 |
| D | - 6% | 5 | -0.37 | 5 |
| G | - 3% | 6 | -0.28 | 6 |
| E | = | 7 | +0.07 | 8 |
| I | + 3% | 8 | +0.33 | 10 |
| L | + 5% | 9 | +0.03 | 7 |
| J | + 8% | 10 | +0.24 | 9 |
| M | +13% | 11 | +2.80 | 11 |
| H | +23% | 12 | +4.64 | 12 |
| B | +28% | 13 | +5.08 | 13 |

## OUT-MIGRATION BIAS

A different but related issue arises in connection with ecological studies in which rates of disorder are related to geographical areas and community living conditions. The investigations by Faris and Dunham (1939) and by Shaw and Mackay (1942) in Chicago pioneered this form of inquiry. Most of these early studies were limited by a reliance on hospital or crime statistics which provide a very uncertain guide to true prevalence, and by a lack of detailed information on the conditions of life in the groups or areas studied. Moreover, it became apparent quite early that some of the findings on high rates of mental illness in certain city districts might simply be an artifact resulting from the drift of such people into areas of lodging houses and poor accommodation (Hare, 1956). That artifact can readily be taken into account in cross-sectional studies by restricting the sample to people born and bred in the area to be studied (Rutter et al., 1975). But less attention has been paid to the possibility that the high rates of sickness might be a consequence of healthy people being more likely to move out of the area. Short-term longitudinal studies are needed to examine the possibility of selective out-migration.

This issue arose in connection with our comparisons of child psychiatric disorder in London and the Isle of Wight (Rutter et al., 1975). Psychiatric problems were twice as common in London children, even those born and bred in London to parents also born and bred in the metropolis. The question of selective out-migration was examined by a means of a separate 4 year follow-up study of adult patients' families and of control families. The results showed that out-migration from London was not related to psychiatric status of adults or children or to family discord and disturbance. The artifact of selective out-migration could be excluded. The artifact of selective in-migration had previously been ruled out by showing that at the time of study, in-migrants to London did not differ in psychiatric state or family circumstances from those already living in the city. That almost deals with the artifacts arising from selective migration, but not quite. It could be that people coming to London from country areas differed systematically from the families left behind. That possibility required another form of longitudinal study, but unfortunately not one carried out.

AGE OF ONSET DIFFERENCES

The data considered so far have been concerned with the
use of longitudinal data to determine when behavioral changes
took place in order to focus on possible causal factors.  The
importance of timing the onset of psychiatric disorder is
shown in another context by the data from a parallel but
different longitudinal study.  This took place on the Isle
of Wight and again, younsters were followed through from 10
years of age (Rutter, Tizard & Whitmore, 1970) to 14 or 15
years of age (Graham & Rutter, 1973; Rutter, Graham, Chadwick & Yule, 1976).  We were interested in the question of
whether there was anything special about psychiatric disorders
arising during the adolescent age period.  That problem required both longitudinal and cross-sectional data.  Adolescents with psychiatric disorders were identified through a
total population cross-sectional epidemiological study.  This
involved screening with questionnaires and tests and then a
very detailed clinical study of some 600 younsters using inter
views with the parents, the teachers and the adolescents themselves.  By these means, 156 14-to 15-year olds with a handi-
capping psychiatric disorder were identified, as shown in
Table 8.

TABLE 8

AGE OF ONSET IN ADOLESCENT PSYCHIATRIC DISORDERS

|       | Before 10 years | After 10 years | Total |
|-------|-----------------|----------------|-------|
| Boys  | 43 (69.3%)      | 53 (56.4%)     | 96    |
| Girls | 19              | 41             | 60    |
| Total | 62              | 94             | 156   |
| Sex Ratio | 2.3 : 1     | 1.3 : 1        |       |

$$X^2 = 2.13; \quad 1 \text{ d.f.}; \quad \text{N.S.}$$

The next task was to determine when these disorders began. This required longitudinal data. The same cohort of Isle of Wight children had been studied in much the same way four years earlier at age 10 years (Rutter, Tizard & Whitmore, 1970). In parallel with the cross-sectional study at 14-15 years, there was a systematic follow-up of all the children previously identified as having psychiatric disorder at 10 years. Using these data, the 156 adolescents with psychiatric disorder were subdivided into the 62 who already showed psychiatric problems in middle childhood and the 94 whose difficulties began at some time between 10 and 14 years. This set the scene to examine the question of whether these two groups of psychiatric disorders differed in any systematic way. Some of the key findings are summarized in Table 9.

Comparison of the left hand and middle columns shows that the adolescent disorders which began in early or middle childhood were strongly associated with various forms of family disturbance or psychopathology and were strongly associated with scholastic difficulties, especially reading retardation. In all cases there were marked differences from the control group (not shown in the table). In sharp contrast, the disorders which began de novo during early adolescence were less often associated with family difficulties (although marital discord was still significantly more common than in the control group), and not associated at all with scholastic problems. It seemed that in some important respects the psychiatric disorders arising for the first time during the pubertal years were different from those arising earlier in childhood. The differences with respect to family disturbance and educational problems were not explicable in terms of diagnostic differences between the groups. On the whole, the diagnostic pattern was fairly similar except that both depression and school refusal were more common in the youngsters whose disorders began during adolescence.

However, there was another difference between the two groups which had to be taken into account. By definition, the disorders beginning before age 10 years were chronic conditions which must have lasted at least 4 years, and in practice had usually lasted some 7 years. In contrast, the new disorders must have been more acute in that they could not have lasted more than 4 years and often the duration was much shorter. In order to determine whether chronicity explained the findings, comparison needs to be made with the

TABLE   9

FAMILY AND EDUCATIONAL VARIABLES AND TIME
OF ONSET OF DISORDER

| | New Disorders (at age 14yr) n = 94 | Persistent Disorders (Fm 10-14yr) n = 62 | Non-Persistent Disorders (after age 10yr) n = 45 |
|---|---|---|---|
| Not living with both natural parents | 18.2% | 37.3%** | 25.5% |
| Poor marriage | 20.8% | 30.2% | 18.9% |
| Child been in care | 8.3% | 32.8%*** | 8.7%+ |
| Maternal psychiatric disorder | 17.6% | 30.2% | 21.4% |
| Reading Retardation (age 10 yrs) | 3.3% | 14.3%* | 11.1% |
| Reading Retardation (age 14 yrs) | 2.2% | 21.4%*** | 13.3%++ |
| Mean I.Q. | 105.0 (s.d.=17.14) | 102.0 (s.d.=15.09) | 102.3 (s.d.=20.60) |
| Mean Arithmetic Score | 31.4 (s.d.=11.68) | 23.2*** (s.d.=10.82) | 27.9 (s.d.=13.00) |

Differences between new disorders and persistent disorders

    \* $p < 0.05$

    \*\* $p < 0.025$

    \*\*\* $p < 0.001$

Differences between persistent disorders and non-per. disorde:

    + $p < 0.001$  ($x^2 = 7.28$; 1 d.f.)

Differences between new disorders and non-persistent disorder:

    ++ $p = 0.015$  (Fishers Exact Test)

children who showed psychiatric problems at 10 years but who did not at 14 years (the group shown in the right hand column of the Table). Their disorders, too, by definition could not have lasted more than 4 years. Nevertheless, in that group, there was still a strong association with scholastic difficulties, so this association must be a function of age of onset, and not of chronicity. On the other hand, the non-persistent disorders at age 10 years also showed a lesser connection with family difficulties so this may be a function of how long disorders last. The finding that psychiatric disorders beginning in adolescence are less likely than those beginning in earlier childhood to be associated with educational difficulties parallels the similar finding by Robins and Hill (1966) with regard to age of onset of delinquency. The next issue, of course, is what is special about adolescence? What factors do lead to psychiatric problems arising for the first time at this stage in development? Naturally, these are questions which must concern us but they take us too far from the methodological issues to be considered in this symposium.

## PREDICTIVE VALIDITY

The issue of predictive validity, by its nature, obviously required longitudinal data. Psychiatric disorders in childhood have sometimes been dismissed rather lightly on the grounds that they are only transient phenomena in essentially normal children (Shepherd et al., 1971). Our data clearly indicate that this is not so. However, that is not the main issue for concern in the present context. Rather, the questions to be posed are: how should predictive validity be assessed and do different conclusions stem from different methods of analysis? To discuss these issues, behavioral scale data on a general population sample of children followed over a four year period will be used.

First, predictive validity may be determined by means of the product moment correlation between children's scores at year '0' and their scores four years later. The correlation found was 0.25, highly significant statistically but, of course, it accounts for only some 6 per cent of the variance. One might reasonably conclude that this shows very weak predictive validity of negligible practical importance.

However, the same data may be analyzed in a different way using the behavioral scale score to identify behaviorally de-

TABLE 10

CONTINUITIES IN BEHAVIORAL DEVIANCE

|  |  | Behavioral Deviance at Year 4 | | | | | |
|  |  | GIRLS | | BOYS | | TOTAL | |
|  |  | % Deviant | (Total N) | % Deviant | (Total N) | % Deviant | (Total N) |
| Behavioral Deviance at Year 0 | Non-Deviant | 15.8 | (171) | 12.1 | (140) | 14.3 | (311) |
|  | Deviant | 33.3 | ( 21) | 38.3 | ( 67) | 37.5 | ( 88) |
| Inter-year correlation | | $r = 0.14$ | | $r = 0.31$ | | $r = 0.25$ | |

viant children. These data indicate that well over twice as
many of the children deviant at the start of the study were
deviant 4 years later compared with those initially non-
deviant. This suggests a quite useful level of prediction,
apparently better than that shown by the correlation coefficient, although the data are the same in both cases.
Even so prediction is still fairly modest.

But the data may be analyzed yet another way. Both the
analyses mentioned so far have dealt with data at only two
points in time. If the behavior scale has any unreliability
(and all scales have), then the prediction will be lowered by
this unreliability. What happens if data at several points
in time are brought together, thus reducing unreliability and
focussing on persistent problems of most clinical interest?
The findings are shown on the bottom half of Table 11.

Behavioral scale data were available at 5 points in
time over a four year period. Children who had deviant
scores on at least 3 out of the 5 occasions were considered
to show persisting deviance. This applied to 63 of the 426
children - 14.7 per cent in all. Of these 63 children, no
less than 45 (71.4 per cent) were identified as deviant on
the first occasion. Only 18 (5.3%) of the 338 children who
were initially non-deviant, later showed persistent deviance.
In sharp contrast persisting deviance was ten times as frequent (51.7%) among youngsters with deviant scores on the
first occasion. In short, a behavioral scale score at one
point in time was a highly successful predictor of persisting behavioral deviance.

The point being made is that these three analyses all
concern the same set of data on the same children over the
same period of time. Yet it has been possible by different
statistical techniques to suggest very low continuity, moderate continuity and very high continuity for the same behavior.
None of these analyses are 'wrong.' Each provides a valid
but different facet of the same picture. It is important to
recognize how far it is possible to influence the conclusions
drawn by the statistical techniques used, a point also made
by Jencks et al. (1973) in a different connection.

The examination of persisting deviance had a particular
advantage in this study. The data already mentioned refer to
the control group for a study of the children of psychiatric

TABLE 11

PERSISTENCE OF BEHAVIOR DEVIANCE OVER FOUR YEARS

| Children of Patients | Non-Deviant No | % | Deviant(Emotional) No | % | Deviant(Conduc No | % |
|---|---|---|---|---|---|---|
| | Initial Behavior Rating | | | | (Teachers Scale) | |
| No Deviance | 91 | | -- | | -- | |
| Fluctuating | 50 | | 14 | | 8 | |
| Persisting Deviance | 10 | (6.6) | 12 | (46.2) | 39 | (82.9) |
| TOTAL | 151 | | 26 | | 47 | |
| Controls | | | | | | |
| No Deviance | 222 | | -- | | -- | |
| Fluctuating | 98 | | 24 | | 20 | |
| Persisting Deviance | 18 | (5.3) | 13 | (35.1) | 32 | (61.5) |
| TOTAL | 338 | | 37 | | 52 | |

patients. The top half of the table provides the comparable
findings for these patients' children. At each point during
the four years of the study, behavioral deviance was slightly
more common in the patients' children than in the controls
but the differences were fairly small. However, behavioral
deviance was more persistent in children of patients than in
the controls with the result that 27.2 per cent of the children in the patients' families showed persisting deviance (as
assessed from teacher's reports) compared with only half that
proportion (14.7 per cent) among the controls. In short,
longitudinal data were needed to bring out the true extent
of the difference between the groups.

Other issues regarding predictive validity can be demonstrated by examination of findings on two rather different
variables. First, there are the findings regarding personality disorder in adults. The data stem from a four year longitudinal study of all newly referred psychiatric patients
with children below the age of 15 years who lived in one
London borough. The designation of personality disorder was
made only if there was persistently abnormal behavior and persisting social handicap going back to adolescence or very
early life - a rather narrower definition than employed by
many psychiatrists.

TABLE 12

PRESENCE OF PERSONALITY DISORDER AND
PERSISTENCE OF PSYCHIATRIC SYMPTOMS

| | PERSISTENCE DURING PERIOD 1 to 4 YEARS AFTER INITIAL CONTACT | | | |
|---|---|---|---|---|
| | No Symptoms after 1st yr. | Symptoms < 2 years | 2-3 years | > 3 years |
| No personality Disorder (n=70) | 14.3% | 41.4% | 22.9% | 21.4% |
| Personality Disorder (n=42) | 7.1% | 21.4% | 16.7% | 54.8% |

Table 12 shows the persistence or non-persistence of psychiatric symptoms in adult patients. The results show that the prognosis was much worse for those with a personality disorder. Over half had symptoms for at least 3 of the 4 years of follow-up - a proportion much higher than in the group without personality disorder. It may be concluded that the diagnosis of personality disorder had quite reasonable predictive validity over a 4 year period. Nevertheless, it should be added that three patients with that diagnosis showed a complete loss of symptoms and of social handicap. With a sufficiently major change in social circumstances even life long problems may remit.

However, do the findings mean anything more than that symptoms present for a long time are more likely to go on being present than symptoms present for a short time? Table 1 shows that they do. In patients without personality disorder, the duration of symptoms was of negligible prognostic significance. Even among patients with symptoms of over 5 years duration, only a quarter had symptoms for as much as 3 out of the next 4 years.

TABLE 13

DURATION OF SYMPTOMS PRIOR TO REFERRAL AND
PERSISTENCE OF PSYCHIATRIC SYMPTOMS

| Duration of Symptoms | PERSISTENCE DURING PERIOD 1 to 4 YEARS AFTER INITIAL CONTACT | | | |
|---|---|---|---|---|
| | No symptoms after 1st yr. | Symptoms $<$ 2 years | 2-3 years | $>$ 3 years |
| Less than 1 yr. (n = 40) | 17.5% | 40.0% | 22.5% | 20.0% |
| 1 - 5 years (n = 19) | 10.5% | 47.4% | 21.1% | 21.1% |
| 5 years or more (n = 11) | 7.7% | 36.4% | 27.3% | 27.3% |

(This table excludes patients with personality disorders).

TABLE 14

PREDICTIVE VALIDITY OF MARRIAGE RATING

| Initial Marriage Rating | Predominant Marriage Rating over 4 Year Follow-Up (Wife's account) | | | | | |
|---|---|---|---|---|---|---|
| | No discord | | Discord | | Separation/Divorce | |
| | No | (%) | No | (%) | No | (%) |
| 'Good' (1/2) | 28 | (93.4) | 1 | (3.3) | 1 | (3.3) |
| 'Fair' (3/4) | 21 | (65.6) | 9 | (28.2) | 2 | (6.3) |
| 'Poor' (5/6) | 10 | (33.3) | 12 | (40.0) | 8 | (26.7) |

No discord vs Discord/Break up $X^2$ for trends 40.37; 2 d.f.; p < 0.001

Table 14 shows the predictive validity of the initial rating of the marriage based on the wife's account - the data being from the same study. Among the group initially rated as having a markedly poor marriage, over a quarter divorced or separated during the next four years, compared with only 3 per cent of those with a good marriage as rated at the time of first contact. The presence of marital discord during the 4 year period of follow-up showed an even stronger association with the initial marriage rating. It may be concluded that the marriage rating had very good predictive validity (Quinton, Rutter & Rowlands, 1976).

IMPLICATIONS FOR LONGITUDINAL ANALYSIS
OF CAUSAL RELATIONSHIPS

The evidence that our ratings of psychiatric state and of family relationships have a high predictive validity is reassuring insofar as it shows that the findings refer to persisting phenomena of some importance. However, the very fact of predictive validity limits the use of longitudinal analysis to delineate causal relationships. One of the notions behind our four year longitudinal study of patients' families was that we could use longitudinal data to study

the development of disorders in the children.  As it turned
out, we have been able to do that in only a very limited way
because most children with behavioral deviance at the start
of the study continued to have problems throughout the follow
up period and very few children without difficulties at the
beginning became deviant during the next four years.  The
cross-sectional data obtained at the point of first contact
with the families showed that disorder in the children was
most strongly associated with disturbed intrafamilial relatic
ships and secondarily with the presence of personality disorder in the parents.  However, the nature of parental symptc
matology seemed of little significance to the child.  On the
other hand, the extent of the child's exposure to and involve
ment in parental symptoms was important as shown by Table 15
which gives the findings for the first year of the follow-up
period.

The rate of psychiatric disorder in the children with
only slight exposure to parental symptomatology was low -
indeed it was lower than the average for the general population.  The rate of  disorder was slightly raised if the
child was exposed either to neurotic symptoms or to parental
irritability/hostility.  But the rate was markedly increased
if the child was exposed to both types of symptomatology.

TABLE 15

EXPOSURE TO PARENTAL SYMPTOMS AND
DISORDER IN THE CHILD

CHILD

| EXPOSURE | % deviant on teachers scale | | % with psychiatric disorder assessed on interview/mother | |
|---|---|---|---|---|
| | % | (Total n) | % | (Total n) |
| Low | 9.5 | (42) | 4.4 | (46) |
| Neurotic or Hostile | 19.2 | (26) | 7.1 | (28) |
| Neurotic and Hostile | 61.1 | (18) | 42.9 | (14) |
| Symptoms both parents | 40.0 | (30) | 53.8 | (26) |

Whether only one or both parents had psychiatric symptoms mattered less. The finding was interesting in that it implied that disturbed family relationships were much more damaging in the context of neurotic disturbances in the parents than if they occurred in isolation. Data not included in Table 15 showed that psychotic symptoms were of little import in this connection.

Finally, our data showed that very young children in patients' families developed psychiatric disorder and that these disorders proved to be remarkably persistent. Psychiatric disorder rarely developed for the first time during later childhood. Similar findings from other studies have led investigators to include that the first few years of childhood are critical for later development. It is necessary to point out that this does not follow from the research findings, as our data show. Not much attention has been paid in the literature to the question of persistence of family disadvantage and to the question of how frequently families cease to be disadvantaged. The findings on the predictive validity of marriage and parental disorder measures indicate only too clearly that, once present, disadvantage tends to go on being present. Children develop disorder when young because family disadvantage is already present then. They less often develop new disorders later simply because family disadvantage less often develops for the first time in later childhood. Longitudinal studies in themselves provide no answer to whether some stages in childhood are more critical than others for particular aspects of development. They may be, although this has only been demonstrated in a few instances. The hypothesis of critical periods required populations in which serious disadvantage ceases after the early years of childhood and populations in which serious disadvantage begins for the first time during later childhood. Comparisons of such populations have rarely been made.

## CONCLUSIONS

Longitudinal data are invaluable in the determination of biases resulting from non-response, from selective input and from out-migration. They are essential for the determination of patterns associated with differences in the age of onset of disorders, and for the assessment of predictive validity. However, they are more limited for the detection

of causal relationships than is sometimes supposed.  Lastly,
the impression of behavioral continuities in development will
be much influenced by the method of statistical analysis
employed.


REFERENCES

Gath, D., Cooper, B., and Gattoni, F.E.G.  Preliminary
    communication:  Child guidance and delinquency in a
    London borough.  Psychological Medicine, 1972, 2, 185-
    191.

Graham, P., and Rutter, M.  Psychiatric disorders in the
    young adolescent:  A follow-up study.  Proceedings of
    the Royal Society of Medicine, 1973, 66, 1226-1229.

Hare, E.H.  Mental illness and social conditions in Bristol.
    Journal of Mental Science, 1956, 102, 349-357.

Jencks, C., Smith, M., Acland, M., Bane, M.J., Cohen, D.,
    Gintis, H., Heyns, B., and Michelson, S.  Inequality:
    A reassessment of the effect of family and schooling
    in America.  London: Allen Lane, 1973.

Power, M.J., Benn, R.T., and Morris, J.N.  Neighbourhood,
    school and juveniles before the courts.  British
    Journal of Criminology, 1972, 12, 111-132.

Quinton, D., Rutter, M., and Rowlands, O.  An evaluation of
    an interview assessment of marriage.  Psychological
    Medicine, 1976, 6, in press.

Robins, L.N., and Hill, S.Y.  Assessing the contribution of
    family structure, class and peer groups to juvenile
    delinquency.  Journal of Criminal Law, Criminology,
    and Political Science, 1966, 57, 325-334.

Rutter, M.  A children's behaviour questionnaire for com-
    pletion by teachers:  Preliminary findings.  Journal
    of Child Psychology and Psychiatry, 1967, 8, 1-11.

Rutter, M.  Why are London children so disturbed?  Proceed-
    ings of the Royal Society of Medicine, 1973, 66, 1221-
    1225.

Rutter, M., Cox, A., Tupling, C., Berger, M., and Yule, W. Attainment and adjustment in two geographical areas: I. The prevalence of psychiatric disorder. British Journal of Psychiatry, 1975, 126, 493-509.

Rutter, M., Graham. P., Chadwick, O., and Yule, W. Adolescent turmoil: Fact or fiction? Development of Medicine in Child Neurology, 1976, 1, 35-56.

Rutter, M., Tizard, J., and Whitmore, K. (Eds.), Education, health and behaviour. London: Longmans, 1970.

Shepherd, M., Oppenheim, B., and Mitchell, S. Children's behaviour and mental health. London: University of London Press, 1971.

Wall, W.D., and Williams, H.L. Longidutinal studies and the social sciences. London: Heinemann, 1970.

West, D.J., and Farrington, D.P. Who becomes delinquent? Second report of the Cambridge study in delinquent development. London: Heinemann Educational, 1973.

## Open Discussion

Greenhouse:   I think you made the point that it takes
a longitudinal study to detect certain kinds of non-response
bias; but now you have shown that there may be a non-response
bias in your longitudinal study which may not be detectable.
Your findings indicate that the deviants do not show up in
the same proportion as the non-deviants and that in turn
indicates a rather bad characteristic of the longitudinal
study when you have drop-outs.

Rutter:   The point, surely, is not whether longitudinal
or cross-sectional studies are superior.  Rather, it is that
studies with a high non-response rate are open to serious
bias.  This applies to both longitudinal and cross-sectional
investigations so that in both it is essential to keep the
proportion of non-responders to a minimum.  Non-response is
not necessarily more frequent or more serious in longitudinal
studies; indeed some of the worst instances of high non-response rates concern cross-sectional inquiries.

Robins:   I think the important thing is that you know
in a longitudinal study if you've lost cases.  You often
don't know that in a cross-sectional study.

THE ROCHESTER ADAPTIVE BEHAVIOR INVENTORY:   A PARALLEL
SERIES OF INSTRUMENTS FOR ASSESSING SOCIAL COMPETENCE
DURING EARLY AND MIDDLE CHILDHOOD AND ADOLESCENCE

Fredric H. Jones
Department of Psychiatry
University of Rochester Medical School
Rochester, New York

## INTRODUCTION

Garmezy (1970) and Jones (1973) have stressed the
importance of developing age-appropriate measures of social
competence throughout the childhood years and of relating
these measures to behavioral and psychiatric outcomes of
interest.  Immediate objectives of such research would be
both to provide predictors of poor psychiatric outcomes in
order to identify children at "high-risk" for adaptive
failure and to guide efforts aimed at early remediation and
prevention by pinpointing specific deficit areas.

———————————

Support for the work reported here was provided by NIMH
Grant #MH-28836-01 (The University of Rochester Child and
Family Study), The Grant Foundation (The Rochester Early
Childhood Study), and NIMH Grant #MH-16544 (The Rochester
Developmental Psychopathology Project).  Data presented
from the University of Rochester Child and Family Study
represent the joint efforts of the author and Dr. Lawrence
Fisher, Dr. James Heriot, and Dr. Lawrence Space, co-
investigators.

The author gratefully acknowledges the contributions of
Ms. Jeri Doane, Ms. Celeste Cipro, Mr. Thomas Rice, Ms.
Marie Lee, Ms. Deborah Wiener, Ms. Mimi Lazar, Ms. Paulette
Gagnon and Mr. Robert Eimers for their efforts on various
normative and "high-risk" studies involving the RABI.

The assessment of social competence of children in the
University of Rochester Child and Family Study (URCAFS) and
related studies has focused upon the development of a series
of age-appropriate measures of social competence in children throughout early and middle childhood and adolescence.
This series of instruments, referred to collectively as the
Rochester Adaptive Behavior Inventory (RABI), was designed
to produce both a "fine grain" as well as a global description of the child's behavioral assets and liabilities at
adjacent age periods based upon the parents' report of the
child's behavior. A series of five parallel and age-
appropriate forms of the RABI have been designed to span
the child's development from 2 through 18 years of age.
These forms of the RABI are designated as form A (2-3 1/2
years), form B (3 1/2 - 5 years), form C (5 - 8 1/2 years),
form D (8 1/2 - 12 years), and form E (12 - 18 years).

The utilization by URCAFS of a convergent longitudinal
research design has placed the additional demand on the RABI
that adjacent forms produce comparable measures of specific
areas of social functioning. The purpose of such comparability of measurement would be to facilitate the documentation of the longitudinal course of development of subjects
in a given domain of behavior across a span of time encompassing two or more forms of the RABI. The RABI, therefore,
was designed from its inception specifically for use in
longitudinal research in which the documentation of the
continuity of various manifestations of social competence is
a prime concern.

The documentation of the continuity of various elements
of the adaptive behavior repertoire of children "at risk"
and the assessment of their predictive power to psychiatric
outcomes of interest is one of the primary goals of URCAFS.
Vulnerability or "risk" in URCAFS is defined by the psychiatric history of one parent of an intact family, either
mother or father. The index parent of risk must have at
least one psychiatric hospitalization with symptoms which
produce a consensual diagnosis of schizophrenia, borderline
schizophrenic or nonschizophrenic made blindly by URCAFS
personnel from available records in which diagnostic labels
have been deleted. The assessment of the children in URCAFS
takes place initially in cohorts of vulnerable male children
who are 4, 7, and 10 years of age. According to the convergent longitudinal design planned for URCAFS, this assessment

is repeated for all children three years later when the children are 7, 10, and 13 years of age. It is therefore possible to document convergence of measurement at 7 years of age where the intake assessment of the 7 year old cohort and the follow-up assessment of the 4 year old cohort converge and at 10 years of age where the intake assessment of the 10 year old cohort and the follow-up assessment of the 7 year old cohort converge.

In addition to this convergence of child measures within the URCAFS project, careful interdigitation of assessment has been planned with the Rochester Developmental Psychopathology Project (RDPP), under the directorship of Dr. Arnold Sameroff and Dr. Melvin Zax of the University of Rochester and the Rochester Early Childhood Study (REC) under the directorship of Dr. Fredric Jones and Dr. Arnold Sameroff. These two projects constitute a combined longitudinal study of risk, control and normative samples of children in which assessments for varying groups of subjects focus upon a broad range of contextual, behavioral and interactional variables within the child-rearing system. Data collection begins prenatally with the mother, and further assessments occur with the mother and child immediately after birth, and at 4 months, 1 year, 2-1/2 years, and 4 years after birth. Assessment of social competence of all of these subjects at 2-1/2 and 4 years of age utilizes the RABI (Forms A and B). This assessment of the RDPP/REC "high-risk" and control samples dovetails at 4 years of age with the 4 year old cohort of URCAFS so that the assessment of social competence in children utilizing the RABI in these two projects spans the age range of 2-1/2 years to 13 years. Table 1 depicts this scheme of interdigitation and convergence of child assessment based upon the various forms of the RABI.

In addition, various other major "high-risk" projects are employing the RABI which should increase the comparability of findings and make possible the pooling of subjects across ongoing "high-risk" studies. Subsequent to a "high-risk" mini-conference on child and adult assessment held in Rochester in November, 1974, "high-risk" projects at the University of St. Louis School of Medicine under the direction of Dr. E.J. Anthony ("Adolescents and Adults at Genetic Risk for Psychosis") and at the University of Minnesota under the direction of Dr. Norman Garmezy ("Project Competence")

Table 1

Convergence in the assessment of childhood social competence utilizing the Rochester Adaptive Behavior Inventory (RABI) within the University of Rochester Child and Family Study (URCAFS) and overlap in assessment between URCAFS and th Rochester Developmental Psychopathology Project and the Rochester Early Childhood Study (RDPP/REC), The Family and Child Development Study (Harvard), Project Competence (Minnesota), Adolescents and Adults at Genetic Risk for Psychosis (St. Louis) and the UCLA Family Project (UCLA).

| RABI Form | Age of Assessment | RDPP/ REC | URCAFS 4 year Cohort | URCAFS 7 year Cohort | URCAFS 10 year Cohort | Harvard | Minne- sota | St. Louis | UCLA |
|---|---|---|---|---|---|---|---|---|---|
| A | 2-3½ | X | | | | | | | |
| B | 3½-5 | X | X | | | | | | |
| C | 5-8½ | | X | X | | X | | | |
| D | 8½-12 | | | X | X | X | X | | |
| E | 12-18 | | | | X | | | X | X |

have opted to utilize the RABI in the follow-up of their respective risk samples which were first seen in early and middle childhood. Other projects are utilizing variations of the RABI which should also produce comparable data. For example, the UCLA Family Project under the direction of Dr. Eliot Rodnick and Dr. Michael Goldstein has utilized a forerunner of the RABI, form E (13-16 years old), in its assessment of their adolescent "risk" samples (Jones, 1974) and the Family and Child Developmental Study at Harvard Medical School under the direction of Dr. Henry Gurnebaum has utilized a combined version of forms C and D (7 and 10 years old) in their assessment of a "risk" sample spanning middle childhood.

It should be noted, however, that the assessment of social competence in children with its emphases upon the development of the RABI is only a part of a broader assessment of the social-emotional functioning of the child in URCAFS. Other procedures include a psychiatric diagnostic evaluation, a pediatric neurological examination, a multi-variate assessment of intelligence along with preliminary visual and auditory screening examinations, an extensive assessment of the child's functioning in school based upon school records and peer and teacher ratings, a normative test of object conservation and a related Piagetian-based assessment of social egocentrism, projective testing which includes the Rorschach, TAT and Foulds test, the Children's Manifest Anxiety Scale, and the Missouri Children's Behavior Checklist. In addition, the children participate in various laboratory family interaction tasks including a parent-child free-play interaction, a referential communication task, and the consensus Rorschach which provide added opportunity for direct observation of the child's behavior in a variety of settings.

## BACKGROUND

A review of instruments available for assessing social competence throughout childhood during the design phase of URCAFS highlighted some serious shortcomings of available assessment devices for meeting the needs of the convergent longitudinal design planned for the project. Most serious was the lack of any parallel series of adaptive behavior inventories or symptom scales which might provide analogous assessments from 4 through 13 years of age. The demand for a high degree of interdigitation of measurement at points of convergence in the convergent longitudinal design therefore ruled out the use of available measures.

A second drawback in available assessment instruments was their use of a checklist or rating scale format in which the informant was forced to make judegments between response intervals that were either undefined or defined by standard labels such as "always," "sometimes," and "never," etc. These two formats, while quick and inexpensive to administer as clinical screening devices, have a number of liabilities for longitudinal research. As Novick, Rosen-feld, Bloch and Dawson (1966) have pointed out, such formats introduce error due to (a) the high reading level required on many items, (b) the common requirement to make judgments along abstract dimensions which requires skills often lacking in informants, (c) a typically long and repetitive format which produces fatigue and rapid or casual responding, (d) the susceptibility of such judgments to response sets such as acquiescence or denial and, in the case of rating scales, a tendency to score toward the center or extremes, (e) the lack of a clearly specified time referent, and (f) the lack of a procedure of self-correction or erroneous responses due to misperception of the child's behavior or misinterpretation of the intent of the item. One additional shortcoming not mentioned by Novick et al. which is particularly serious when any kind of rating scale is involved, is the lack of specific, quantitative definitions of scalar intervals so that informants are not forced to rely on personal, idio-syncratic norms in order to estimate what might constitute "often" or "seldom" or "too much" or "too little."

The amount of error variance introduced into an in-strument in these various ways was unacceptable for the purposes of the present project since it would "muddy" the data upon which the demonstration of convergence would be based and would therefore greatly reduce the likelihood of successful convergence. Data analysis of behavioral surveys at the descriptive level is typically via factor analysis or some other multivariate procedure that reduces a large number of specific and relatively unstable single items to a manageable number of more stable composite variables such as factors or clusters. Yet multivariate procedures such as factor analysis are seriously affected by the presence of large amounts of error variance in the data which compounds

geometrically with the extraction of each additional factor.
Consequently, the factoring of behavioral survey data has
typically produced either factor solutions with many factors
which lack clarity, interpretability and replicability or
few factors which, while interpretable, lack differentiation. This situation has led Peterson (1960, 1965) and
Walker (1967) to assert that the only factors which show up
consistently in the literature which produce high interjudge
agreement on similarity of content are the "broad" factors
variously named "externalizing" (activity, approach, extro-
version, or when defined by symptoms, acting out, aggression,
delinquency or under-socialization) and "internalizing"
(control, withdrawal, introversion, or when defined by
symptoms, inhibition, neuroticism, or oversocialization).

The demands of the present study were for a highly
differentiated picture of the children's adaptive behavior
repertoire which was analogous at adjacent age periods so
that a measure of a given domain of behavior at one age
period could be shown to converge or be similar to a pur-
ported measure of the same domain of behavior measured at a
later age period. This meant that the instruments used had
to be not only parallel in design at adjacent age periods
but also had to produce analogous factor structures. Using
conventional procedures, one would have to choose between
either the convergence of "broad" factors which could be
clearly identified from two sets of data at adjacent age
periods or the use of more differentiated factor structures
which would probably not replicate at adjacent age periods.
This consideration, once again, necessitated the development
of a new set of assessment instruments, ones which could
generate "clean" data capable of producing both a differentiated picture of adaptive behavior as well as a similar
picture at adjacent age periods.

As a means of avoiding the above mentioned sources of
contamination and error in the data, the RABI employs a
fundamentally different format than that typically used in
behavioral surveys. The format is that of a clinical interview of the parents based upon many specific, behaviorally
oriented questions. Each question is accompanied by a scale
specific to that time, each point of which is operationally
defined. Questions are scored by the interviewer rather the
parent after careful probing of each question. A standard
set of interviewing procedures is used to obtain sufficient
information to produce a clear and unequivocal scoring of

the item. Since this process of "cross examining" the
parents eliminates most of the sources or error mentioned by
Novick et al., the RABI is freed of many of the biases
typically attributed to parental reports of ongoing child
behavior. This assessment, therefore, capitalizes on the
major strength of the parental report in that it is based
upon the observation of an extremely large sample of behavior. The various forms of the RABI contain from 110 to
145 items. Identical items and scales are used on adjacent
forms of the RABI wherever possible, and items are retained
on forms for all ages well beyond that in which the behavior
in question might be expected to appear or drop out in an
effort to facilitate the convergence of adjacent forms.
Consequently, there is in excess of 70% item overlap between
all adjacent forms of the RABI.

The composition of the RABI was derived from the results
of longitudinal high-risk research, the extensive body of
factor analytic studies of various adaptive behavior scales
and symptom checklists, and applied behavioral research on
aggression. To begin with, critical aspects of the assessment of social competence in children have been delineated
by recent "high-risk" research at UCLA and at the University
of Minnesota. Data from the UCLA Family Project (Goldstein,
Judd, Rodnick, Alkire, & Gould, 1968; Jones, 1973, 1974)
have underlined the relative importance of the child's
social functioning within the home as an index of competence.
These findings also underscore the importance of assessing
competence globally as well as in terms of specific functions.
First, due to the exploratory nature of the study and its
explicit interest in pathogenic family interaction patterns,
adaptive adequacy was assessed in a wide spectrum of stimulus situations both inside and outside the home. And,
secondly, due to pilot data indicating that summed measures
of social competence were difficult to equate with psychopathology in a more clinical sense, a single global rating
of "level of pathology" was developed at intake and follow-
up in addition to the spectrum of social competence meaures.
Evaluation of the follow-up data for the first 24 male
subjects showed three indices to correlate highly with the
global rating of level of pathology outcome. They were the
global rating of level of pathology at intake (r=.58) and
two measures of the extent of the child's belligerence
toward his parents over issues of autonomy and irresponsi-
bility (r=.45 and .46). On the global rating two-thirds of

the least adequate group at follow-up were also members of
the least adequate group at intake, subjects who at both
points in time exhibited behavior that stood out as being
extremely maladaptive or bizarre.

Data from the Minnesota Vulnerability Research Project
(Achenback, 1966; Garmezy, 1970) has also helped delineate
major aspects of the patterning of adaptive behavior during
childhood. Work by the Minnesota group in isolating age-
appropriate behavioral predictors of psychological adequacy
has attempted to extend into childhood those measures of
social competence in adults which have been most valuable in
predicting the outcome of hospitalization due to schizophrenia. In research which has attempted to isolate in-
dicants of good vs. poor premorbid adjustment in hospitalized adults, two systems of partialing subject variance have
repeatedly demonstrated significant predictive power. The
first, typified by the Phillips Scale of Premorbid Adjustment (Phillips, 1953), conceptualizes social competence as
the sum of adequacy of functioning in three major behavioral
domains: economic (academic achievement and job level and
stability), social, and psychosexual. The second, developed
in the work of Phillips and Rabinovitch (1958), contrasts
subjects along the dimensions of internalization vs. ex-
ternalization. Extending the work of Phillips and Rabinovitch, Achenback (1966) found patterns of "internalizing"
and "externalizing" behavior to account for most of the
common variance in a factor analysis of childhood symptom
data obtained from clinic records.

As mentioned earlier, this patterning of symptoms by
factor analysis has been replicated repeatedly in the psychological literature, and this literature was the second major
source of input into the construction of the RABI. Valuable
precedents were available in both the general developmental
literature (Cattell & Gruen, 1953; Emmerich, 1964, 1966) and
in the clinical literature dealing with the adaptive behavior
of children in schools (Alkire, 1969; Conners, 1969; Digman,
1963; Emmerich, 1966; Kohn & Rosman, 1972; Ross, Lacy &
Parton, 1965; Walker, 1967), in the home with parents (Collins,
Maxwell & Cameron, 1962; Conners, 1970; Dreger, 1964;
Jenkins & Glickman, 1946; Miller, 1967; Patterson, 1964;
Peterson, 1961; Schaefer, 1971), and specifically with
delinquents (Peterson, Quay, & Tiffany, 1961; Quay & Quay,
1965; Stott, 1960). This literature has served not only to
guide the development of the general outlines of the RABI,

but it has also suggested many "narrow" factors pertaining to the adaptive behavior of children and specific items by which to define them. These precedents have been used as the basis for "building in" comparable factor structures in the various forms of the RABI throughout the childhood years.

A third major source of input into the construction of RABI items was the social learning literature on aggressive and oppositional behavior within the home. Work by Patterson and his associates has described the development of a reciprocal reliance upon "pain control tactics" by parent and child as basic to the shaping and maintenance of aggressive and oppositional behavior in children (Patterson, 1970, 1971). This pattern, which Patterson refers to as "the coercion cycle," tends to be highly stable over time due to the unique pattern of mutual reinforcement delivered by the participating parties to each other. This interaction pattern resembles that of many of the families of the least competent children in the UCLA Family Project whose children were described as being highly belligerent, oppositional and irresponsible. Work by Patterson (1974) has also documented ways in which high-rate problematic behaviors such as oppositionalism and belligerence are shaped into producing low-rate high-intensity deviant behaviors which might be described clinically as extreme or bizarre. This literature in conjunction with the UCLA findings placed a high priority upon assessing the children's patterns of maladaptive behavior with their parents within the home, particularly in regard to aggressive, oppositional and irresponsible behavior patterns.

On the basis of the literature cited above and related studies, it was possible to develop some preliminary assumptions concerning those patterns of behavior in childhood which might indicate vulnerability. On the basis of the UCLA Family Project data (Jones, 1974) and the Social Learning literature as well as school data collected by Norman Watt and his associates (Watt, 1972), patterns of extreme oppositionalism and aggression within the home or school might well be regarded as signs of risk. On the basis of these two separate sets of findings from home and school settings, one might expect that children who "acted out" in the home would do the same in school. However, Wahler (1975) has produced data based upon repeated observations of specific behavioral categories in home and school settings which indicate that specific deviant behaviors are highly situation specific. Nevertheless, we would expect marked "acting out" in the home setting to correlate with dysfunction in school in either academic or behavioral areas or both, although the specific nature of the problem behaviors may be different between settings.

Data from the UCLA Family Project also suggest some hypotheses relating internalizing symptom patterns to the child's school functioning (Jones, 1974). In the UCLA adolescent clinic sample, subjects with marked patterns of passivity who tended not to confront parents but who also did little of what was expected of them around the home presented a nearly universal picture of underachievement in school. Once again, while specific patterns of behavior might be expected to vary greatly from child to child, we would predict some moderate level correlations between internalizing behavior patterns as perceived by the parents and poor or apathetic performance at school.

An additional assumption based on the findings of the UCLA Family Project (Jones, 1974) and that of Masterson (1967) is that the presence of any extreme or bizarre behavior pattern or extreme incompetence in many areas of functioning is highly stable across time and a most ominous sign of vulnerability. As mentioned above, Jones (1974) in conducting a four year follow-up of a clinic sample of adolescents found that two-thirds of the most disturbed subgroup of subjects, those who showed some form of extreme or bizarre behavior, were among the most disturbed subgroup of subjects four years later and were showing signs of marked psychopathology or overt decompensation. Masterson as well produced similar data showing that, from adolescence to adulthood, the more incompetent individuals indeed do not "grow out of it." Since the Global Rating of Psychopathology from the RABI contains a broad spectrum of information which includes anecdotal comments from the parents about extreme patterns of behavior, we expect to find stronger correlations between the level of school functioning and the Global Rating of Psychopathology than from more limited measures of internalizing or externalizing patterns of behavior.

Assumptions concerning the continuity of specific areas of functioning across time in the children are more difficult to develop since so little is known about developmental changes in the composition of the child's behavioral re-

pertoire over time. For those factors which have a clear
"health/sickness" polarity inherent in the items, any
precipitous movement toward the "sickness" end would
naturally be regarded as a possible sign of risk, although
the meaning of such shifts would have to be interpreted in
the light of follow-up data. However, the methodology
available for describing, analyzing, and interpreting longitudinal changes in the rates of children's behaviors is in
its infancy. Recent reviews of the developmental literature
by Kessen, Haith, and Salapatek (1970) and by Sameroff and
Chandler (1975) have concluded that there is minimal evidence for continuity in development in spite of our common
sense view that such stabilities must exist. Consequently,
Sameroff and Chandler argue for an abandonment of unifactorial
models of causation in favor of a more complex transactional
model. The University of Rochester Child and Family Study,
the Rochester Developmental Psychopathology Project and the
Rochester Early Childhood Study and other high risk projects,
many of which utilize the RABI, should provide an opportunity
to test out a variety of models for describing various kinds
of longitudinal continuity and discontinuity in the development of both normal and deviant behavior.


                              PROCEDURES


     The RABI is administered as a clinical interview in a
conversational manner allowing the subject freedom to elaborat
and to pursue related issues. Items are paraphrased and
examples given where necessary to insure that the parents
have a clear understanding of the intent of the question
and a consistent understanding of the definitions of key
terms. Interviewers are trained in skills of clinical interviewing and probing of specific response categories as well
as protocol scoring prior to their interviewing of subjects
so that they can produce a protocol scorable by a blind
scorer at 90 percent item agreement. Probing of questions
focuses upon clarifying the meaning of questions and upon
eliciting sufficient information to permit scoring of the
items with a high degree of confidence. Probing typically
seeks examples of the behavior in question on the part of
the index child and specifications of "how many?," "how
often?," and "with whom?" Where more abstract judgment is
required, informants are presented with a forced choice
after initial probing to ascertain that portion of the scale

in which the judgment should fall. Finally, if difficulty
persists, the interviewer presents a verbal description of
the "kind of child" which might typify neighboring response
categories, and the informants are asked to choose the one
most like their child (i.e., a matching task). Scales are
bipolar on many items to permit the quantification of competence as well as incompetence so that a more thorough
picture of the balance of the subject's behavioral assets
and liabilities may be obtained. In addition, each form of
the RABI has a specified time frame ranging from 6 months
(forms A and B) to one year (forms C, D, and E) within which
behavioral assessment is limited.

Following the administration of the RABI to the parents,
a summary of information contained in the RABI is prepared.
In URCAFS this summary consists of a one-page (single-
spaced) written synopsis of all item responses and anecdotal
comments made by the parents called a "Thumbnail Sketch."
In the normative work, the synopsis is shortened to a list
of behavioral assets and liabilities according to standard,
predetermined categories. The purpose of these procedures
is both to summarize the quantitative information in the
RABI and to preserve the richness of information contained
in the anecdotal narrative of the parents which may accompany the items. This "RABI summary" has been most worthwhile
as a means of recording anecdotal reports of low frequency,
high intensity symptomatic behaviors which might be quite
meaningful from a clinical point of view but which are often
excluded from multivariate data reduction procedures.

From this "Thumbnail Sketch" (URCAFS) or from the list
of assets and liabilities (normative) the interviewers then
make their Global Rating of Psychopathology. The "Global
Rating" is made on a five-point scale adapted from Glidewell,
Domke, and Kantor (1963) comprised of the following five
categories:

  1.  Above average adjustment:  a happy child who tends
  to be superior in his relationships with others and in
  his accomplishments. Minor problems are overshadowed
  by his considerable strengths.

  2.  No significant problems:  a child who is generally
  happy and accomplishes reasonably well the things that
  usually go with his age and level of development. A
  few slight problems may be present but he handles them
  adequately.

3.   Sub-clinically disturbed:   a child who is not as
happy as he might be and has moderate difficulties
getting on.   Growing up represents something of a
struggle.

4.   Clinically disturbed:   a child who has, or, at his
present rate is likely to have, serious problems of
adjustment and needs clinical help because of such
problems. Certain aspects of his relationships with
others and/or his accomplishments are markedly deficient
in spite of some compensating social assets.

5.   Seriously disturbed:   extreme or bizarre behavior
or problems of adjustment that are intense and over-
shadow social skills which are limited and generally
inadequate.

Reliability of scoring has been assessed in two separate
studies for both the RABI items and for the Global Rating of
Psychopathology. Reliability data is available for the first
66 subjects of URCAFS (forms B, C and D) as well as for a
normative sample of 162 two and one-half year old males
(form A). Assessment of reliability for the items of the
RABI protocol was derived from the blind scoring of audiotape
recordings of RABI interviews by research staff members
trained in the administration of the RABI.  Assessment of
reliability for the Global Rating of Psychopathology was
based upon the blind scoring by members of the research
staff of the two types of summaries of the subjects' behavior
the Thumbnail Sketch in URCAFS and the listing of the subject's behavioral assets and liabilities in the normative
work.  Thus, in URCAFS, reliability of the Global Rating
represents independent blind ratings from a common summary
(the Thumbnail Sketch), whereas with the normative sample,
reliability represents independent blind ratings from
independently constructed summaries.

Reliability of RABI item scoring in URCAFS was assessed
on approximately every seventh protocol (10/66), and reliability of the Global Rating was assessed for 26 of the 66
subjects.  Reliability was calculated for the RABI items in
terms of the percent item agreement. On the ten protocols
for which reliability of item scoring was assessed, the
median percent item agreement was 94 percent with a range of
87 percent to 96 percent. For the Global Rating, scorers
agreed on 24 of 26 ratings for 92 percent agreement.

Reliability of RABI item scoring for the normative sample of 2 1/2 year old males was also conducted on approximately every seventh protocol (21/162), and reliability of the Global Rating was assessed for 20 subjects. Reliability was calculated for the RABI items both as a percent item agreement and as a correlation between item scores on the 21 sets of protocols. The median percent item agreement was 93 percent with a range of 80 percent to 99 percent. The median intercorrelation between the same 21 sets of protocols was .97 with a range of .93 to .99. Percent item agreement is obviously a conservative estimate of reliability for the RABI. This is due, most likely, to the fact that, on the basis of the amount of information generated by the interview, independently derived item scores almost never disagree by more than one scalar interval. For the Global Rating, scorers agreed on 17 of 20 for 85 percent agreement. Apparently rating from a common summary generated somewhat higher agreement than rating from separately derived summaries (92 vs. 85 percent).

Although inter-rater agreement on the Global Rating was high, all raters were members of the author's research staff who had been fully trained in RABI procedures. Since several major "high-risk" projects have opted to utilize the RABI in an effort to facilitate the comparison and pooling of data, reliability between projects has been a major concern. In an effort to standardize interviewing and rating procedures, staff members of projects utilizing the RABI have been trained in Rochester whenever possible. To further standardize the Global Rating score, actuarial procedures based upon weighted and summed item scores are being developed and have been completed for form A. Using this score as a reference point, investigators can then generate an "adjusted" Global Rating based upon anecdotal information obtained during the interview if they so desire.

PRELIMINARY FINDINGS

Although the various forms of the RABI were developed during the years 1973-1975 and have therefore been in use only a short time, some preliminary findings are available from the norming for males of form A (2-3 1/2 years) and from preliminary data analyses for URCAFS. These findings provide at least a glimpse of what one might expect from ongoing normative and "risk" research.

Normative Studies: Preliminary data analysis at the descriptive level has been completed for a normative white, male, middle-class sample of 162 children (form A). Factor analysis was performed on 100 of the 110 RABI items with 10 items being omitted due to missing data since several toilet training and sibling oriented items were not applicable in many cases. Items were excluded if they were unanswered over 5 times, and item grand means were substituted for what little missing data remained. A varimax criterion of oblique rotation was used in the factor analysis and a factor loading cutoff of .35 was used for the inclusion of items into a factor. No items were omitted from the factor analysis due to small item response variance because of the investigators' interest in obtaining at least one factor describing extreme or bizarre behavior (which is infrequent by definition) as a possible potent predictor of psychological vulnerability. Factor solutions extracting 2 through 15 factors were run, and the 10-factor solution was chosen on the basis of inspection as providing a maximum of behavioral differentiation with a maximum of factor clarity and interpretability.

Factor analysis of the RABI produced a relatively clear and highly differentiated profile of the adaptive behavior repertoire of the 2-1/2 year old male. Table 2 presents items in each factor and their factor loadings. The 10 factors of the preferred varimax solution were labelled in terms of the negative or pathological end of the item scales. The factors were: (1) angry, oppositional, defiant; (2) social isolation; (3) easily upset, complaining; (4) quiet, sad; (5) fearful of strangers and other caretakers; (6) dependent, demanding; (7) anxious; (8) strange or extreme behavior; (9) fantasy play and feminine preference; and (10) immature, unhappy.

All factors were correlated with the Global Rating of Psychopathology to provide an estimate of the relative contribution of these various problem areas to the Global Rating Score. Factors which correlated significantly with the Global Rating of Psychopathology were Factor 1, Angry, Oppositional, Defiant ($r=.45$, $p<.01$), Factor 2, Social Isolation ($r=.18$, $p<.05$), Factor 7, Anxious ($r=.22$, $p<.01$), and Factor 8, Strange or Extreme Behavior ($r=.27$, $p<.01$). The correlations of the factors with the Global Rating of Psychopathology may represent nothing more than the relative

Table 2

RABI Factors for 2 1/2 Year Old Males With
Variable Number, Meaning and Factor Loadings

| No. | Meaning | Loading |
|-----|---------|---------|

Factor 1:  Angry, Oppositional, Defiant

| No. | Meaning | Loading |
|-----|---------|---------|
| 79 | gets angry or tantrums when he cannot get his own way | .74 |
| 78 | is often oppositional and defiant toward parents | .65 |
| 73 | gets angry or tantrums when parents stop him from doing something he wants to do | .63 |
| 72 | parents describe him as stubborn | .60 |
| 24 | gets very upset at play if he doesn't get his own way | .58 |
| 19 | bosses peers and insists on having his way | .57 |
| 71 | disobeys when parents tell him to stop doing something | .57 |
| 80 | often tantrums | .57 |
| 84 | becomes oppositional when parents try to push him to do something | .56 |
| 70 | does not accept prohibitions from parents | .55 |
| 53 | gets angry with other kids, is easily provoked | .52 |
| 69 | is oppositional when asked to do something by parents | .49 |
| 74 | when he gets upset at parents, he stays upset for a long time | .46 |
| 20 | is not friendly in relating to other children | .45 |
| 83 | often kicks or hits parents | .43 |
| 21 | has difficulty sharing toys | .40 |
| 86 | resents criticism by parents, talks back | .39 |

Table 2 (Con't.)

| No. | Meaning | Loading |
|-----|---------|---------|
| 51 | tends to be sulky or sad | .38 |
| 77 | gets upset when play is interrupted by routines | .36 |
| 55 | is generally loud and boisterous, obnoxious | .35 |

Factor 2:  Social Isolation

| | | |
|-----|---------|---------|
| 9 | usually plays alone | .73 |
| 10 | spends most of his time playing by himself | .69 |
| 11 | has few friends in neighborhood | .63 |
| 92 | members of the family tend not to show affection openly | .54 |
| 95 | is not curious about sex and never asks where babies come from | .42 |
| 14 | rarely has fun in an exuberant fashion | .38 |
| 94 | the family rarely does enjoyable activities together weekly | .35 |

Factor 3:  Easily Upset, Complaining

| | | |
|-----|---------|---------|
| 40 | often comes to mother crying or complaining about being hurt at play | .55 |
| 47 | gets upset when he breaks something or does something wrong | .48 |
| 18 | gets upset and cries easily from teasing or bullying at play | .46 |
| 81 | demands that mother get him things he is capable of getting for himself | .40 |

Table 2 (Con't.)

| No. | Meaning | Loading |
|-----|---------|---------|

Factor 3 (con't.)

| 52 | rarely gets thrilled or squeals with laughter at play | .38 |
| 26 | often complains about bodily aches and pains | .36 |
| 75 | parents criticize rather than explain when reprimanding | .36 |
| 76 | when parents scold, the child gets upset | .35 |

Factor 4:  Quiet, Sad

| 54 | is usually passive and quiet | .61 |
| 56 | is rarely talkative | .58 |
| 55 | is rarely loud or boistrous | .46 |
| 12 | prefers to play by himself when he could be playing with other kids | .45 |
| 51 | tends to be sad and rarely smiles | .36 |
| 28 | has poor health and is often sick | .35 |

Factor 5:  Fearful of Strangers and Other Caretakers

| 37 | is very shy or even hides when meeting a strange adult | .69 |
| 5 | withdraws or refuses to interact with other caretakers | .64 |
| 1 | cries, clings and is upset when left with other caretakers | .62 |
| 2 | stays upset for a long time when left with other caretakers | .59 |

Table 2 (Con't.)

| No. | Meaning | Loading |
|-----|---------|---------|

Factor 5 (Con't.)

41  stays close to mother and does not explore
    in stores, parks, and public places                .51

36  when outside of the home, he becomes afraid
    when mother is out of his sight                    .48

Factor 6:  Dependent, Demanding

39  always follows mother around the house and
    likes to be near her                               .56

68  always wants to be "mother's little helper"        .51

42  usually seeks mother's help to do anything
    that is difficult                                  .50

43  constantly demands mother's attention to
    play or interact                                   .50

44  is a very "finicky" eater                          .45

31  often has nightmares                               .43

45  has to be coaxed or spoon fed at most meals        .41

46  has an aversion to getting messy at play           .35

Factor 7:  Anxious

29  tends to be tense, jittery and nervous             .60

90  the family is not a close family                   .48

35  is afraid of the dark                              .44

65  has had a period during which he acted
    unusually upset                                    .42

31  often has nightmares                               .39

30  has nervous habits                                 .37

Table 2 (Con't.)

| No. | Meaning | Loading |
|-----|---------|---------|

### Factor 8: Strange or Extreme Behavior

| No. | Meaning | Loading |
|-----|---------|---------|
| 62 | has expressed ideas or fantasies that worry parents or seem strange | .56 |
| 97 | when entertaining himself, he sometimes engages in strange or bizarre behavior | .50 |
| 88 | he rarely shares his experiences or activities with parents | .48 |
| 64 | often seems to be involved in aimless activity or "off somewhere else" | .45 |
| 25 | has been willfully destructive of toys and property | .44 |
| 7 | rarely goes out on errands, visits, etc. with mother | .42 |
| 23 | is often hurtful or cruel to other children | .40 |

### Factor 9: Fantasy Play and Feminine Preference

| No. | Meaning | Loading |
|-----|---------|---------|
| 67 | often engages in imaginary play | .76 |
| 66 | has imaginary playmates and adventures | .68 |
| 99 | plays role of girl or mommy in make-believe play | .46 |
| 100 | has made statements about wishing he were a girl | .42 |

### Factor 10: Immature, Unhappy

| No. | Meaning | Loading |
|-----|---------|---------|
| 61 | acts babyish for his age | .49 |
| 93 | is not an affectionate child | .44 |
| 32 | is a restless sleeper | .37 |
| 49 | is generally unhappy or down | .37 |
| 64 | often seems involved in aimless activity | .35 |

weights which the scorers tend to assign these various
domains of behavior in their ratings. However, it may also
indicate that the problem behaviors described in factors 1,
2, 7, and 8 tend to be either more pervasive characterlogi-
cal features of the child's behavior repertoire (factors 1,
2 and 7) or particularly alarming features of the child's
behavior (factor 8).

The results of this normative work indicate that the
RABI is a highly reliable instrument for assessing social
competence at 2-1/2 years of age which produces a well
differentiated picture of the child's adaptive behavior
repertoire. The factor clarity and high degree of behavioral
differentiation which was obtained from such young children
is noteworthy. Apparently, the adaptive behavior repertoire
of the child reaches a high degree of elaboration by 2-1/2
years of age and can hardly be characterized as simplistic
relative to later childhood. This high level of description
at such an early age suggests that the RABI format has been
successful to a considerable degree in minimizing the types
of error variance which typically "muddy" the factor solutions of adaptive behavior and symptom inventories.

Description of the URCAFS Sample:  At the present time
the RABI has been administered to a considerable portion of
both the normative and URCAFS "high-risk" samples of 4 and 7
year old males, and a comparison of the distribution of
these subjects on the RABI Global Rating of Psychopathology
may provide a means of determining the relative degree of
deficit, if any, of the "risk" children.  In the norming of
the RABI, subjects are chosen from newspaper reports of
birth in the Rochester area at the desired time interval
prior to testing, so the term "normative" with these samples
should be regarded in a statistical rather than a clinical
sense. Frequency distributions of the various normative and
"risk" samples are presented in Table 3.  Judging from these
data, the "risk" sample is markedly skewed toward the pathological end of the Global Rating of Psychopathology and may
therefore represent a significantly heightened degree of
vulnerability as compared with the normative sample of
children.  Roughly 28% of the "risk" sample is contained
in category 4 ("clinically disturbed") and category 5
("severely disturbed") of the Global Rating compared with
only 6% of the normative sample.  In contrast, only 46%
of the "risk" sample is contained in category 1 ("above

Table 3

Distribution of Four and Seven Year Old Normative and URCAFS
"High-Risk" Male Subjects on the Global Rating of
Psychopathology Derived from the RABI

| Global Rating | | Normative Subjects | | | URCAFS Subjects | | |
|---|---|---|---|---|---|---|---|
| | | 4 | 7 | Total | 4 | 7 | Total |
| 1 | N | 14 | 10 | 24 | 1 | 2 | 3 |
| | % | 13 | 13 | 13% | 4 | 10 | 7% |
| 2 | N | 63 | 49 | 112 | 10 | 8 | 18 |
| | % | 61 | 63 | 62% | 38 | 40 | 39% |
| 3 | N | 23 | 12 | 35 | 7 | 5 | 12 |
| | % | 22 | 16 | 19% | 27 | 25 | 26% |
| 4 | N | 4 | 6 | 10 | 6 | 5 | 11 |
| | % | 4 | 8 | 6% | 23 | 25 | 24% |
| 5 | N | 0 | 0 | 0 | 2 | 0 | 2 |
| | % | 0 | 0 | 0% | 8 | 0 | 4% |
| Total | N | 104 | 77 | 181 | 26 | 20 | 46 |

average adjustment") and category 2 ("no significant problems") of the Global Rating as compared with 75% of the
normative sample. This concentration of almost five times
more risk than normative subjects in the "disturbed" categories of the Global Rating attests not only to the likelihood of heightened vulnerability in the children but also
to the utility of the RABI and the Global Rating for purposes
of sample description in terms of a "health-sickness" dimensio

URCAFS Cross-Project Data Analysis:  Preliminary data
analysis on the first 66 URCAFS subjects revealed some relationships between the RABI data and the findings of other
investigators studying children's behavior in URCAFS which
support some preliminary hypotheses. These findings, however,
must be regarded as tentative due to the small sample size.

Most of the significant findings were obtained from the
broader or more encompassing measures of competence generated from the RABI. In addition to the Global Rating of
Psychopathology, indices of externalizing and internalizing
symptom patterns were obtained form the RABI for purposes of
preliminary analysis by clustering all items common to the
4, 7, and 10 year old forms of the RABI which dealt explicitly
with aggression or oppositionalism on the one hand and fear,
inhibition and social withdrawal on the other hand. Items
were eliminated from the clusters which failed to achieve a
corrected part/whole correlation on their respective clusters
exceeding the .01 level of significance. This clustering
was in lieu of factor analyses of larger normative samples
which are presently being collected. In addition to the
Global Rating and the two cluster scores from the RABI
(externalizing and internalizing), the cross-project data
analysis also included the factor scores from the Missouri
Children's Behavior Checklist or MCL (Sines, Pauker, Sines &
Owen, 1969) as additional meures of competence in the home
setting. The factor scores provided by the MCL are labelled
aggression, inhibition, hyperactivity, sleep disturbance,
somatic complaints and sociability.

As noted earlier, one major issue in vulnerability
research is the development of an adequate measure of child
competence and the assessment of their interrelationships.
To approach this problem, relations between the child competence measures of the author's research team (RABI and
MCL) and child competence measures collected by other URCAFS

child assessment teams were analyzed. Measures collected by
other URCAFS child research teams and reported here include
assessment of behavior within the school setting (Dr.
Lawrence Fisher) and I.Q. and social maturity assessment of
the child (Dr. James Heriot and Dr. Lawrence Space). School
measures include teacher and peer ratings of social and
intellectual competence in school, school grades and standardized achievement test scores and scores summarizing information derived from the child's school cumulative record.
I.Q. and social maturity assessment includes psychometric
assessment of intelligence on the WISC and parental judgments
of the child's I.Q. as well as an I.Q. estimate and social
maturity score derived from the Vineland Social Maturity
Scale. These findings are summarized in Table 4 below. All
school related findings are based on the 7 and 10 year old
cohorts only (n=54).

Major hypotheses supported by the data in Table 4 relate to the "broad band width" or more global measures of
child competence derived from the RABI and MCL. By far the
most and the largest correlations were between the Global
Rating of Psychopathology and the various measures of school
functioning and intelligence. In fact, the Global Rating
correlated significantly and in the expected direction with
nearly every peer and teacher rating, with grades and
achievement test scores, with cumulative record scores for
overall school adjustment and emotional stability and with
I.Q. and social maturity scores. This confluence of parent,
teacher and peer judgments as well as intelligence test
scores argues persuasively for the existence of a sizable
"G" factor of competence in addition to factors which are
situation specific.

The magnitude of the correlations between parental
reports of competence (RABI AND MCL) and the school measures
falls off as the unitary index of competence is partialled
into its component parts. The RABI cluster scores for
externalizing and internalizing symptom patterns, for
example, have relatively weak correlations with the school
measures as compared to the Global Rating. The factor
scores for the Missouri Checklist as well are small compared
to the Global Rating, and those which are largest come
from the two factors which account for most of the variance
in almost all symptom checklists, aggression and inhibition.
The number of significant correlations between more circum-

Table 4

Intercorrelations of Social Competence Measures from the RABI and Missouri Children's Behavior Checklist with Measures of Competence at School Based on Peer and Teacher Ratings, Grades, Achievement Testing, and Cumulative Records and with Intelligence and Social Maturity Assessments

| | N | RABI | | | MISSOURI CHECKLIST | | | | | |
|---|---|---|---|---|---|---|---|---|---|---|
| | | Global Rating | External-izing | Internal-izing | Aggression | Inhibition | Hyperac-tivity | Sleep dis-turbance | Somatic Complaint | Socia-bility |
| I. School: Peer Sociometric Rating | | | | | | | | | | |
| 1. Bright compliant student | 54 | -.29* | .02 | -.19 | -.21 | -.14 | -.14 | .16 | -.05 | -.06 |
| 2. Intrusive student | 54 | .21 | .22 | -.10 | .05 | -.02 | .15 | -.21 | -.15 | -.02 |
| 3. Dull student | 54 | .38** | .14 | -.20 | .13 | .18 | .11 | -.14 | -.04 | -.22 |
| 4. Friendly student | 54 | -.26* | -.07 | -.33** | -.16 | -.35** | -.17 | -.04 | -.09 | -.11 |
| II. School: Teacher Rating Scale | | | | | | | | | | |
| 1. Social competence | 53 | -.36** | -.23 | -.35** | -.35** | -.29 | -.07 | -.15 | -.14 | .00 |
| 2. Social compliance | 53 | -.32* | -.20 | .03 | -.18 | -.17 | -.23 | .23 | -.06 | .02 |
| 3. Cognitive competence | 53 | -.43** | -.15 | -.06 | -.21 | -.16 | -.20 | .10 | -.08 | .06 |
| 4. Motivation | 53 | -.39** | -.19 | -.06 | -.35** | -.34** | -.39** | .05 | -.09 | -.02 |
| 5. **Mean rating** | 53 | -.51** | -.23 | -.16 | -.30* | -.25 | -.31* | .09 | -.08 | .05 |
| **III. School: Peer Rating Scale (Mean)** | 54 | -.40** | -.13 | -.17 | -.16 | -.16 | -.21 | .10 | .02 | .02 |
| IV. School: Grades | | | | | | | | | | |
| 1. Total grades, numerical | 40 | -.38** | -.11 | -.19 | -.12 | .06 | -.18 | .07 | .18 | .14 |
| 2. Total grades, Language Arts | 45 | -.39** | -.22 | -.09 | -.25 | -.19 | -.12 | .02 | .19 | .17 |
| 3. Total grades, Social Studies | 36 | -.26 | -.17 | .08 | -.16 | -.05 | -.25 | -.06 | .30 | -.07 |
| V. School: Achievement Testing | | | | | | | | | | |
| 1. Total numerical | 38 | -.39* | -.04 | -.35** | -.04 | -.03 | -.10 | .19 | -.03 | .10 |
| 2. Total verbal | 42 | -.44** | -.04 | -.06 | -.16 | -.09 | -.11 | .14 | -.11 | .12 |
| 3. Composite score | 42 | -.43** | -.05 | -.21 | -.11 | -.06 | .16 | .16 | -.05 | .11 |
| VI. School: Cumulative Record Factors | | | | | | | | | | |
| 1. Work habits | 51 | .21 | -.17 | -.22 | .12 | .13 | -.21 | .15 | -.03 | -.05 |
| 2. Specific academic competencies | 43 | -.03 | -.01 | -.11 | .13 | .03 | -.14 | .38* | -.11 | -.00 |
| 3. Overall school adjustment | 48 | -.32* | -.14 | -.21 | -.06 | .08 | -.06 | .05 | -.13 | -.12 |
| 4. Emotional stability | 52 | -.30* | -.13 | -.18 | .07 | -.04 | -.28* | .25 | .09 | .01 |
| 5. Likability | 32 | -.15 | .04 | -.01 | -.17 | -.13 | .00 | -.07 | .27 | .04 |
| VII. Intelligence Assessment | | | | | | | | | | |
| 1. Full Scale WISC | 55 | -.33** | -.18 | -.16 | -.18 | -.21 | -.02 | -.02 | .00 | .11 |
| 2. Parental Estimate of I.Q. | 55 | -.29* | -.04 | -.07 | .06 | .07 | -.10 | .21 | .15 | .05 |
| 3. Vineland I.Q. Estimate | 55 | -.35** | -.21 | -.20 | -.08 | .06 | .12 | .12 | -.09 | .15 |
| III. Vineland Social Maturity Scale | 55 | -.17 | -.02 | .10 | -.17 | .07 | -.01 | .19 | -.05 | .26 |

p .01 = **   p .05 = *

scribed areas of competence on the MCL (hyperactivity, sleep disturbance, somatic complaint and sociability) does not exceed chance. On the basis of these data one might conclude that competence is a multifaceted and additive function. Since its form varies from situation to situation depending upon the stimulus and contingency characteristics of each situation, the chances of relating meaures in one setting to those in another setting probably increase in proportion to the number of aspects of competence which are pooled in the respective assessments. Correlations between various measures of intelligence such as the full scale WISC, parental estimate of I.Q. and the Vineland I.Q. estimate are also strongest for the Global Rating of Psychopathology. Once again, correlations between intelligence measures and more circumscribed domains of social competence wash out.

A related issue of importance is whether or not specific behaviors in one setting can be predicted from unique behavior patterns in another setting. Data relating to this question came primarily from the relationship between the two sets of internalizing and externalizing measures (RABI and MCL) and the various school meaures. It was hypothesized that children perceived as highly aggressive and disobedient in the home would be perceived as troublemakers and underachievers by teachers and would be disliked by peers. This prediction was particularly borne out by the correlations between the MCL factor of aggression and teacher perceptions of the child as being of low social competence ($r=-.35$, $p < .01$) and as having low motivation ($r=-.35$, $p < .01$). Teacher ratings of social compliance ($r=-.18$) and cognitive competence ($r=-.21$) were also suggestive of a generally negative teacher evaluation which was further reflected in the mean teacher rating score across all of the above categories ($r=-.30$, $p < .05$). This pattern of relationships most likely suggests that children who are perceived as aggressive by their parents at home manage to generate negative evaluations on the part of their teachers at school as well. However, correlations with peer ratings failed to follow the predicted pattern indicating, perhaps, that peer status is a far more complex phenomenon than is teacher approval which is more directly a function of the child's disruptiveness and motivation to work in class.

Correlations between measures of internalizing behavior (RABI) or inhibition (MCL) within the home and measures of school performance also followed predictions in terms of teacher ratings. Congruent with previous research (Jones, 1974), children with marked internalizing patterns of behavior were seen by their teachers as having relatively low general competence (r=-.35, p <.01 on the RABI and r=-.29, on the MCL) and as being unmotivated (r=-.34, p <.01, MCL). In addition, and also congruent with previous research on an adolescent sample (Jones, 1974), children exhibiting marked internalizing patterns of behavior had relatively low peer status and appeared somewhat socially isolated. Correlations between the "internalizing" or "inhibition" scores on the RABI and MCL and peer ratings of "friendly student" were -.33 on the RABI (p <.01) and -.35 on the MCL (p <.01).

In contrast to these correlations between the "broad band width" indices of competence in the home and the various school measures, all hypotheses of a more atomistic nature, relations between "narrow band width" factors from the MCL and specific behaviors at school, washed out. This supports the results of Wahler (1975) who failed to find significant correlations between highly circumscribed behavioral measures collected via naturalistic observation in the home and at school for clinic referred children. Apparently, the stimulus and contingency factors affecting specific elements of the behavior repertoire of children are different enough between these two settings to render a close matching of problematic behaviors of children at home and at school relatively unlikely.

## OVERVIEW

The development of the RABI represents an attempt to supply age-appropriate and comparable meaures of social competence throughout childhood in a form optimal for assessing continuities of behavior in longitudinal research. In so doing, the RABI attempts to capitalize on the observations of the informant who knows the child best, the parent, but free from many of the contaminants that often render parental reports dubious. Hopefully, this effort will ultimately do much to operationalize "risk" in terms of the child's functioning apart from the parents' psychiatric status. The capacity to separate "risk" from "nonrisk" children early in their lives is one of the basic prerequisites for systematic progress in prevention by the mental health professions. In addition, the capacity to assess competence or "risk" in a comparable fashion throughout childhood is a prerequisite for sophisticated outcome research that traces the course of social adaptation for treated and untreated "risk" children and their controls. The development of the Rochester Adaptive Behavior Inventory is an element in this endeavor which, conveniently, is in a form readily usable as a standard intake and follow-up interview in a child clinic. Hopefully, the RABI will help make "risk" and outcome research economically feasible within the ongoing functioning of many child treatment centers.

## REFERENCES

Achenback, T.M.  The classification of children's psychiatric symptoms: A factor analytic study. Psychological Monographs, 1966, 80, 6, (whole No. 615).

Alkire, A.A.  Social power and communication within families of disturbed and nondisturbed adolescents. Journal of Personality and Social Psychology, 1969, 13, 335-349.

Cattell, R.B. and Gruen, W.  The personality factor structure of 11-year old children in terms of behavior rating data. Journal of Clinical Psychology, 1953, 9, 256-266.

Collins, L.F., Maxwell, A.E., and Cameron, C.  A factor analysis of some child psychiatric clinic data. Journal of Mental Science, 1962, 108, 274-285.

Conners, C.K.  A teacher rating scale for use in drug studies with children. American Journal of Psychiatry, 1969, 126, 152-156.

Conners, C.K.  Symptom patterns in hyperkinetic, neurotic and normal children. Child Development, 1970, 41, 667-682.

Digman, J.M.  Principal dimensions of child personality as inferred from teachers' judgments. Child Development, 1963, 34, 43-60.

Dreger, R.M., Lewis, P.M., Rich, T.A., Miller, K.S., Reed, M.P., Overlade, D.C., Taffel, C., and Flemming, E.L. Behavior classification project. Journal of Consulting Psychology, 1964, 28, 1-13.

Emmerich, W.  Continuity and stability in early social devel-
    opment.  Child Development, 1964, 35, 311-332.

Emmerich, W.  Continuity and stability in early social develo
    ment, II.  Teacher ratings.  Child Development, 1966,
    37, 17-27.

Garmezy, N.  Vulnerable children:  Implications derived from
    studies of an internalizing-externalizing symptom dimens
    In Zubin, J. and Freedman, A.M. (Eds.), Psychopathology
    of adolescence.  New York:  Grune and Stratton, 1970,
    pp. 212-239.

Glidewell, J.C., Domke, H.R. and Kantor, M.B.  Screening in
    schools for behavior disorders:  use of mothers' reports
    of symptoms.  Journal of Educational Research, 1963, 56,
    508-515.

Goldstein, M.J., Judd, L.L., Rodnick, E.H., Alkire, A., and
    Gould, E.  A method for studying social influence and
    coping patterns within families of disturbed adolescent
    Journal of Nervous and Mental Disease, 1968, 147, 233-2

Holloway, H.D.  Reliability of the children's manifest anxie
    scale at the rural third grade level.  Journal of
    Educational Psychology, 1958, 49, 193-196.

Jenkins, R.L. and Glickman, S.  Common syndromes in child
    psychiatry.  American Journal of Orthopsychiatry, 1946,
    16, 244-245.

Jones, F.H.  Current methodologies for studying the develop-
    ment of schizophrenia:  A critical review.  Journal of
    Nervous and Mental Disease, 1973, 157, 154-178.

Jones, F.H.  The prediction of outcomes in early adulthood
    from measures of social competence, coping style, and
    overall level of psychopathology.  Journal of Nervous
    and Mental Disease, 1974, 159, 20-39.

Keller, E.D. and Rowley, V.N.  Junior high school and
    additional elementary school normative data for the
    children's manifest anxiety scale.  Child Development,
    1962, 33, 675-681.

Kessen, W., Haith, M.M. and Salapatek, P.H. Human infancy: A bibliography and guide, in P.H. Mussen (Ed.), Carmichael's Manual of Child Psychology, (3rd edition), Vol. 1, New York: Wiley, 1970, pp. 287-361.

Kohn, M. and Rosman, B.L. A social competence and symptom checklist for the preschool child: Factor dimensions, their cross-instrument generality, and longitudinal persistence. Developmental Psychology, 1972, 6, 430-444.

Masterson, K.F., Jr. The symptomatic adolescent 5 years later: He didn't grow out of it. American Journal of Psychiatry, 1967, 123, 1338-1345.

Miller, L.C. Dimensions of psychopathology in middle childhood. Psychological Reports, 1967, 21, 897-903.

Novick, J., Rosenfeld, E., Block, D.A. and Dawson, D. Ascertaining deviant behavior in childhood. Journal of Consulting Psychology, 1966, 30, 230-238.

Patterson, G.R. An empirical approach to the classification of disturbed children. Journal of Clinical Psychology, 1964, 20, 326-337.

Patterson, G.R., and Reid, J.B. Reciprocity and coercion: Two facets of social systems. In C. Neuringer and J. Michael (Eds.), Behavior modification in clinical psychology. New York: Appleton-Century-Crofts, 1970, pp. 133-177.

Patterson, G.R. and Cobb, J.A. A dyadic analysis of "aggressive" behaviors. In J.P. Hill (Ed.), Minnesota Sumposium on Child Psychology, Minneapolis: University of Minnesota Press, 1971, Vol. 5, pp. 72-129.

Patterson, G.R. A basis for identifying stimuli which control behaviors in natural settings. Child Development, 1974, 45, 900-911.

Peterson, D.R. The age generality of personality factors derived from ratings. Educational and Psychological Measurement, 1960, 20, 461-474.

Peterson, D.R.   Behavior problems of middle childhood.
    Journal of Consulting Psychology, 1961, 25, 205-209.

Peterson, D., Quay, H.C., and Tiffany, T.C.   Personality
    factors related to juvenile delinquency.  Child
    Development, 1961, 32, 355-372.

Peterson, D.R.   The scope and generality of verbally defined
    personality factors.  Psychological Review, 1965, 72,
    48-59.

Phillips, L.   Case history data and prognosis in schizo-
    phrenia.  Journal of Nervous and Mental Disease, 1953,
    117, 515-525.

Phillips, L., and Rabinovitch, M.S.   Social role and patterns
    of symptomatic behaviors.  Journal of Abnormal and Social
    Psychology, 1958, 57, 181-186.

Quay, J.C., and Quay, L.C.   Behavior problems in early ado-
    lescence.  Child Development, 1965, 36, 215-220.

Rolf, J.E.   The academic and social competence of children
    vulnerable to behavior pathologies.  Journal of
    Abnormal Psychology, 1972, 80, 225-243.

Ross, A.O.,Lacy, H.M., and Parton, D.A.   The development of
    a behavior checklist for boys.  Child Development, 1965,
    36, 1013-1027.

Sameroff, A.J., and Zax, M.   Perinatal characteristics of the
    offspring  of schizophrenic women.  Journal of Nervous
    and Mental Disease, 1973, 157, 191-199.

Sameroff, A.J., and Chandler, M.J.   Reproductive risk and the
    continuum of caretaker causality.  In F.D. Horowitz, M.,
    Hetherinton, S., Scarr-Salapatek and G. Siegel (Eds.),
    Review of child development research, Vol. 4, Chicago:
    SRCD, 1975, pp. 186-244.

Sameroff, A.J.   Psychological needs of the mother in early
    mother-infant interactions.  In G. Avery (Ed.),
    Neonatology:  Pathophysiology and management of the
    newborn.  New York: Lippincott, 1975, pp. 1023-1042.

Schaefer, E.S.   Converging conceptual models for maternal
    behavior and for child behavior.  In J.C. Glidewell (Ed.),
    Parental attitudes and child behavior.  New York:  Thomas,
    1961, pp. 124-146.

Sines, J.O., Pauker, J.D., Sines, L.K., and Owen, D.R.
    Identification of clinically relevant dimensions of
    children's behavior.  Journal of Consulting and
    Clinical Psychology, 1969, 33, 728-734.

Stott, D.H.   A new delinquency prediction instrument using
    behavioral indicants.  International Journal of
    Social Psychiatry, 1960, 6, 195-205.

Wahler, R.G.   Some structural aspects of deviant child be-
    havior.  Journal of Applied Behavior Analysis, 1975,
    8, 27-42.

Walker, R.N.   Some temperament traits in children as viewed
    by their peers, their teachers and themselves, Mono-
    graphs of the Society for Research in Child Development,
    1967, 32, 6 (whole No. 114).

Watt, N.F.   Longitudinal changes in the social behavior of
    children hospitalized for schizophrenia as adults.
    Journal of Nervous and Mental Disease, 1972, 155, 42-54.

GENERAL DISCUSSION OF SECTION III


Formal Discussant:  Leonard Heston

I want to make two rather obvious points that need to
be re-stated occasionally.  First, there is a very large
body of evidence that with respect to almost any behavioral
trait, the correlation between relatives is very high.  Even
given all the problems with our measures and all the dis-
claimers that we usually make, the correlation between relatives remains one of the strongest relationships in all of
biology.  Whether we're talking about diagnoses, IQ estimates
or even cruder scales measuring pathology of some kind, the
correlations between relatives are stronger, for example,
than are found in diabetes.  Now at the same time, there is
also great variability within families; that is, even in
families with all sorts of psychopathology, there will be
some members, who do extremely well.  There are also spora-
dic cases who do very poorly in otherwise healthy families.
Why this family clustering?  Why this vulnerability/invul-
nerability dimension?  Surely these are among the most critical questions that we can ask.  From this, it seems very
obvious to me that we must study relatives at any excuse,
any chance.  In most studies, sibships would be the natural
way to begin.  It seems to me that many studies including
many reported here, would be greatly strengthened by including
at least sibling pairs, even if the total number of subjects
studied were not changed.  Although there are some kinds of
studies in which families will be irrelevant, I think we
should think very carefully and several times before design-
ing family relationships out of our studies.

The second point I want to make relates to the two main
reasons for studying environment in schizophrenia.  The
first of these is to discover an environmental cause of
schizophrenia.  Nearly all of the research that's been done on
environmental factors in schizophrenia has been of this kind.
Now this is perfectly legitimate; it has not been productive,
but it is a perfectly legitimate sort of research to do.  Perhaps the study of amphetamine psychosis as a phenocopy of
schizophrenia and a few others have demonstrated sufficient
causes, but by and large the effort has not been a very productive one.  The second reason for studying environment in
schizophrenia is to discover the environmental events that

contribute to the gene-environment interaction. Now this, it seems to me, is an extremely practical enterprise. It's pertinent in view of what we do know and is a very sensible way to proceed. But to study environmental factors entering into the gene-environment interaction, the genotype must be controlled for. The essential question is, what environments act positively and negatively on vulnerable genotypes, and it's quite useless to ignore the genotype. Again, family relationships must be studied to do the research. There's no way to get at the answer that I see without taking this into consideration, and yet it very often is not. Although most high-risk studies in fact consider family relationships as a feature of risk, and I think that's very good, they tend not to state their findings in the gene-environment interaction framework.


Formal Discussant:  Arnold Sameroff

I want to discuss why it is that we see so little continuity in behavior when we'd like to see so much. Let me describe to you in very simplistic terms some models of development which have been typically used to study these issues. The first might be called the main effect or medical model. It is used, for example, in the standard nature vs. nurture position. On the nature side, it is argued that if a child has a good constitution, he's going to have a good outcome, independent of his environment, whether that be good or bad. If he has a bad constitution, then he'll have a bad outcome independent of his environment. On the nurture side, the view is that if the child has a good environment, then his outcome is going to be good, independent of whether his constitution is good or bad; and if his environment is bad, his outcome will be bad independent of his constitution.

We all recognize that these are simplistic views. Anyone who has searched for a single constitutional factor, whether schizophrenic genes or low IQ genes, in order to predict developmental outcomes, also finds people with exactly the same characteristics who do not end up as predicted. And similarly for many of the environmental variables, one finds exactly the same thing. There's no evidence that any single variable will predict developmental outcome. An improvement is made by adopting a second model, the interaction model. It's the one typically used in most developmental hypotheses.

An example are the hypotheses about environmental/consti-
tutional interaction.  If you have a good constitution and
a good environment, you'll have a good outcome.  If you
have a bad constitution, but you manage to get into a good
environment, you'll have some kind of medium outcome; and
if you have a good constitution but somehow you get into a
bad environment, you'll also have an intermediate outcome.

The diathesis stress theory of schizophrenia is another
example of this model.  That theory states that if a child
is born with a diathesis, a weakness of some sort, he is
constitutionally disadvantaged.  The level of stress in his
environment will then determine what his outcome will be.
This child will always carry that gene, that diathesis.  If
the stress environment goes over a certain threshold, at any
time, the child will break down.  Current models of IQ, such
as the Jensen model, are similar.  These theories propose that
blacks, for example, are limited by their genetic endowment.
It won't matter what kind of environment they get into, there
will be a maximum limit to their intellectual development.

The interactional model is an improvement statistically.
Most of our data have shown that if you take both environment
and constitution into account, you can do much better at
predicting than taking either one alone.  But the model has
two major difficulties.  The first is that it is a statistical model, that is, it tells you statistically what the probability for a deviant outcome is for each combination of
constitution and environment, but it doesn't explain how
those outcomes come about.  It doesn't explain what actually
happens when a child with one type of constitution gets
into one kind of environment, and why that combination produces a specific outcome.

But there's a more important criticism, the model assumes
that both constitution and environment are static in time,
a child has a good or bad constitution and that will always
be true; or conversely, that a child has a good or bad environment, and that will always be true.  On the contrary,
there is a great deal of research now showing that constitution and environment are in a constant transaction.  I
use the word "transaction" to focus attention on the mutual
interchanges between organism and environment over time.

I think the distinguished research of Dr. Thomas and
Dr. Rutter and their associates has shown this clearly.  For

example a mother who might originally be considered as quite
normal, might have a child with a specific negative characteristic, colic or whininess or prematurity, which would
convert this normal mother into a bad one. She may become
anxious, or guilty, or hostile towards the child and alter
her relation to the child. This may lead the child to become more difficult, more cranky, or more colicky, in turn
convincing the mother that she really has got a rotten kid,
which in turn will affect the next stage in the child's
development. In this kind of social transaction over time
one has to know at each point what is the nature of the
relationship between the child and its environment.

I think we need to use this transactional model more
frequently. One way is to study how children in general
change with age, and to determine why it is that some don't
change. There seems to be in the field of schizophrenia
research a consistent flip-flop in emphasis on either environment or constitution. At one time there were family
studies that focused on the environment, e.g., the schizo-
phrenogenic mother. Now we have a return to a constitutional emphasis found in the recent array of genetic studies.
The most telling of these genetic studies are where children of schizophrenic women who are adopted by non-schizophrenic women show a fairly high rate of later psychiatric
disorder. The implication is that little importance is
given to the character of the families these children get
into. What counts is the genetic endowment that the children
bring into the situation. We have found in our research at
Rochester, that severely mentally-ill mothers and their
babies may have many problems around the time of childbirth.
In our sample, of the 29 children born to schizophrenic women,
six were placed in either adoptive or foster homes, four of
these infants spent the newborn period in a special care
nursery: 3 because of premature births, while the fourth had
a heart murmur. This information provides a different picture of what kind of infant is going into the adoptive mother's
home. It's not always a child who was a normal, average
baby, bound to please any adoptive mother, but rather a child
coming out of a special care nursery, a premature infant who
may look different, who was delayed in getting into the
adoptive home, and who now presents the initial ingredient of
a stressful transactional relationship. The closer we study
the actual lives of our subjects, the more complexity we find
in their behaviors and in their interactions with others.

Open Discussion:

Rutter:  Yes, I agree, but surely the need is for
empirical means of determining whether or not these are
interaction or transaction effects, rather than reliance
or alternative conceptual models.  A simple analysis of 2
by 2 tables provides the means to do this.  Transaction
implies that the presence of one variable influences the
frequency of occurrence of another.  Interaction means that
the presence of one variable increases the effect of another
(i.e., the effect of the two variables in combination is
greater than the sum of the effects of the two when they occur
in isolation).  This may be illustrated by the analyses that
David Quinton and I (1976) undertook with respect to the
associations between chronic psychosocial disadvantage and
multiple hospital admission as independent variables and
later emotional disturbance as the dependent variable.  The
basic data are summarized in Table 1.  First, associations
may be looked at in the usual way.  Emotional disturbance
was twice as common in children from disadvantaged homes as
in those from more favored family circumstances (47% vs 22%;
i.e. q/r vs h/i).  Emotional disturbance was also associated
with multiple hospital admissions (12 1/2% vs 2 1/2%, i.e.,
e+n/h+q vs d+m/g+p).  Transaction may be examined by determining if multiple hospital admissions were more likely in
children from chronically disadvantaged homes.  It was found
that they were twice as likely (8% vs 4%; i.e. , o/r vs f/i)
indicating that chronic disadvantage made it more probable
that children would be admitted to the hospital several times—
a transactional effect.  Interaction may be examined by
determining if the association between multiple hospital
admission and emotional disturbance was greater in the
presence of chronic disadvantage than it was in its absence.
The findings showed that it was (that is the difference between 15% and 2% was greater than that between 9% and 3%;
i.e., n/q:m/p exceeded e/h:d/g).*  In short, in this case
there were independent effects, transaction effects and interaction effects.

_____

*Not all of these differences reach statistical significance –
see Quinton and Rutter (1976) for details.  However, the
point of presentation here is the mode of analysis rather
than the substantive findings.

Table 1*

Teacher Questionnaire Findings

|  |  | No Disturbance | Emotional Disturbance | Total |
|---|---|---|---|---|
| (A) | Low Psychosocial Disadvantage | | | |
| | 0 or 1 hospital admission | 110 (a) | 30 (b) | 140 (c) |
| | 2+ hospital admissions | 3 (d) | 3 (e) | 6 (f) |
| | | 113 (g) | 33 (h) | 146 (i) |
| (B) | High Psychosocial Disadvantage | | | |
| | 0 or 1 hospital admission | 51 (j) | 40 (h) | 91 (i) |
| | 2+ hospital admissions | 1 (m) | 7 (n) | 8 (o) |
| | | 52 (p) | 47 (q) | 99 (r) |

*From Quinton and Rutter, 1975.

While the above table provides the necessary data,
interaction effects are more easily seen by presenting the
figures in a graphical form as in Figure 1. This gives the
findings from a study looking at the associations between
brain damage and psychiatric disorder according to the
presence or absence of psychosocial adversity (Rutter, 1976).
The slope of both lines shows that psychiatric disorder is
more frequent in children from disadvantaged homes. The
fact that the upper line is considerably above the lower line
indicates that brain damaged children are much more prone
to psychiatric disorder irrespective of the presence of
psychosocial adversity. The finding that the slopes of the
two lines are generally similar indicates that there is no
substantial interaction effect. In other words, both brain
damage and psychosocial adversity predispose to psychiatric
disorder in children and the effects are additive. But there

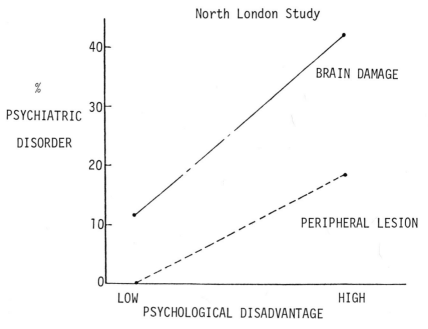

Figure 1

Psychiatric disorder and
Psychosocial Disadvantage

is no interaction; that is the psychiatric risk associated
with brain damage is not a result of the damage rendering
the child more vulnerable to psychosocial stresses.  This
negative finding is all the more striking and important because it runs counter to many people's expectations.  It
also emphasizes the need to differentiate between additive
and interactive effects, effects which have often been mis-
leadingly regarded as synonymous.


Thomas:  We tend to get stuck with the assumption of
continuities in development, I know we did, and the interaction model tends to perpetuate that.  The question of discontinuities in development which Arnold (Sameroff) has
raised and which we have been struggling with I think is to
some extent a watershed issue in looking at longitudinal
studies.  I'm not sure, Mike (Rutter), that these kinds
of charts can tease out the differences between them because you can get these kinds of charts which look interactional and yet may not be.  We have had a number of interesting instances in tracing development over many years
of several populations in which a change, a new aspect of
the child's characteristics have come out, for example, a
new talent, a new attribute, or an attribute which originally
was considered difficult temperamentally but at a later
age did not cause difficulty in terms of parent reaction.
Therefore, a marked shift in the course of development
takes place.  If this is not kept in mind, then one has a
problem understanding the relationship.  If serial cross-
sectional studies are carried out and miss the period at
which the shift takes place, then the results cannot be
interpreted, or even the logic of the sequence of development may be missed.  This is another reason why longitudinal studies have a power, in spite of all their difficulties,
which even serial cross-sectional studies do not have.


Vaillant:  I have two statements about long-term studies.
First, regarding the concern that it's precisely the deviant
people who don't consistently return in a longitudinal study.
If you have a real longitudinal study, that does not mean a
follow-up at just one point, but a follow-up at several
points, and if you keep following people up you keep finding
them - even the deviant ones - and so fill in the missing
cells.  Repeated follow-up provides information you can't get
any other way.  Second, if you want longitudinal studies to

predict the future consistently rather than inconsistently, you measure what the person does well, rather than what the person does badly. If you focus on individual successes at any given point, they will predict the future better than if you focus on failures.


Rutter, M.  Brain damage syndromes in childhood:  Concepts
    and findings.  Journal of Child Psychology and
    Psychiatry, in press.

Quinton, D., and Rutter, M.  Early hospital admissions and
    later disturbances of behavior:  An attempted repli-
    cation of Douglas' findings.  Developmental Medicine
    and Child Neurology, 1976, 18, 447-459.

# Section IV

# Follow-up Studies of Psychiatric Patients

# LONGITUDINAL RESEARCH ON PSYCHOPATHOLOGY IN PSYCHIATRIC

# PATIENTS: SOME ASSETS AND LIABILITIES

Robert Cancro
Department of Psychiatry
New York University Medical Center
550 First Avenue
New York, New York

It has been often observed that to know a person or even an organization you must have the opportunity to live with him and observe his actions closely over time. My introduction to the Society for Life History Research in Psychopathology occurred when I joined. The procedural activities involved in this serious life event were to put my mailing address on the bottom of a sheet of paper and send it off to Minnesota. The Society had an unadorned quality not unlike Robert Hall. It was devoid of officers, committees, dues, tax exemption, and even a constitution. On November 1, 1973, in deference to the complexity of our times, a committee was formed to consider the future directions -- if any -- of the organization. The urgency of the questions posed to the committee led to a luncheon meeting on May 22, 1975. These events might cause the casual observer to conclude that the Society is extraordinarily liberal and manifests a passionate aversion to structure. Certainly, its interest in the longitudinal study of psychopathology suggests if not a preference at least sympathy for subjective impressions. It is instructive, therefore, that the conclusions drawn from this life history "study" of the Society are as spurious and superficial as those drawn by certain life history researchers studying other groups. The Society does not harbor scientific neohippies but rather some of the most rigorous colleagues who accept the challenges of longitudinal research without compromising their methodologic integrity. Virtually every member has done research on this afternoon's topic and is painfully familiar with the methdologic problems of the area. Furthermore, a number of the previous speakers have skillfully

covered many of the salient issues in depth.  This review
must, therefore, lack novelty for an audience such as this,
but will hopefully compensate for this deficiency through
its succinct redundancy.

We shall define longitudinal research in psychopathology, in very broad terms, as that research which is conducted
over time and which studies the multiple and changing
relationships of psychopathology over that time period.  It
may, for example, involve the use of pre-post designs on the
same individuals or the use of matched groups of subjects
who are at different points.  The techniques vary but the
emphasis is on what happens over time rather than a cross-
sectional view.  The often used, but unfortunately quite
misleading, analogy is that of multiple sequential photo-
graphs, i.e., a motion picture film, versus a still photo-
graph.

The question must arise as to why a small band of
individuals pursues a far from universally popular research
strategy.  It is simplistic to argue that the reason lies in
the inherent superiority of the approach -- even if it were
to be true.  The personal preferences and values of the
investigator are real determinants, since the interest in or
curiosity about what happens to research subjects in the
future is not universally shared.  There are individual
differences among investigators as to what constitutes an
interesting question.  Longitudinal approaches lend themselves well to certain classes of questions and not to
others. These personal factors play a role in determining
the vitality and size of the research community engaged in
longitudinal research.

Beyond the human factor, there are other and powerful
reasons for using this strategy.  At a basic level of hypothesis generation, the naturalistic observation of the phenomena in question over a period of time is an essential
prerequisite.  Yet, interestingly enough it is often unmet.
Many younger colleagues who have trained since the advent of
the phenothiazine and community mental health center eras,
have, for example, never seen a hospitalized drug-free
schizophrenic.  It would be more accurate to say that they
have never admitted a patient to hospital referred with a
diagnosis of schizophrenia who is drug free. Unfortunately
most of those referred with a nonschizophrenic misdiagnosis
are also medicated to various degrees.  There is an explicit

warning in the experience of Spohn, et al (1971) who repeated a group of psychophysiologic measures in a sample of
normals and chronic schizophrenics after withdrawing their
medication and found that certain of the between-group
differences in the measures were related to phenothiazines
and not to schizophrenia. One need not return to Kraepelinian
predetermination, to recognize the vital importance of the
natural course of the pathology in the most probable environmental setting. I do not wish to leave the impression
that medication is the problem. Rather, it is an example of
those external events which make longitudinal observation of
the natural phenomena difficult. The internal urgencies
which reduce efforts at longitudinal observation and research
seem to be more related to a kind of impatience which is to
science as antimatter is to matter. The rush to get into
print, particularly newsprint, is a threat to the integrity
of our scientific effort.

Once having obtained the basic experience of observing
people over time, we can move on to more formal hypothesis
generation. Here the blending of correlational techniques
with the longitudinal approach lends itself extremely well.
The correlational approach is often downgraded by the use of
the adjective "mere." It is a useful and powerful technique when used correctly. It can identify the independent
variables which are related to the dependent variable in a
particular sample. It can reveal intercorrelations and
complex correlations which are not intuitively obvious.
Through the use of Simon's method (1957) and other more
recently devised statistical techniques (Blalock, 1961;
Vroom, 1956), causal inferences can be drawn from correlational studies done on longitudinal data. In this way, the
relatively simple correlational analysis can be enhanced.

At the level of hypothesis testing, other speakers have
addressed themselves to the variety of statistical methods
available for the rigorous analysis of data derived from
longitudinal studies and their limitations. The problems of
analysis are obvious but not insurmountable. The longitudinal strategy is inherently powerful for dealing with
certain kinds of questions. These studies are ideally
suited to separate state from trait dependent variables. If
a person shows a particular attentional disinterest in the
environment during a depressive illness, the knowledge of
his pre- and/or postdepression attentional pattern would be
vital in deciding whether this attentional mode is a state-

related deficit or a trait-related variant. Many other
kinds of investigations are strengthened by the longitudinal
approach and its value need not be defended here.

We shall now turn to the more narrow issue of individuals first studied after becoming identified as ill. These
people can be admitted to the study population immediately
upon being labeled ill or at some later date. The second
division of this population is based on the prospective or
retrospective nature of the analysis. In summary, there are
four possible combinations of these divisions. The population can be obtained either immediately or later and
studied either retrospectively or prospectively. Obviously,
the world of the life history researcher is never simple
over time and with a little resourcefulness can be made even
more complex. For example, first admission decompensations
can be mixed with recent readmissions showing little change
from preadmission symptomatology but whose environment can
no longer maintain them. Retrospective data can be obtained
while prospective observations are being made. In this way,
no source of potential information, confusion, error, or
aggravation is neglected. A common practice is to obtain
historical data from the patient and/or his family, supplement it with data on variables derived from direct observation of present behavior in the artificial and unnatural
environment of the hospital, and then put these data from
very different sources into the same matrix. There is little
reason to assume that data derived from a parent's recollec-
tion of premorbid behavior after the patient is hospitalized
does not differ in fundamental ways from data drawn from the
observation of ward behavior. I would be hard pressed as to
which is more reliable or valid but comfortable as to the
need for caution in their analysis, particularly when
realizing that different methods of analysis can yield
different results.

The study population -- people labeled ill -- is
naturally occurring and suffers, therefore, from all the
endemic deficiencies of natural as opposed to synthetic
groups. We are all familiar with the effects of confounding
variables, problems of baseline measures, initial value
problems, etc. How to interpret longitudinal data in
naturally occuring groups is troublesome. The synthetic
group, on the other hand, may produce a happier period of
analysis but the leap from it to the real world is not

without danger. There are problems with nylon as well as with wool and its apparent superiority diminishes as an exponential function of closeness.

Th need for controls remains in the study of naturally occuring groups, but the investigator must be more imaginative in applying them than in a preselected population. Obviously, the pursuit of rigor should not be mindless nor result in controlling away the object of study.

The complexity of the interrelationships also poses special problems. An example that illustrates how subtle the obvious can be may be informative. Some fifteen years ago I obtained a sample of consecutive male admissions with a diagnosis of schizophrenia. The Prognostic Rating Scale (1953) prospectively predicted the duration of hospital stay. There was no relationship between age or history of prior hospitalization and either the Prognostic Rating Scale or the duration of hospitalization. Recently, this sample was reviewed in response to a request from a colleague who needed a consecutive admission sample. In response to an independent suggestion from a second colleague, the sample was divided into first admission and readmission subsamples. The Prognostic Rating Scale no longer predicted for the first admission group. This group was younger and the predictive power of marital status which loads the Prognostic Rating Scale apparently is only manifest when the group members are old enough for marital status to have differential predictive value. We had never looked at the results from this perspective. The data must be carefully digested and its study not restricted to readily available computer programs. We must reflect on the data and this requires time.

The next problem to be faced is that while patient populations are naturally occuring, they are also man made. Diagnosis is a clinical judgment and not an absolute measure. We need not be ashamed of reliabilites in the range of .5 - .7 but conversely we can not ignore the consequences of this moderate reliability. The validity of our diagnostic classifications is a separate question which will not be developed in this presentation.

The operational definition of both dependent and independent variables poses problems. A simple clinical

notion such as social withdrawal becomes enormously complex
when studied closely.  Should withdrawal be approached
quantitatively?  If so, can we simply count the number of
friends?  Who decides if they were friends?  What is the
number of friends that indicates withdrawal?  Is the number
the same for quiet people?  Is the quality of the social
contacts more important than the quantity?  The list goes on
as a function of the care of the investigator.  The problems
are the same for outcome variables.  Everyone can tell if
the patient is better, but cannot tell how they know it.  It
is not a trivial task to operationalize this subjective
global impression into a useful measure.

    The study of individuals after they have become iden-
tified as ill is complicated by the effects of the processes
of identification and treatment as well as the consequences
of the illness.  Labeling a person as mentally ill changes
not only his self image but how he is seen and treated by
others.  Being hospitalized carries a stigma which influences
the course of many future events.  Psychiatric treatment of
any sort has a variety of consequences.  Patients often fear
that their status will become known, and live with this fear
and its effects.  Receiving medication or ECT has a variety
of psychological and social meanings and consequences which
can confound the picture and influence the future -- the
so-called Eagleton effect. These are all sources of variance
which are unique to becoming a mental patient and which must
be recognized in our research designs.

    There are problems and limitations in all longitudinal
research which go beyond the specific ones cited for research
on individuals who have been identified as ill.  Longitudinal
research is very time consuming.  The older researcher may
not be able to wait twenty years and the younger researcher
may not want to.  Careers are advanced and grants are
obtained on the basis of current rather than future research
publications.  The furor to publish mitigates against good
longitudinal research.  So too does the understandable
desire to see your results before your maker.  Longitudinal
research is expensive.  Partially the expense is a function
of the time involved in doing the work.  It is also related
to the sheer mass of the data resulting from a longitudinal
study.  Interpreting longitudinal data is much more complex
and time consuming.  The research team must be supported
while it thinks for extended periods of time.  In principle

no one would object to this expense, but in practice it is
rarely protected from budgetary deprivations.

The problem of patient attrition is formidable.  It is
estimated that 20 percent of the American population moves
each year.  A five year period of data gathering might,
therefore, lead into an earlier than ancitipated data
analysis stage.  Hopefully, mental patients are less mobile
and/or less affluent and may move less.  Beyond the problem
of geographic loss of the sample, there is the further
attrition related to dropouts.  The patients decide not to
come back.  They no longer wish to participate.  Both of
these sources of attrition may be nonrandom.  The patients
who move away or drop out of the study are not necessarily
the same as those who do not.  Perhaps the best antidote to
the dropping out is a strong personal relationship with the
patient and/or his family.  Nevertheless, a good insurance
policy would include a very large initial group.  As with all
insurance, it does not return what is lost but does defray
the cost.

All longitudinal research that starts with adults has a
population which is characterized by a fully developed
central nervous sytem.  This fact precludes the study of the
interactions that go on earlier which may be different in
important ways.  Similarly, the personality of adult subjects is relatively formed.  We can assume that the same
events have different effects at different points in the
evolution of the personality. Starting with an adult personality excludes certain sources of potential information.

The longitudinal study of the patient must be placed in
a social context.  The patient cannot be studied in vacuo.
This requires additional efforts on the part of the researcher
and increasingly requires an interdisciplinary team with all
of the problems that go with working in a group.  Solitary
longitudinal research is not a practical alternative.  The
splendid isolation described by Federn (1952) has no place
in longitudinal research.  The hierarchical arrangement of
the team is more ambiguous and less constant than in many
other research endeavors. Each specialist speaks in a dom-
inant voice in a limited area.  To borrow an ethological
analogy, there is relative rather than absolute dominance in
the group.  This is a situation which is not born equally
well by all colleagues.

Finally, one must consider the ethical problems raised by longitudinal research. This is particularly important today since lawyers seem determined to expose subjects to more serious risks in order to protect them from less serious ones. If informed consent involves telling the subjects the hypotheses of the research and the basis for them, many longitudinal studies -- particularly the high-risk studies -- are in a dilemma. There is a profound difference, for example, between being told that the investigators wish to study the children of women who were in a mental hospital to see if there are any effects and being told that the investigators believe the children have a much better chance of becoming mentally ill. It should be emphasized that the beliefs and anticipations of researchers are not always borne out by experience, and, therefore, may not constitute informed consent but rather misinformed consent. The term at-risk can have a very different meaning to a researcher and to a parent. Furthermore, if we believe that labeling the children is in itself harmful, we must speculate as to the consequences on the individuals who refuse to participate but have been informed about the hypotheses of the study.

After listing even a portion of the problems and limitations involved in doing longitudinal research in general and post-illness research in particular, one may wonder as to the wisdom of the approach. The difficulty does not reside in the method but rather in the nature of complex open systems such as man. Any clinical research that is nontrivial is extraordinarily complex. The extreme complexity can discourage the initiation of efforts to study the problem. But for those who prevail in the face of the difficulties the longitudinal method has genuine benefits. It is not the Rosetta Stone which will decipher human psychopathology. It is not the only way. Longitudinal research is only one of several valid approaches but it is in my judgement, the most powerful and appropriate strategy to study, conceptualize, and influence psychopathology.

REFERENCES

Blalock, H.M.  Causal Inferences in Non-Experimental Research Chapel Hill: North Carolina Press, 1961.

Federn, P. Ego Psychology and the Psychoses. New York: Basic Books, 1952.

Phillips, L. Case history data and prognosis in schizophrenia. Journal of Nervous and Mental Disease, 1953, 117, 515-525.

Simon, H. Models of Man. New York: Wiley, 1957.

Spohn, H.E., Thetford, P.E., and Cancro, R. The effects of phenothiazine medication on skin conductance and heart rate in schizophrenic patients. Journal of Nervous and Mental Disease, 1971, 152, 129-139.

Vroom, V.H. A comparison of static and dynamic correlational methods in the study of organizations. Organizational Behavior and Human Performance, 1956, 1, 55-70.

# LIFE HISTORY CHARACTERISTICS OF RESPONDERS TO DRUG AND

## SOCIAL THERAPY IN SCHIZOPHRENIA

Solomon C. Goldberg and Nina R. Schooler
Psychopharmacology Research Branch
National Institute of Mental Health
Rockville, Maryland

Gerard E. Hogarty
Department of Psychiatry
University of Pittsburgh
Pittsburgh, Pennsylvania

The study to be described here begun in 1968 and involving some 370 patients in three clinics, has been partially reported in separate papers dealing with selected points of focus. Here we will take the opportunity to present the results of the study as a whole and to offer an integration that was not possible in the individual papers.

The study was addressed to two major research questions. First, can maintenance CPZ treatment in the community sub-stantially forestall the relapse of schizophrenics who have recently been discharged from the hospital? Clinical experience indicated that neuroleptic drugs such as CPZ were capable of reducing the symptoms of schizophrenics suffering an acute episode, ultimately leading to discharge from the hospital in the vast majority of cases. These very same patients were then frequently being rehospitalized after relapse in the community. How strong would drug treatment be in reducing relapse? Were there some patients who could remain in the community without drug treatment and were there some patients who would relapse despite receiving drug treatment? What are the differential characteristics of such patients?

In England, Leff and Wing (1971) observed that patients with very good prognostic signs were able to stay in the community without drugs while patients with very poor prognostic signs relapsed despite getting drugs; only those patients with mid-range prognostic signs seemed to benefit from drug treatment.

In the United States, Goldstein's results (1970) suggested that good premorbid schizophrenics show no benefit from drug treatment (in terms of symptom reduction in an acute episode) in an inpatient setting; only the poor premorbids showed a drug-placebo difference.

Our study was begun with every confidence that maintenance CPZ treatment would on the average, forestall relapse in schizophrenic patients. Drug efficacy was no longer a question. Rather, ours was a question of how strong the drug effect was, and since there are limits to any treatment, how to define those limits. To do this kind of limit testing study required a large sample and a demonstration of replicability in different clinical settings.

The second research question was concerned with the possible effects of a social therapy on the relapse and community adjustment of schizophrenics. One reason social therapy is commonly offered to schizophrenics is that while drugs render the patient relatively free of symptoms, the patient needs help in being established in some instrumental role, whether as a student, wage earner, or housewife. Without such aid, the patient might simply occupy the role of "patient" in a room at home instead of on the hospital ward. Within manpower limits, such a social therapy is offered to many patients discharged to the community. There was not a strong expectation that social therapy would diminish the likelihood of relapse since relapse was usually a matter of symptom exacerbation, and there was no strong evidence that social therapy could affect symptoms. Our expectation was that the quality of community adjustment for those who did not relapse would be enhanced by social therapy

## METHOD AND PROCEDURE

Following discharge from three Maryland state hospitals, schizophrenic patients from Baltimore were randomly assigned at clinic intake to major role therapy (MRT), a combination of intensive social casework and vocational rehabilitation

counseling.  All patients were stablized on chlorpromazine
treatment for two months and then randomly assigned identical-
looking tablets of chlorpromazine or placebo.  The study
required 120 patients from each of the three clinics.
Patients, stratified by sex, were randomly assigned to all
possible combinations of drug-placebo and MRT-no MRT.
Although the goal for total sample size was only 360, a
total of 374 patients actually were studied. The study was
conducted at three clinics for two purposes; to obtain a
sizable sample within a reasonable amount of time and to
enable us to examine the consistency of results across
facilities.  A result was not considered a result unless it
was consistent across clinics.  Relapse was defined as
clinical deterioration of such magnitude that rehospitaliza-
tion was imminent.  About 75 percent of relapsed patients
were actually hospitalized.

The minimal dose of coded study medication (chlorpromazine or placebo) was 100 mg/day.  At clinic intake, the
average chlorpromazine dose, or its equivalent, was $280 \pm$
145 mg/day.  At the point of random assignment (two months)
an average chlorpromazine dose of $265 \pm 135$ mg/day was
prescribed.  Drug survivors averaged $270 \pm 140$ mg/day
throughout the two years of study and placebo survivors
averaged $275 \pm 190$ mg/day.

Drug relapsers in the first and second year averaged
$295 \pm 180$ mg and $245 \pm 130$ mg/day, respectively; placebo
relapsers averaged $330 \pm 200$ mg/day and $265 \pm 130$ mg/day in
the first and second years.

The MRT was administered by social workers with MSW
degrees and with an average of nearly seven years' experience
(range five to ten years).  Most were graduates of more
functional (Rankian) schools of social work.  The MRT was
viewed as a psychosocial, problem-solving method designed to
respond to the interpersonal, personal, social and rehabili-
tative needs of study patients and their families.  An
effort was made merely to evaluate the needs of non-MRT
patients. When indicated, non-MRT patients were referred to
other community resources, but the referral was not routinely
followed through. The MRT attempted an approximate solution
of practical problems, which frequently includes situational
crises.  The primary goal toward which social workers were
directed was the resolution of personal and environmental

problems that directly affected the patient's performance as a homemaker or as a real or potential wage earner. Otherwise therapeutic objectives ranged from improving the quality of interpersonal relationships and ameliorating social isolation, to the rudiments of self-care, financial assistance, and medication maintenance. Principles of practice included acceptance, clarification, material and emotional support, and appropriate assurance.

The MRT and non-MRT patients were equally prepared for the study and similarly urged to take medication and comply with scheduled clinic appointments. These efforts to insure adherence to the study design by non-MRT patients act to blur the distinction between the two treatments. They might better be labelled "high" and "low" sociotherapy. This ambiguity represents an unavoidable defect in the controlled study of the psychotherapies; one that has the effect of weakening tests of comparative efficacy.

## RESULTS

Figure 1 shows the cumulative relapse rates for each of the treatment combinations. By the end of two years there was a sizeable drug-placebo difference such that about 80% of those on placebo relapsed, while the comparable figure for drug was about 48%. At the same time there was essentially no effect over the two years from the social therapy, Major Role Therapy (MRT).

## Predictor Analysis Procedure

Using "months until relapse" as the dependent variable, a series of analyses of variance were performed within a factorial design where the factors were drug, MRT, clinic, and predictor. The drug factor had two levels, MRT had two, clinic had three, and various other predictors had from two to four levels. The predictors were a series of personalistic variables concerning the patients' social and psychiatric history.

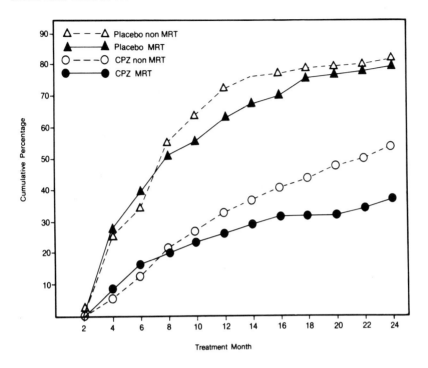

Figure 1

Cumulative relapse rates for each treatment group.
Major role therapy indicated by MRT.


General Predictors

There were three main kinds of results. First a number
of the predictors showed main effects and did not interact
with other factors. These variables were associated with
"months until relapse" in the same strength regardless of
which treatment was received and regardless of which clinic
was examined. By and large, as expected, patients with
"bad" signs relapsed earlier, e.g., patients with more
outpatient experience and less stability rated by family.

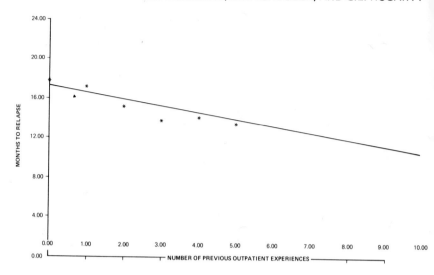

Figure 2


Predictor by Drug Interactions

A second result of more pertinence to our research
questions showed a number of predictors interacting with the
drug variable, so that patients with good signs showed a
larger drug-placebo difference than did those with poor
signs.  There was little difference on placebo between
patients with good and poor signs; the difference between
"goods" and "poors" was mainly in the drug treated patients.
This point is illustrated in Figure 4 showing the greatest
drug-placebo difference with less autism observed by the
psychiatrist; in Table 1 with a more favorable family attitude toward study participation and in Table 2 with females.
These results are counter to those cited by Goldstein et al.
which suggested that we would find a stronger drug effect
for poor than for good prognosis patients.  To support the
Leff et al. results, we should find a drug effect for middle
prognosis patients but not for very good or very poor prognosis patients.  Our results do support the Leff et al.
findings on patients with poor signs but are completely
counter to their results on patients with good signs.

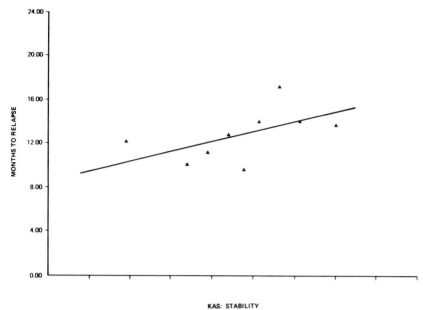

KAS: STABILITY

Figure 3

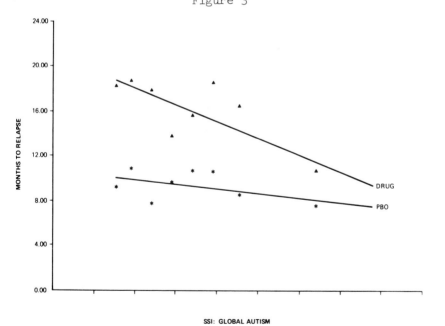

SSI: GLOBAL AUTISM

Figure 4

Table 1

Predictors of Months Until Relapse

Relative's Attitude Toward Study
Participation X Drug Treatment

$F = 5.19$, DF 1, 318    p   .025

|                   | CPZ  | PBO  |
|-------------------|------|------|
| Favorable         | 17.5 | 9.8  |
| Neutral or Opposed| 17.2 | 11.5 |

MRT Effects on Relapse in Patients with Good and
Poor Prognostic Signs

A number of predictors were found to interact with MRT.
These results show MRT to forestall relapse in patients with
good prognostic signs but to hasten relapse in patients with
poor signs. Moreover, the "toxic" effect in the "poors" is
larger than the "therapeutic" effect in the "goods." These
results were a complete surprise since there had been no
expectation that the social therapy would affect relapse at
all. This point is illustrated in Figure 5 on disorganized
hyperactivity; Figure 6 on anxious depression; and Figure 7
motor retardation.

Effect of Treatment on Adjustment of Non-Relapsed Patients

One of our questions was whether MRT could enhance the
quality of adjustment in patients who at the end of two
years had not relapsed. Most of the nonrelapsers were on
drugs with a smaller number on placebo. With this subsample,
a drug by MRT by clinic factorial analysis was performed
with regard to a variety of dependent variables representing
community adjustment after 24 months of treatment. The
findings show a large number of disordinal interactions such
that MRT enhances adjustment in drug treated cases but
worsens adjustment in placebo cases. A few illustrative
cases are given in Figures 8, 9, 10, and 11.

Table 2

Drug by Sex Interaction on Months in the Community
(2 Years)

|  | Drug | Placebo |  |
|---|---|---|---|
| Men | M = 14.40 | M = 10.14 | 12.31 |
|  | N = 74 | N = 71 |  |
| Women | M = 19.5 | M = 10.38 | 15.24 |
|  | N = 105 | N = 93 |  |
|  | 17.4 | 10.3 |  |

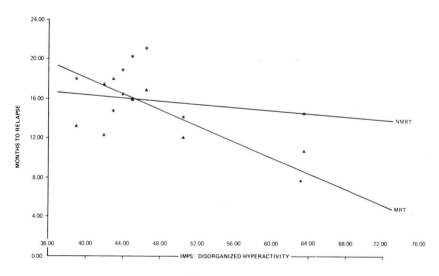

Figure 5

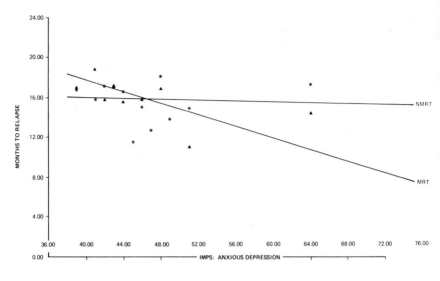

Figure 6

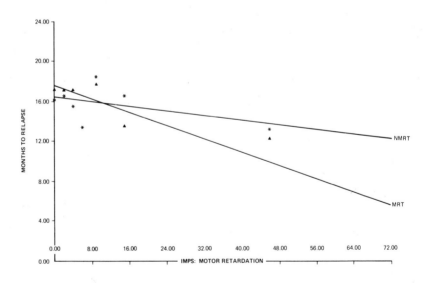

Figure 7

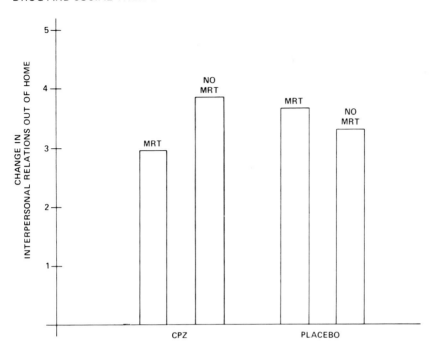

Figure 8

Drug by MRT Interaction

$F = 6.94$, $df = 1$ & $96$, $p = .01$


DISCUSSION

The first question addressed by this research is "who needs drugs and who does not." The conclusions of Leff and Wing are that only patients in the middle prognostic range benefit from drug treatment; patients with good prognostic signs tend not to relapse even without drugs, while patients with poor prognostic signs tend to relapse even through drug treated. Our results agree with only half of their contention in that we find larger drug-placebo differences in forestalling relapse in the "good" rather than the "poors." Leff and Wing drew their conclusion by the finding that good prognosis patients not on drugs were not different in relapse rate from mid-range prognosis patients who were drug treated. Since in their study good prognosis patients could not be included in the random assignment procedure, they could not, as we did, compare drug with placebo on patients with good prognostic signs. Our results are somewhat consistent with theirs in that we find smaller drug effects for patients with poor prognostic signs.

Our most surprising findings are those concerning our social therapy, MRT. There was no expectation that MRT would have any effect on relapse and, indeed, on the average it does not. It is only when predictor variables reflecting good and poor signs are taken into account that MRT makes a difference. That MRT has a positive effect on patients with good signs is gratifying and reasonable. However, when a

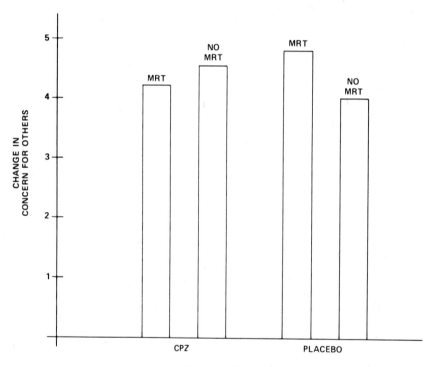

Figure 9

Drug by MRT Interaction

F = 3.93   df = 1 & 84   p = .05

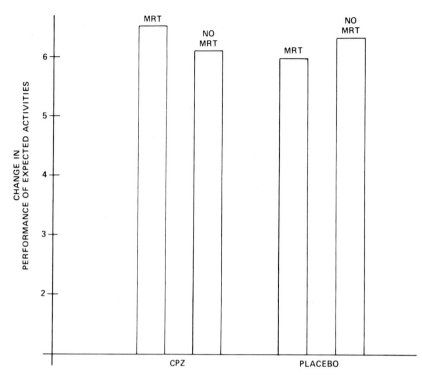

Figure 10

Drug by MRT Interaction

$F = 4.21$, $df = 1 \& 85$   $p = .043$

humanitarian and well intentioned therapy such as MRT is shown to have a detrimental effect on patients with poor signs, some explanation is demanded.

Equally puzzling is our result concerning MRT on the quality of adjustment of nonrelapsed patients. Here our expectation was that MRT would enhance adjustment in both drug and placebo treated patients. It was thus surprising that in placebo-treated patients who had not relapsed, MRT was detrimental to the quality of their adjustment. Those patients who survive two years in the community without drug treatment are undoubtedly different in kind from those who need drugs to do so. The question is what kind of patients are harmed by MRT? At this time, one can only offer a specu-

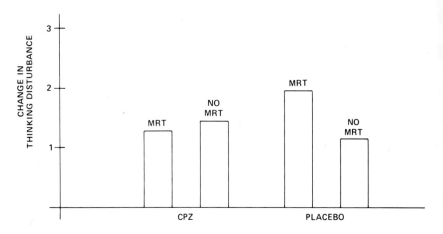

Figure 11

Drug MRT Interaction
F = 8.17, df = 1 & 84  p = .005

lative hypothesis which bears some similiarity to ideas that
have been published by Shakow (1962), Silverman (1964),
Venables and Wing (1962), Brown, Birely and Wing (1972), but
mainly McGhie and Chapman (1961), and probably others.  The
hypothesis proposes that poor prognosis schizophrenic patient
suffer from an inability to distinguish and filter out the
vast amounts of irrelevant stimulation in one's stimulus
field.

To quote from McGhie and Chapman's patients:

Patient 13:  "If I am talking to someone they only need
to cross their legs or scratch their heads and I am
distracted and forget what I was saying.  I think I
could concentrate better with my eyes shut."

Patient 19:  "It must look queer to people when I laugh
about something that has got nothing to do with what I
am talking about...you see, I might be talking about
something quite serious to you and other things come
into my head at the same time that are funny and this
makes me laugh."

The patient's recognition of his inability to filter the
irrelevant results in a panic and a high arousal state.
High arousal in similar kinds of patients has been shown by
Venables and Wing (1962). In the words of McGhie and
Chapman's patients:

Patient 2:   "When you feel yourself going into sort of
a coma you get really scared...You tremble and panic.
It's like no other fear on earth."

One way of defending against this mental state is for
the patient to reduce his cognitive field to a size he can
manage. Thus Venables and Wing (1962) find hyperarousal
related to withdrawal in non-paranoid chronic schizophrenic
patients and Silverman (1964) speaks of similar patients
being reducers of their stimulus fields rather than being
augmenters. Again in the patient's own words:

Patient 13:   "I think I could concentrate better with
my eyes shut."

Patient 22:   "If it is just one person who is speaking
that's not so bad, but if others join in, then I can.'t
pick it up at all."

Patient 14:   "I don't like moving fast. I feel there
would be a break if I went too quick. I can only stand
that a short time and then I have to stop. If I carried
on I wouldn't be aware of things as they really are.
Everything would be a jumbled mass. I have found that
I can stop this happening by going completely still and
motionless. When I do that, things are easier to take
in."

Given an intervention (MRT) which hopes to train the
patient to behave like a more responsible adult and to
enlarge and enrich his stimulus field, he will be provoked
into a mental state that he can no longer manage, resulting
in a panic and exacerbation of symptoms. The goals of our
social therapy MRT were indeed to aid the patient in becoming more responsible and independent. This kind of push
to enrich one's world may be more complex than poor prognosis patients can handle.

Somewhat similar conclusions are drawn by Brown, Birely and Wing (1972). "In the presence of a socially intrusive relative, for example, (the patient) is unable to withdraw and any residual or latent thought disorder will become manifest as expressed delusions or odd behavior. This condition will be accompanied by a high level of "arousal" ...too enthusiastic attempts at reactivating unprepared long-stay patients have been shown to lead to sudden relapse of symptoms that had not been present for years."

It might also be that drug treatment acts to reduce one's stimulus field and thus protects against the confusion of figure and ground. Thus MRT effects on patients with poor signs should have been more evident in less protected placebo patients; however, this expectation was borne out only in one variable which showed a drug by MRT by predictor inter-action on "months to relapse." In this predictor variable (Figure 12) the MRT effects (positive for "goods" and negative for "poors") were found as hypothesized in the placebo but not the drug cases.

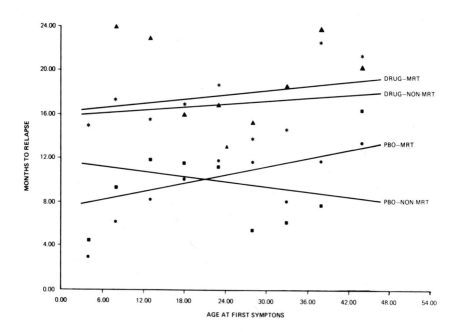

Figure 12

Our results on nonrelapsers has a similar explanation although here one must recall that we are not dealing with relapse but with better and worse adjustment in patients who have not and are not relapsing. Here, the hypothesis is that placebo patients who are not protected by drug from a larger undifferentiated stimulus field are more subject to the negative effects of MRT.

A further point of interest about the "toxic" effects of MRT in "poor" patients is that it may well represent the same kind of environmental stress that will provoke clinical schizophrenia in high genetic risk subjects who are not yet schizophrenic. We tentatively equate high risk with poor prognosis on the basis of McCabe et al. (1971) showing this relationship. The kind of message contained in MRT, i.e., to behave like a responsible adult, is the middle class achievement message which can have beneficial effects for those whose mental tolerance for enrichment and multiplexity is high. The "message" intended by parents and teachers and peers to be beneficial is possibly selectively stressful for individuals at high genetic risk for schizophrenia. One difficulty with past environmental stress theories of schizo- phrenia is that they suppose that some kind of environmental condition or stimulus, such as double-bind will be stressful to everyone. Given a genetic substrate, the stress is additive and pushes a predisposed individual over the "brink." Perhaps we must begin to consider a different kind of nature- nurture interaction in which a given environment condition might be beneficial for some, but "toxic" for others.

## REFERENCES

Brown, G.W., Birely, J.L.T., and Wing, J.K. Influence of family life on the course of schizophrenic disorders: A replication. British Journal of Psychiatry, 1972, 121, 241-258.

Goldstein, M.J. Premorbid adjustment, paranoid status and patterns of response to Phenothiazine and acute schizo- phrenia. Schizophrenia Bulletin, 1970, 3, 24-37.

Hogarty, G.E., Goldberg, S.C., Schooler, N.R. and Collaborative Study Group. Drug and sociotherapy in the after-
care of schizophrenic patients. III Adjustment of
nonrelapsed patients. Archives of General Psychiatry,
1974, 31, 609-618.

Leff, J.P. and Wing, J.K. Trial of maintenance therapy in
schizophrenia. British Medical Journal, 1971, 3, 559-
604.

McCabe, M.S., Fowler, R.C., Cadoret, R., and Winokur, G.
Familial differences in schizophrenia with good and
poor prognosis. Psychological Medicine, 1971, 1, 326-
332.

McGhie, A., and Chapman, J. Disorders of attention and
perception in early schizophrenia. British Journal of
Medical Psychology, 1961, 34, 103-117.

Shakow, David. Segmental set. Archives of General Psychiatry
1962, 6, 1-17.

Silverman, Julian. The problem of attention in research and
theory in schizophrenia. Psychological Review, 1964,
71, 352-379.

Venables, P.H. and Wing, J.K. Level of arousal and the
subclassification of schizophrenia. Archives of
General Psychiatry, 1962, 7, 114-119.

Open Discussion

Vaillant: Could you explain what you call good prognostic signs? They don't seem to be the ones that people
like Langfeldt, Hoch, and Zubin and Stephens report who
reviewed the prognostic literature in schizophrenia.

Goldberg: First, we had a number of variables describing the patient's present state or past history that were to
be tested as predictions. Some of them were level of psychopathology taken at that time.

Vaillant: Well, why do you use that when level of psychopathology has never been a very good predictor of schizophrenic remission during the acute episode?

Goldberg: In this study in addition to our acute study in 1964 and the study by Klein and Fisk, among others, level of psychopathology is a good predictor. I'm only saying that here is a variable, level of psychopathology, and on the "more" end of that variable we're getting, for instance, larger drug placebo differences and also on the "more" end we're getting positive MRT effects. Now with any one of our predictor variables, I think that there would be very good agreement as to what the more and less end was, like a greater amount of psychiatric experiences is worse than less, and so on.

Vaillant: Why do you use idiosyncratic prognostic variables when there are perfectly good prognostic variables in the literature which don't need agreement but have been empirically shown?

Goldberg: Well, I think that we used practically everything that was in the literature, and what predicts outcome is not as settled an issue as you imply.

Vaillant: The composites of which you used to define your good prognosis schizophrenics?

Goldberg: We didn't define patients in that way, we had variables which we were testing out in this study as predictors. All we know at this point is that on each variable there is a classically admitted good end and bad end. I don't think anybody here would go counter to what the good and bad ends are on any one of those variables. The only thing I'm doing now is not testing what has been in the literature as good and bad prognostic signs, I'm only saying that on these variables you get a certain pattern of results on the good end that is different from what you get on the bad end.

Cancro: But there are no absolute goods. The judgment of "good" has to be placed within a context. A variable may be good in the sense of nice, but it may not be good in the sense of predicting a good prognosis.

Goldberg:  Good prognosis is not an empirical matter in this study.  For instance, with certain "classical" good prognosis variables that a lot of people have researched, I can show you that the outcome of patients with that classically good sign is not invariably good but depends on treatment received.

Carpenter:  I think many of us would disagree as to what is the good and bad prognostic end of some of the scales. The anxious-depression score is an example.  Some would consider anxiety and depression as measured on the IMPS as a good prognostic indicator.  The same comment applied to your cautionary note that arousing psychotic symptoms in a chronic group is a bad sign.  I don't know that there is any general agreement that symptom arousal in a chronically ill person is considered bad.  The warning you make not to be too active with interventions or too eager to effect change because it may give rise to psychotic symptoms is controversial. Active psychotic symptoms in chronically institutionalized patients may be a good sign, although it certainly creates a management problem.  I do think Vaillant's point is true.  There is no uniform view about what is good and bad.

Goldberg:  Okay, I agree there is no uniform view of good and bad.  I can only say that we tested almost every variable anyone ever proposed, as a prognostic sign.  We hoped to save ourselves from this statistically large number of tests by replication.  The predictors that don't show up consistently in 3 clinics we do not consider as significant results. My retreat goes back simply to describe the nature of the variable.  Perhaps you can say that in schizophrenia anxious depression is a positive sign rather than a negative one, but all I'm saying is that the characteristic, more psychopathology, shows a certain pattern which is consistent all the way through these symptoms.

Cromwell:  With regard to good vs. poor prognostic signs, I agree with Will Carpenter.  My colleagues and I found the same thing in about 900 patients at the Danville VA Hospital.  The more chronic or poor in prognosis they were, the lower they were in affective measures such as agitated depression.  The higher or more severe the patient on this index, the better the prognosis.  The term prognostic signs, has taken on a traditional meaning.  It seems simpler semantically just to use the word "descriptor."

LONG-TERM FOLLOW-UP OF JUVENILE AND ADULT DELINQUENCY
WITH SAMPLES DIFFERING IN SOME IMPORTANT RESPECTS:
CROSS-VALIDATION WITHIN THE SAME RESEARCH PROGRAM*

Merrill Roff
Institute of Child Development
University of Minnesota

Problems of crime and the correctional system have received a great deal of attention in recent years. This set of studies presents some factual information bearing on these problems. This has been obtained from follow-ups covering periods of from 10 to 35 years using populations which had already been studied for shorter periods of time. These were parts of a comprehensive program of life history studies dealing not only with offenses but also with other kinds of problem behavior.

Two kinds of samples are employed in the follow-ups presented here: (1) a large sample for which childhood peer status scores are available and (2) earlier samples for which histories of juvenile delinquency and adjustment to military service had already been obtained. For both of these, an intensive follow-up has been made through the adult period in terms of their contacts with the law and the correctional system.

---

*This research program has been supported in part by the United States Air Force School of Aviation Medicine, the National Institute of Mental Health, the United States Army Research and Development Command, the United States Office of Education, the State of Minnesota's Governors Commission on Crime Prevention and Control, and the University of Minnesota Graduate School.

The significance of childhood peer status as a predictor of adult problems has been indicated in a series of studies (Roff, 1957, 1960, 1961, 1963, 1965, 1966, 1970; Roff, Mink & Henrichs, 1966). These findings triggered a large-scale study of peer status in about 18,000 Minnesota elementary school children (plus another 18,000 in Texas) for whom peer choice information was obtained in the early 1960's. Results of the follow-up of the entire Minnesota group in terms of their juvenile delinquency records has been presented earlier (Roff, Sells & Golden, 1972; Roff, 1972, 1975). This paper presents a follow-up of this group into the adult period.

The second group of samples consisted of individuals with histories of juvenile delinquency who were born in the years 1928 through 1936. Follow-up studies have been made with large samples of these individuals in terms of their military service histories, in general during the Korean War period. An earlier control group, born in the years 1915 through 1923 and randomly selected from the grade school population had been similarly followed through their military service period (in World War II).

A follow-up has now been made in terms of contacts with the law occurring during adulthood for both these groups. Individuals in the Korean War Sample were 38-46 years old at the time of follow-up while the controls were about 55 years of age.

In addition to following up contacts with the law in these two sets of samples as far into adulthood as possible, three additional associated studies are described. From the peer sample, (1) the relation between peer scores and child guidance clinic contact has been examined, (2) the relation between sibling concordance in juvenile delinquency and a history of adult offenses has been analyzed, and (3) for a delinquent group who had been confined in a training school, the relation was studied between evaluations made during and at the end of confinement by correction system personnel and behavior of inmates after release.

PEER STATUS SCORES, SOCIOECONOMIC STATUS,
AND JUVENILE DELINQUENCY

Paper status scores of third- through sixth-grade pupils of entire school populations were obtained in two

Minnesota cities (Minneapolis and St. Paul) in the early sixties. Peer choices in each class were made only within sex groups. Each child indicated the four children he/she liked best and the two he or she liked least. Peer scores were obtained by combining the Like-Most choices and the Like-Least choices received by each pupil from his same sex classmates with teacher ratings of peer status. The original peer study has been described in full elsewhere (Roff, Sells, and Golden, 1972).

The composite peer score, which will be used in the present paper, consists of a weighted combination of two times the Like-Most score minus the Like-Least score plus the teacher rating score (the higher the score the greater the peer acceptance). These scores were transformed into scaled scores with an average value of 5.0 and a standard deviation of 1.0, with a distribution that tended toward the normal and was symmetrical. This means that there were more individuals in the center of the distribution than at either extreme, so that scale units of the same size would contain different numbers of persons at different parts of the scale.

Peer score results were analyzed separately for eight different socioeconomic levels (1=high SES; 8=low SES) based on census data for income and education of adults in the census tracts of each city for each school district. The results for these eight SES groups are reported as if they were separate populations.

In one city, the entire public school population including all socio-economic levels was studied. In the second, the entire school population was not needed to reach the pre-set target sample size. Consequently, only schools from the lower socioeconomic half of the city were utilized. These were employed because they contained more problem children. It was found that the proportion of delinquents in the low peer status group was consistently greater than the number in the high and middle peer score groups in each of the seven upper SES levels. In the lowest group, however, the number of delinquents was approximately as great in the high as in the low-choice group (Roff, 1972; Roff, Sells and Golden, 1972). There were no delinquents at all among the high and middle peer choice boys in the SES groups 5 and 6, and only one in group 7. There were however several low-choice boys with delinquency records. At SES

level 8 at least as many high-choice as low-choice boys had
delinquency records.  The same regular relationship of peer
scores and delinquency was observed among girls at all SES
levels without the departure from expectation noted for boys
at the lowest socioeconomic level (Roff, 1975).

PEER STATUS, SOCIOECONOMIC LEVEL, AND CHILD
GUIDANCE CLINIC CONTACTS

Table 1 shows the number of subjects with a child
guidance clinic contact, in relation to their peer scores
and SES, for a portion of our male peer group elementary
school sample.  This portion consisted of a substantial
number of consecutive cases who were among the oldest of the
peer sample.  Apart from the age factor, the sample was
unbiased.

There were no cases where a peer score of 6.5 or better
was associated with a history of child guidance contact,
while there were 16 cases from approximately the same number
in this sample with scores of 3.4 and below. In this sub-
sample, the peer scores have selected a group which is
problem free in terms of child guidance clinic contact.  A

Table 1

Number of Subjects with Child Guidance Clinic Contact
in Relation to Peer Scores and Socioeconomic Status

| Peer Scores | Socioeconomic Quartile | | | | |
|---|---|---|---|---|---|
| | I | II | III | IV | Total |
| 6.5 and up | 0 | 0 | 0 | 0 | 0 |
| 5.5 - 6.4 | 2 | 2 | 5 | 2 | 11 |
| 4.5 - 5.4 | 7 | 8 | 5 | 4 | 24 |
| 3.5 - 4.4 | 7 | 5 | 9 | 6 | 27 |
| 3.4 and below | 4 | 6 | 4 | 2 | 16 |
| Total | 20 | 21 | 23 | 14 | 78 |

direct comparison may also be made between those with peer scores of 5.5 to 6.4 and those with peer scores of 3.4 to 4.4. There were 11 guidance clinic contacts in the higher group and 27 in the lower, a ratio of about 2 1/2 to 1. There is no relation between socioeconomic level and clinic contact for this group except for a somewhat smaller number in the lowest socioeconomic quartile.

### PEER STATUS, SOCIOECONOMIC LEVEL AND CONFINEMENT IN CORRECTIONAL INSTITUTIONS

Because the peer group boys were at most 25 years of age at the time of the follow-up, their histories of institutionalization were far from complete. Nevertheless, it is of interest to trace the course of their institutional histories up to that age, and to study the relation between peer scores, socioeconomic status, and confinement. The institutions to which the males could be sent may be described briefly as follows:

(1) County Home School for Boys: Each of the·two counties in this study had its own training school to which juveniles were sent when it seemed desirable to get them out of the situation in which they had been living. Earlier work in this program has indicated that of those sent to a County Home school about one in five progressed to the next higher level which is the

(2) State Training School for Boys: This "receives all boys committed to the Youth Conservation Commission by the juvenile courts of the state" (Directory of Minnesota Government Agencies). It has two associated forestry camps to which some of the members were assigned. In general, boys cease to become eligible for the STS upon reaching their 18th birthday, at which time they become eligible for the

(3) State Reformatory for Men, which may retain custody of them until the age of 25. After that age, they are sent instead to the

(4) Minnesota State Prison.

Earlier work has indicated that about one in five juveniles on probation who are sent to the county training

school progress to the next stage - the state training
school or reformatory. We have a sequence where only one in
five at one level go on to the next level of confinement.

From the total male peer sample in Minneapolis of
3,380, the number who went to the State Training School for
Boys was 131 or about 4 percent. About twice as many juveniles were sent from families in the lowest of the eight
SES groups as from those in the fifth.

The relationships between high and low scaled peer
scores and confinement in the three most serious institutions are shown in Table 2. These values indicate a definite relationship between peer scores obtained during the
grade school period and later confinement.

The groups shown for the three institutions were not
independent. Of the 46 persons between the ages of 18 and 25
at the Minnesota State Reformatory, 37 (80 percent) had
previously been confined at the State Training School. All
but two of the 46 Reformatory inmates had been confined in
the State Training School or the earlier County Home School
for Boys. Of the six in the sample sent to the State
Prison, four had been incarcerated in both the State Training School and the Minnesota State Reformatory. It should
be noted that while these six indiividuals had records of
multiple confinement, they comprised only a fraction of the
the total Minneapolis sample. These findings, then, show
marked attrition at every stage of the correctional procedure
from one level to the next. The majority, and sometimes the
great majority, of individuals at any stage do not progress
further. This should be realized whenever the entire correctional system is viewed, and opinions expressed as to its
effectiveness.


PEER SCORES, SOCIOECONOMIC LEVEL AND
POST-JUVENILE OFFENSES

A follow-up study was made of the post-juvenile offenses
of all males from the peer study with delinquency histories
(1729 cases) and of the 3287 cases without histories of
juvenile delinquency. Individuals in the peer study were
born predominantly in the years 1950-1953. In 1974, they
would have been between 21-24 years of age. This is, of

Table 2

Scaled Peer Scores and Confinement in
Correctional Institutions

| | | Scaled Peer Score | | |
|---|---|---|---|---|
| Correctional Institutions | N | High Peer Scores | Middle Peer Scores | Low Peer Scores |
| State Training School | 131 | 19 | 51 | 61 |
| State Reformatory | 46 | 9 | 14 | 23 |
| State Prison | 6 | 0 | 1 | 5 |

course, closing the books rather early in their post-
juvenile careers.  Some of the older samples described below
given an indication of what the subsequent histories of
subsamples like these would be.

Of those with histories of juvenile delinquency, 427 or
24.7 percent had adult offenses recorded.  For those without
a history of juvenile delinquency, 134 or 4.1 percent had
adult offenses recorded.  This is about one-sixth the
frequency in former juvenile delinquents.  In spite of the
higher number of adult offenders among former juvenile
delinquents, it should be emphasized that three out of the
four former delinquents did not have a record of adult
arrest.

The relationships among peer scores, socioeconomic
level and number of adult offenses for the group with
juvenile delinquency histories are shown in Table 3.  This
group has been divided into those whose offenses were drug
related and those whose offenses did not involve drugs, on
the hypothesis that the association between socioeconomic
status and offense might be different.  This turned out to
be so.  Those with drug involvement showed little
or no SES trend, while those without drug involvement showed

Table 3

Post-Juvenile Arrests of Males with
Histories of Juvenile Delinquency

A.  Not Drug-Involved

| Peer Score | Four Lower SES Octiles | | | | |
|---|---|---|---|---|---|
| | 5 | 6 | 7 | 8 | Total |
| 6.5 and higher | 0 | 1 | 2 | 5 | 8 |
| 5.5 - 6.4 | 10 | 13 | 16 | 18 | 57 |
| 4.5 - 5.4 | 23 | 20 | 28 | 54 | 125 |
| 3.5 - 4.4 | 14 | 21 | 32 | 32 | 99 |
| 3.4 and lower | 13 | 9 | 7 | 11 | 40 |
| Totals | 60 | 64 | 85 | 120 | 329 |

B.  Drug-Involved

| Peer Score | Four Lower SES Octiles | | | | |
|---|---|---|---|---|---|
| | 5 | 6 | 7 | 8 | Total |
| 6.5 and higher | 0 | 0 | 0 | 2 | 2 |
| 5.5 - 6.4 | 6 | 3 | 5 | 6 | 20 |
| 4.5  5.4 | 12 | 7 | 9 | 12 | 40 |
| 3.5  4.4 | 5 | 5 | 5 | 7 | 22 |
| 3.4 and lower | 4 | 6 | 2 | 2 | 14 |
| Totals | 27 | 21 | 21 | 29 | 98 |

the familiar increase in the number of offenses as socio-economic level decreased.

The relation between peer scores and arrests in those not drug-involved and the drug-involved is both similar and different. For these two groups the proportion of those with the lowest peer score to those with the highest is similar, 5 to 1 and 7 to 1 respectively. On the other hand, there are almost twice as many with peer scores in the below-average interval as in the above-average interval for the nondrug involved, while there is little difference in the drug involved cases. The drug involved group is less than one-third the size of the other.

SIBLING CONCORDANCE AND JUVENILE AND ADULT DELINQUENCY

Results are presented for cases from only one city since complete family information was not readily available in the other one. The sample of siblings was restricted to those who were in the total peer sample, that is, to those siblings in the third, fourth, fifth, and sixth grades. We thus missed certain older siblings who may have had histories of delinquency and certain younger ones who had not yet reached the delinquency age, or had not yet been born. With this limitation, we have a complete picture for a total sample of 6663 children. The ratio of delinquent boys to girls was about two to one in this sample. The number of sets of siblings and the number of sets and individuals showing some juvenile delinquency are shown in Table 4.

Analysis of the data on males according to the relation-ship of various sibling combinations and juvenile delinquency history to number of adult offenders indicated clearly the need for large samples in research of this kind, since with the breakdown employed, some of the combinations yielded frequencies that were unsatisfactorily small. The sibling sets containing girls only were not analyzed since the kind of adult follow-up made for males was not made for females.

Not surprisingly, in the groups of siblings with only one delinquent member, it was most often the delinquents rather than the nondelinquents who became adult offenders. Quasi-percentages were obtained by dividing the total number of individuals with adult offenses by the total number of

Table 4

Occurrence of Juvenile Delinquency in Sibling Sets

| Sets of Siblings | | Number of Children (Siblings) |
| --- | --- | --- |
| Total | 1321 | 2875 (out of total sample of 6663) |
| With no delinquent | 901 | 1921 |
| With one delinquent | 278 | 619 |
| With more than one delinquent | 142 | 335 (303 delinquent) |

groups of siblings from which they come. These order themselves in an interesting way. Individuals from sibling sets with more than one delinquent show 32 percent with adult offenses. Individuals who were the only delinquents in their set of siblings show 18 percent with adult offenses. Nondelinquent members of sets with only one delinquent show only 2 percent with adult offenses. The difference between these numbers is marked and suggests that those from multiple delinquent sibling sets show more adult offenses than delinquents from single-delinquent sets, who in turn show more adult offenses than the nondelinquent members of the single-delinquent siblings sets.

POST-SERVICE ADJUSTMENT OF OLDER INDIVIDUALS WITH HISTORIES OF JUVENILE DELINQUENCY AND OF A CONTROL GROUP

In order to obtain a picture of the continuation of criminal behavior further into the adult period, use was made of some large samples studied as long as 20 years ago. Follow-up studies were made of large samples of indivudals with histories of either child guidance clinic contacts or juvenile delinquency who were born in the years 1928 through 1936. For the delinquent groups, complete histories of their juvenile delinquency records had been obtained. For those with military service, their subsequent military records have also been obtained. In this study, adult offense histories have been updated to the present time.

In the analyses of military service data, outcome in service was classified into four categories:

1.   The noncommissioned or petty officer or officer group includes all those who had such status at the completion of their period of active duty with an honorable discharge. They are referred to as the "promoted" or "good adjustment" group.

2.   Recruit-Private-Private First Class (RCT-Pvt-Pfc) or equivalent includes cases who did not achieve noncommissioned status but were not disciplinary problems. Some of these cases had rather brief terms of service (early medical discharges, those with only six months active duty).

3.   The minor disciplinary problem group includes those who had multiple disciplinary offenses that were not serious enough or numerous enough to result in a discharge.

4.   The unsatisfactory group indicates all those who received a discharge other than an honorable one, with a disciplinary component in the picture.

Of these outcome categories, the first and the fourth are of primary interest since a comparison of these two groups contrasts those who entered service and made a relatively good adjustment, with those who had unsatisfactory outcomes. The data from these two outcome categories showed that subjects with a history of juvenile delinquency but who had not been confined in a training school had a favorable outcome ratio of about 3.5 to 1. Of those who had been sent to the state training school or reformatory as juveniles, the ratio was more than 5 to 1 unsatisfactory.

The outcome in service for those confined in the county training school but not at a state reformatory is about one satisfactory to one unsatisfactory. Their outcome is thus intermediate between those who were never confined and those who went to the state reformatory.

### Earlier Control Sample

For comparison with an earlier group of problem cases who were in service during World War II, a group of 900 cases was randomly selected from the Minnesota public school files (100 cases each for nine consecutive years, 1915-1923). Of the original 900, 686 were found in selective service records (either registration for the service or actual entry into the service). For the 530 of these who actually entered the service, a follow-up review of their records was made. Of the entire group of 686 registered, six were rejected because of serious misconduct, psychopathic personality, etc. Of the 530 who entered the service, 90 percent remained in service until released. Six received bad conduct discharges.

A follow-up was made of the adult offense histories of all 686 subjects. The median age of the group in 1974 was 55 years, and it is believed that they have had almost all the arrests they are going to have. Of the six individuals rejected for moral reasons, all six had at least one serious offense after the offense(s) which led to rejection. One of these six is the only chronic case in the entire sample. His confinement record seems almost continuous from the State Training School for Boys when he was 16 to the federal penitentiary in 1969 with a sentence long enough to keep him there to the present time. He did not limit his activities t Minnesota; he was also confined in the states of Iowa, Wiscon Illinois, Michigan, and Missouri. It should be emphasized that he was the only one of our 686 comparison cases to have a record of that duration and scope.

Of those receiving bad conduct discharges, three of the six had post-service offense records in Minnesota. For one of the others, discharge resulted from a civilian arrest in another state, and for one there was no post-juvenile record available apart from military service.

### Juvenile Delinquent Sample Born 1928-1936

Later follow-up indicated that those in the juvenile delinquent sample with poor outcome in service had a much greater frequency of post-service offenses than did those with good outcomes. Table 5 gives frequencies of individuals with adult offenses with different combinations of

Table 5

Number with Adult Offenses Born in 1928-1936 Classified by
Juvenile Confinement or Non-Confinement and Service-Related
Histories, for Successive Age Periods

| In-Service | | 18-22 | | 23-29 | | 30-39 | | 40+ | |
|---|---|---|---|---|---|---|---|---|---|
| Total N | | N | % | N | % | N | % | N | % |
| 927 | Non-confined (S)* | 22 | 2.4 | 19 | 2.0 | 20 | 2.7 | 2 | 0.2 |
| 267 | Non-confined (U)* | 97 | 36.3 | 64 | 24.0 | 30 | 11.2 | 3 | 1.1 |
| 127 | Confined County Home School (S) | 14 | 11.0 | 1 | 0.8 | 2 | 1.6 | 0 | - |
| 125 | Confined County Home School (U) | 62 | 49.6 | 42 | 33.6 | 26 | 20.8 | 1 | 0.8 |
| 14 | Confined State Training School (S) | 4 | 28.6 | 1 | 7.1 | 1 | 7.1 | 0 | - |
| 77 | Confined State Training School (U) | 74 | 96.1 | 45 | 58.4 | 38 | 49.4 | 9 | 11.7 |
| Moral Rejects | | | | | | | | | |
| 115 | Non-Confined | 99 | 86.1 | 38 | 33.0 | 20 | 17.4 | 5 | 4.3 |
| 58 | Confined County Home School | 50 | 86.2 | 30 | 51.7 | 16 | 27.6 | 1 | 1.7 |
| 139 | Confined State Training School | 115 | 82.7 | 67 | 48.2 | 34 | 24.5 | 3 | 2.2 |

*Non-confined refers to those who had juvenile offenses but were not confined in any institution as juveniles. The confined group is divided into those who were confined only at the County Home School for Boys and those who were at the State Training School, who may also have been at the County Home School earlier.

(S) Satisfactory outcome in service.

(U) Unsatisfactory outcome in service.

history as juveniles and outcome in service (satisfactory, unsatisfactory) for the age periods 18-22, 23-29, 30-39, and 40 and above. The best post-service outcomes from the delinquent sample born in 1928-36 were shown by a group of 927 who had not been confined as juveniles and had good outcomes in service. Just 63 of these, or 5.8 percent of the total, had any record of offenses between the age of 18 and the present time, when the oldest of these were about 46.

Whether confined or non-confined as juveniles, those having good military service outcomes consistently had the lowest percentage of adult offenses at all age levels. The largest group, those non-confined as juveniles with good service outcomes, had about 2 percent with adult offenses in each of the three youngest age categories; this frequency dropped to 0.2 percent with offenses in the age period 40 and over. The highest frequency at all intervals was shown by the group who had been confined in the state training school as juveniles and had unsatisfactory service outcomes.

The detailed post-juvenile arrest records of the 63 individuals with adult offenses from the group of 927 who had not been confined as juveniles and who had good service outcomes were tabulated for these time intervals. This showed that there were relatively few cases with multiple adult offenses in a single time interval. In general, this group did not appear to be more serious offenders as adults than the randomly selected comparison group. They were not ruined by their contacts with the juvenile probation system.

On the other hand, those who were in the state training school as juveniles and had unsatisfactory service outcomes showed a wide variety of adult offenses. In frequency, they ranged from a single offense sometime within the entire adult period to more than 20 offenses. In this group of 77 cases, the number with no offenses was 3 in the 18-22 period, increased to 39, or more than half, in the 30-39 age period, and to 68, or all but 9, in the 40 plus age period. In spite of the substantial amount of confinement, there is a steady drop in the number of offenses with an increase in age.

## Moral Rejects

Among the sub-samples with greater frequencies of
adult arrests are those rejected by the services for moral
reasons. In general, individuals were not rejected for moral
grounds unless they were either confined or on probration or
parole after their eighteenth birthdays. A history of
juvenile offenses regardless of frequency or seriousness
was not in general disqualifying. Many of those who had
post-juvenile offenses serious enough to lead to rejection
after their eighteenth birthday had earlier juvenile confinement, but some of them did not. This is the explanation
for the relatively similar adult histories of the three groups
of moral rejects.

## PREDICTIVE SIGNIFICANCE OF EVALUATIONS MADE BY CORRECTIONAL SYSTEM PERSONNEL

Previous work has shown the predictive value of both
peer evaluations of grade school children and of judgments
by their teachers. Thus, it might be expected that prediction of subsequent adjustment could be made for those in
a training school or reformatory in terms of the way they
appeared to the persons dealing with them at the time. In
order to explore this hypothesis, abstracts of the evaluations made by correctional system personnel at time of
discharge from parole for a sample of 19 reformatory inmates
with good outcomes in one of the military services were
compared to similar evaluations for another group of 19 from
the same institution with unsatisfactory service outcomes.
When qualitative descriptions were subjected to blind evaluations by readers, the readers consistently discriminated
between the two groups at a much better than chance level
(Table 6).

The first line of Table 6 includes five individuals
whose outlook was classified as good or excellent at the
time of discharge from parole. Four of these five were under
18 at the time of discharge. All of those classified as
good or excellent had a good service outcome. The next
category were those characterized as satisfactory at the
time of discharge. This group of subjects discharged from
parole as satisfactory before the age of 18 came out well in
service by a ratio of 10 to 2. Combination of the first two
categories gives 15 satisfactory in service to 2 unsatisfactory.

Table 6

Evaluations Made by Correctional System Personnel
and Service Outcome

| Predictions from Juvenile Correction Official's Abstracts | Outcome in Military Service | |
|---|---|---|
| | Good | Unsatisfactory |
| Good or Excellent | 5 | 0 |
| Satisfactory before 18 | 10 | 2 |
| Satisfactory age 18 or later | 3 | 5 |
| Unamenable | 0 | 6 |
| Other unsatisfactory* | 1 | 6 |

*
Including such things as "released to other authorities."

Those who were not discharged from parole as satisfactory
until the age of 18 or later (the oldest was 19 1/2) were
satisfactory in service in a ratio of 3 to 5.  Combination
of the two final categories, unamenable and unsatisfactory
gives a ratio of 1 satisfactory to 12 unsatisfactory outcomes in service.  This is in sharp contrast to the 15 to 2
ratio of the first two groups, those with a favorable evaluation at the time of discharge.

The six subjects discharged as unamenable to treatment
represent a group with which our legal system has no adequate way of coping.  They became to old for the reformatory.
Since the time they were confined there, they had not committed recent offenses for which they could be sent to
another correctional institution.  They were thus released
with the recognition that they are likely to get into trouble
wherever they might go.  For one of them the statement was
made that he was unamenable, but it was hoped that he could
get into the armed services and that there he would grow up.
He did get into the armed services but remained unamenable.
Another was discharged rather than kept on probation because

he was considered an undesirable person for a probation officer to have to try to deal with. What should be done with this group poses a difficult question. There is obviously no provision in the law for confining a person in the belief that he is likely to commit an offense.

## INDIVIDUAL HISTORIES OF OFFENSES

Any presentation using average values loses certain information. On the other hand, with samples of this size, a detailed presentation of each case is obviously impossible. To preserve to some extent information about individual cases, tabulations were made of the complete post-juvenile offense histories of selected sub-groups of the total sample. Some observations will be made about a tally of this kind for the control sample, born 1915-1923. The present average age of around 55 for this group is the highest for all our samples.

Of the 686 cases, 41 have a post-juvenile offense record. In the five-year interval from 18 through 22 years, they had an average of about a half an offense per person. Only one person of these 686 was in serious trouble more or less from first to last. He had enough juvenile and post-juvenile offenses to keep him out of service through World War II. He started out his adult career specializing in auto theft. In his thirties he shifted to forgery and fraud. In his forties he returned to auto theft with driving while intoxicated mixed in and was put in prison where he has remained up to the present time. In the age period from 30-39, he had ten offenses recorded. This is more than all the combined offenses of the 685 other cases during this period. If he had been confined during this period, it would have cut the crime rate for this control group in half for that period. This distinction between number of offenders and number of offenses must be kept in mind when reading reports of a rise or fall (more commonly rise) in crime rates. The information needed to make this distinction is almost never presented.

Another individual case should be mentioned. He had no offenses prior to the age of forty and then a run of five offenses within five years. He had no juvenile record and a good military record followed by some post-war college attendance. His offenses were alcohol-connected.

Only two offenses appear for the entire group after the
age of fifty.  Both of these were driving while under the in
fluence of alcohol.  Cross-sectional figures on a national
basis indicate that the relative frequency of all offenses
which are alcohol-connected rises with age, in contrast to
most other offenses which decline with age.

## DISCUSSION

Earlier follow-up studies of the relation between
childhood peer status and adult maladjustment have indicated
that low peer status was significantly related not only to
adult severe bad conduct, but also to adult neurosis,
schizophrenia, schizoid personality and homosexuality.
During adolescence, deviance in each of these categories
tended to approximate more closely the direction of the
eventual adult problem.  Because of this trend, prediction
of specific adult outcome from adolescent scores was more
precise than prediction from earlier peer scores.

One of the two main samples described in this paper was
a large grade school population for whom peer scores had
been obtained earlier.  Histories in this group of both
juvenile delinquencies and confinements and adult difficulties with the law up to the age of 24 give a picture of
the effectiveness both of early peer scores and of histories
of juvenile delinquency and confinement in predicting adult
contacts with the law.

The availability of scores for the entire school population gave perspective to the experience of those confined
in correctional institutions.  The percentage of the total
population, or even of juvenile delinquents, who ever went
to a correctional institution was small and became progressively smaller with successive correctional institutions.  Some relation was apparent between childhood peer
scores and adult confinement, but it was lower than that
with adolescent bad conduct.  Most of those confined at any
age level had been confined earlier, but the majority of
those confined at any age level were not confined at later
ages.

An analysis of sibling concordance in juvenile delinquency showed that delinquent juveniles from sibling sets

with more than one delinquent had about twice as many adult offenses as ones who were the only delinquent in a set of siblings, and about 16 times as many offenses as the non-delinquent members from sibling sets with only one delinquent. Family influence was not all-powerful.

The second major set of samples employed were large groups with histories of juvenile delinquency, who were born from 1928 through 1936. An earlier follow-up through the period of military service was continued to the present time, when these persons are in their early forties. Analyses of both the confinement experiences during the juvenile period and adult contacts with the law show a marked attrition at each of the stages of the correctional process and throughout the succeeding periods of adulthood.

Former juvenile delinquents with good military service records showed no more adult offenses than an earlier randomly selected control group. This was the largest group among the former delinquents. On the other hand, a much smaller group with serious juvenile delinquency and unsatisfactory service outcomes had a much higher offense frequency in the adult period. Not until the age period of 30 to 39 were more than half of them arrest-free.

A third sample was a control group randomly selected from public school files to match an earlier set of problem cases. Among the 686 individuals followed to the age of about 55, there was one chronic male offender who was consistently in trouble and periodically confined from the time he was a juvenile until the time of the present study. He could undoubtedly be classed as a failure of the correctional system. He was but one of a larger number who had been involved with the law at one time or another. The very small number of those getting into trouble with the law during their forties and fifties tended to have alcohol-related offenses.

The predictive significance of the evaluations made by juvenile correctional system personnel at the time of an individual's discharge from parole was assessed for a small group of subjects, from the juvenile delinquency sample, half of whom had good adjustments and half of whom had unsatisfactory adjustments in military service. Those described as having a good or excellent adjustment at the time of discharge from parole uniformly got along well in

military service, while all but one judged "unamenable" or
unsatisfactory had an unfavorable service outcome. The
problem of treatment for this "unamenable" group has not
been solved. This small group is a relatively large part
of the recidivism problem.

On the other hand, the assertion frequently made in the
public press that the correctional system fails all or most
of those with whom it deals is not supported in any way by
the results of this study.

## REFERENCES

Roff, M. Preservice personality problems and subsequent
    adjustment to military service: The prediction of
    psychoneurotic reactions. Rep. No. 57-136. School
    of Aviation Medicine, USAF, 1957.

Roff, M. The relation between certain preservice factors
    and psychoneurosis during military duty. U.S. Armed
    Forces Medical Journal, 1960, 11, 152-160.

Roff, M. Childhood social interactions and young adult bad
    conduct. Journal of Abnormal and Social Psychology,
    1961, 63, 333-337.

Roff, M. Childhood social interactions and young adult
    psychosis. Journal of Clinical Psychology, 1963, 19,
    152-157.

Roff, M. Some developmental aspects of schizoid personality.
    Report No. 65-4, March, 1965, U.S. Army Medical Research
    and Development Command, Contract No. DA-49-007-MD-2015.

Roff, M. Some childhood and adolescent characteristics of
    adult homosexuals. Report No. 66-5, May 1966, U.S.
    Army Medical Research and Development Command, Contract
    No. DA-49-007-MD-2015.

Roff, M. Some life history factors in relation to various
    types of adult maladjustment. In M. Roff and D.F. Ricks
    (Eds.), Life History Research in Psychopathology, Vol.
    1. Minneapolis: University of Minnesota Press, 1970.
    pp. 265-287.

Roff, M.  A two-factor approach to juvenile delinquency and
    the later histories of juvenile delinquents.  In M. Roff,
    L. Robins, & M. Pollack (Eds.), Life History Research in
    Psychopathology, Vol. 2.  Minneapolis: University of
    Minnesota Press, 1972, pp. 77-101.

Roff, M.  Juvenile delinquency in girls:  A study of a recent
    sample.  In R.D. Wirt, G. Winokur, & M. Roff (Eds.),
    Life History Research in Psychopathology, Vol. 4.
    Minneapolis:  University of Minnesota Press, 1975, pp.
    135-151.

Roff, M., Mink, W., and Hinrichs, G.  Developmental Abnor-
    mal Psychology.  New York: Holt, 1966.

Roff, M., Sells, S.B., and Golden, M.M.  Social adjustment
    and personality development in children.  Minneapolis:
    University of Minnesota Press, 1972.

Open Discussion


Sells:  In work that we have done in the last couple
of years, we have found many instances in which special
accommodations appear to exist between certain intervention
groups working with particular deviant sub-samples and the
police, as though they had asked the police to lay off
in order to give them a chance to work their magic.  As a
result, one needs to be very careful in accepting numbers of
arrests and certain other statistics without being very sure
of the relationship that exists.  Frequently such relationships are sensitive and you have to do quite a lot of digging

Roff: We did quite a lot of digging.

Sells:  Yes, I know, but if you go directly to police
departments, it's not always possible to get it.  Most of
your data came out of federal files, if I recall.

Roff:  That was in earlier work.  Here we covered all
levels.

Sells:  One other comment.  I think that the present
laws and regulations concerning confidentiality would probably preclude further new studies of this type.

Roff:  It is hard to tell whether the pendulum has swung
too far on confidentiality or not.

# METHODOLOGICAL ISSUES IN THE STUDY OF OUTCOME

William T. Carpenter, Jr.
Albert Einstein College of Medicine
1300 Morris Park Avenue
Bronx, New York

John S. Strauss
University of Rochester Medical School
300 Crittenden Boulevard
Rochester, New York

## INTRODUCTION

Outcome studies provide the crucial data for evaluating the natural course of an illness, the effect of treatment interventions, and the predictors of outcome. However, major problems have arisen in attempting to develop adequate methodology for these studies. A survey of outcome research from a methodologic perspective shows the progress from rudimentary, unreliable, clinical evaluation of patients to increasing recognition that systematic and reliable data collection are essential aspects of scientific investigation. Even though recent methods do not provide research techniques that are entirely satisfactory, several important advances have been made.

In this report, we will describe methodological developments in the three key aspects of outcome research: the diagnostic description of the cohort to be studied, evalution of prognostic status, and the measurement of course and outcome. We will describe some methods we have used to deal with problems in these areas, and some methodological suggestions for future work. This paper will focus on the functional psychoses, where our experience is greatest. The starting point for this work is the ill patient, with premorbid factors being evaluated retrospectively and outcome being assessed at some future date.

Description and Classification of Patients

Recent developments in interview methods, and mathematical techniques for combining clinical data have provided
improved approaches for classifying psychiatric patients.
Structured and semi-structured psychiatric interview schedules are now available  that permit systematic and reliable
evaluation of patients' clinical status. The resultant
ability to consider diagnostic detail has generated more
clearly defined and operationalized classification systems
(Astrachan et al., 1972; Carpenter et al., 1973; Cooper et
al., 1972; Feighner et al., 1972; Schneider, 1959; Strauss
et al., 1973; Wing et al., 1974; WHO, 1973). Computerized
diagnostic systems which classify patients with 100 percent
reliability are now available in several centers (Wing et
al., 1974; WHO, 1973; Endicott et al., 1972; Spitzer et al.,
1969; Fischer, 1974). Although the validity of these
systems remains to be demonstrated, their diagnostic rules
have the advantage of being completely and precisely defined.

Our work relevant to these aspects of diagnosis and
description, and to the premorbid and outcome characteristics
to be discussed below, was carried out in the context of the
International Pilot Study of Schizophrenia (IPSS) (WHO,
1973). The IPSS is a transcultural psychiatric investigation
of 1,202 patients in nine countries - Columbia, Czechoslovakia
Denmark, India, Nigeria, China (Province of Taiwan), Union
of Soviet Socialist Republics, United Kingdom, and the
United States of America. It was designed as a pilot study
to lay scientific groundwork for future cross-national
studies of schizophrenia and other psychiatric disorders.
Details of the methodology employed in this nine-nation
investigation are provided elsehwere. The collaborating
investigators of the IPSS are listed in Volume I (WHO,
1973). In our work on diagnostic and descriptive issues, we
have been able to analyze data from all nine IPSS centers,
and thus utilize the advantages of a large, multi-center,
cross-cultural design.

The IPSS was designed to study a patient group in each
center that was roughly representative of patients seen in
that center with schizophrenia and other nonorganic psychotic
disorders of relatively recent onset. Such a group was
gathered by screening recently-admitted patients between the
ages of 15-45 who had no evidence of organic, drug or alcohol

related disorders, and who had been hospitalized for less
than two of the previous five years and who had not been
continuously psychotic for longer than three years. For
inclusion in the study, patients had to present at least
suggestive evidence on admission of psychotic symptoms such
as hallucinations, delusions, thinking disorder, bizarre
behavior, or severe withdrawal. The hospital facilities
chosen treated patients representative of those hospitalized
from the catchment areas involved in the project.

Each patient was interviewed by a collaborating psychiatrist using the Present State Examination (PSE) (Wing et
al., 1974; WHO, 1973). This interview schedule contains a
series of 360 items with opportunity for flexible interviewing
to provide systematic inquiry regarding the basic psychiatric
signs and symptoms.

The ratings (absent, questionably present, present
but not continuous or severe, present and severe or continuous,
and categories for missing data) represent the psychiatrist's
judgment regarding the patient's symptoms during the month
prior to the interview. Besides this information on patients'
current symptoms, psychiatric history data were obtained by
using a structured psychiatric history schedule. An "index
diagnosis" for each patient was made by the interviewing
psychiatrist classifying patients according to the categories
of the International Classification of Disease by utilizing
all available information from the research interviews and
case records. Together, information from these sources
provided the basis for the patient evaluation procedures
described below.

## Diagnosis and Description

Utilizing the PSE data and the index diagnoses, we
derived empirically a system for operationalizing the diagnosis of schizophrenia. To accomplish this, we first
randomized patients from each country into study cohorts
containing about 400 diagnosed schizophrenics and about 150
nonschizophrenic patients in each cohort. Cohort A was then
used to develop diagnostic criteria. An analysis of variance (ANOVA) was carried out to determine which of over 400
overlapping sign and symptom variables were most discriminating between the schizophrenic and non-schizophrenic

Table 1

Items from the Present State Examination (PSE) Corresponding
to the 12 Signs or Symptoms; r, Reliability, Intraclass
Correlation; (-) Indicates that Absence of the
Criterion Favors a Diagnosis of Schizophrenia

| Sign or Symptom | PSE Observation or Question | r |
|---|---|---|
| RESTRICTED AFFECT | Blank, expressionless face | .62 |
| | Very little or no emotion shown when delusion or normal material is discussed which would usually bring out emotion. | .63 |
| POOR INSIGHT | Overall rating of insight | .66 |
| THOUGHTS ALOUD | Do you feel your thoughts are being broadcast, transmitted, so that everyone knows what you are thinking? | .95 |
| | Do you ever seem to hear your thoughts spoken aloud? (Almost if someone standing nearby could hear them?) | .74 |
| WAKING EARLY (-) | Have you been waking earlier in the morning and remaining awake? (Rate positive if 1 to 3 hours earlier than usual.) | .83 |
| POOR RAPPORT | Did the interviewer find it possible to establish good rapport with patient during interview? Other difficulties in rapport. | .86 |
| DEPRESSED FACIES (-) | Facial expression sad, depressed | .75 |

Table 1 (Con't.)

| Sign or Symptom | PSE Observation or Question | r |
|---|---|---|
| ELATION (-) | Elated, joyous mood | .73 |
| WIDESPREAD DELUSIONS | How widespread are patient's delusions? How many areas in the patient's life are interpreted delusionally? | .67 |
| INCOHERENT SPEECH | Free and spontaneous flow of incoherent speech. | .74 |
| UNRELIABLE INFORMATION | Was the information obtained in this interview credible or not? | .70 |
| BIZARRE DELUSIONS | Are the delusions comprehensible? | .69 |
| NIHILISTIC DELUSIONS | Do you feel that your body is decaying, rotting? | None |
|  | Do you feel that some part of your body is missing, for example, head, brain, or arms? | .70 |
|  | Do you ever have the feeling that you do not exist at all, that you are dead, dissolved? | .71 |

patients. We then took the 150 most discriminating variables (all at p <.01) and eliminated the least discriminating or obviously overlapping variables. A group of 69 highly discriminating signs and symptoms remained. These 69 variables were then subjected to a step-wise discriminant function analysis to reduce hidden redundancy and to identify the signs and symptoms which, taken together, would be most effective in distinguishing the schizophrenic patients from the non-schizophrenics. A total of 12 signs and symptoms proved optimal (Carpenter et al., 1974).

These 12 symptoms, their constituent PSE items, and their reliability are shown in Table 1. Nine of these symptoms contribute to the likelihood of a schizophrenic diagnosis being given by the IPSS psychiatrists, and the presence of the other three symptoms favors a nonschizophrenic diagnosis. Scoring one point for any of the nine schizophrenic symptoms manifested by a patient, and scoring one point for each of the three non-schizophrenic symptoms absent in a patient, results in a diagnosis score from 0-12. A score of 0 indicates virtually certain nonschizophrenic diagnosis, and a score of 12 indicates a virtually certain schizophrenic diagnosis.

This system was very effective in differentiating schizophrenics from non-schizophrenics in cohort A, from which the system was derived. To determine its general applicability, a replication study was under taken with the other half of the sample, cohort B. The results were similar, as can be seen in Table 2. A chi-square comparison of results in cohort A and cohort B revealed no significant difference.

We advocate the use of this system in schizophrenia research to supplement the clinical diagnostic process. For example, in selecting a patient for a schizophrenia study one could select only patients diagnosed schizophrenic by hospital staff and who also scored 6 points or greater on the 12-point system. This would provide a group where diagnostic criteria were operationally defined, and where the percentage of diagnostic false positive inclusions can be estimated. We would expect only 8-10 percent of patients with 6 points or more not to receive a diagnosis of schizophrenia if only this system were used. The number of false positives would be further reduced by following the usual clinical diagnostic process of considering psychiatric history data as well as symptoms. For example, a patient with a history of manic and depressive episodes could be excluded from the schizophrenia group even if 6 points were obtained on this system.

This 12-point system is intended to assist in selecting patients for study. As such, it enhances the diagnostic homogeneity of study groups and provides explicit criteria for other investigators to apply in replication attempts. However, it is also important to proceed beyond the use of

Table 2

12 Point System for Identifying Schizophrenic Patients

| POINTS | COHORT A | | COHORT B | |
|---|---|---|---|---|
| | SCHIZOPHRENIC (N=407) | NONSCHIZOPHRENIC (N=152) | SCHIZOPHRENIC (N=404) | NONSCHIZOPHRENIC (N=156) |
| 5 or more | 80% | 13% | 81% | 22% |
| 6 or more | 66% | 4% | 63% | 6% |
| 7 or more | 44% | 1% | 39% | 1% |

key diagnostic symptoms to describe adequately the broad
range of presenting psychopathology which can characterize
a study population. For example, the diagnosis of schizophrenia when supported by at least 6 points on the 12-point
system gives no information as to whether the patients are
anxious, or whether hallucinations are common or rare.

To provide such a broad description of symptoms, we
have found it useful to construct psychopathologic profiles
(Bartko et al., 1974). These profiles provide a basis for
defining and comparing patient groups by simultaneously
considering a large number of patient characteristics (WHO,
1973; Bartko et al., 1974). In our work, we have selected
27 psychopathologic dimensions, such as depression, auditory
hallucinations, and restricted affect, as representing
important symptom information for clinical assessment. Each
dimension is made up of all PSE items relevant to that area
of psychopathology.

With this approach, any individual or group of patients
can be represented by a profile, providing a visual and
quantitative description of pathology. Profiles may be
compared, for example, to determine if two groups are
similar in pattern and/or degree of psychopathology. In one
study, we compared outcome in two groups of patients and
used a profile ANOVA to establish that the pattern and level
of psychopathology were the same in both groups. This
careful identification of symptom similarity made the
outcome differences that were found later between these
groups especially striking (Carpenter et al., in press, a).
In another study, profile ANOVA was used to compare presenting psychopathology in the traditional schizophrenic subtypes (Carpenter et al., in press, b). No significant
profile differences were found. For example, paranoid
schizophrenic patients could not be distinguished from
hebephrenic or schizoaffective patients by pattern or degree
of presenting symptomatology.

The value of using a combination of specific symptoms
and profile analyses in this way can be illustrated by a
study comparing hospitalized borderline and schizophrenic
patients (Gunderson et al., 1975). Using the criteria of a
limited number of key symptoms, a cohort of patients had
been separated into borderline and schizophrenic groups.
Besides these criteria, all schizophrenic patients selected

had six or more discriminating symptoms (average of 8 points) which contrasted with the borderline groups which averaged only four of these symptoms. We found that two-year outcome was virtually identical in the two groups of patients.

This finding of similar outcome in the diagnostically distinct groups raised questions regarding the value and limitations of differentiating these two patient groups. Perhaps, since both groups were hospitalized, there may have been no real difference in overall symptomatology. To describe these patient groups further, the profile for each group was determined. These are shown in Figure 1. One can readily see (and ANOVA confirms) that the pattern (p=.026) and level (p=.23 x $10^{-8}$) of manifest pathology is remarkably different.

With this information of clearly different symptom profiles, the similar outcome in these two diverse patient groups becomes even more striking. How is it that patients with such different symptoms and symptom patterns can have similar outcomes? Evaluation of characteristics other than symptoms is needed to find the answer.

ASSESSMENT OF NON-SYMPTOM PROGNOSTIC VARIABLES

Once a study population is adequately defined and described in terms of key diagnostic symptoms and overall symptom patterns, a second group of attributes must be assessed - premorbid and other non-symptom characteristics associated with course and outcome.

The most common problem in this area is that many studies are carried out with little attention given to non-diagnostic prognostic variables. It is as though once a diagnosis were made and the subjects given a label, such as schizophrenia, the prognostic status was known. The assumption of a close correspondence between a symptom-based diagnosis and prognosis is not valid (Strauss et al., 1974a, 1974b; Hawk et al., 1975). In fact, determination of the predictors of outcome has been hindered because investigators have so often failed to separate diagnostic variables from nonsymptom predictor variables. For example, if a patient with nuclear schizophrenic symptoms is already chronic having been hospitalized for two years and had an

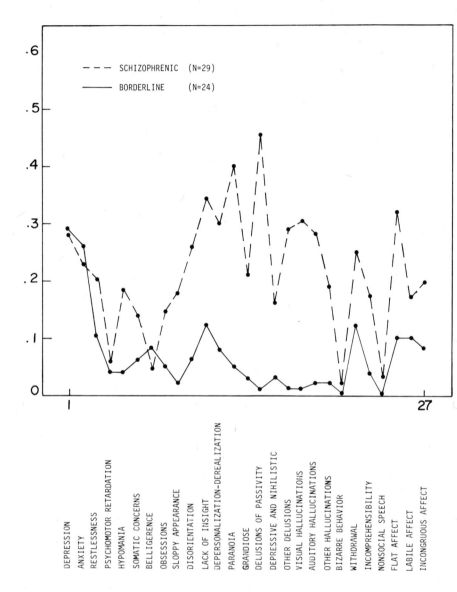

Figure 1
Comparison Between Schizophrenic and Borderline Profiles
on 27 Psychopathologic Dimensions

insidious onset of hallucinations six years ago, one can
justifiably be guarded as to prognosis - but not necessarily
because of the nuclear symptoms.

Another common problem in delineating prognostic
variables occurs when markers of already established chronicity are considered as predictors. For example, the symptom
flat affect, when used as a diagnostic criterion may well
identify with patients who will, on the whole, have a poor
outcome. But flat affect may well have "predictive" power
because it is a concomitant of chronicity rather than a
predictor per se.

One commonly used solution in outcome studies attempting
to evaluate treatment results has been to try to avoid the
problem of controlling for variables of known prognostic
importance by randomizing patient assignments to various
treatment groups. While such a procedure helps eliminate
systematic bias, it does not assure that prognostically
similar groups will emerge. This was illustrated in a
recent report in which two patient groups were formed by
random assignment and received different treatments and had
different outcomes. The investigators had the wisdom also
to collect and analyze crucial prognostic data. Unfortunately, despite random assignments, the better outcome group
also had the better prognostic characteristics (Glick et
al., 1975).

Many investigators have contributed to the task of
separating diagnostic variables from predictors (Astrup et
al., 1966; Garmezy, 1965; Langfeldt, 1937; Nuttall et al.,
1965; Phillips, 1953; Phillips, 1966; Raman & Murphy, 1972;
Stephens & Astrup, 1965; Swensen & Pascal, 1954; Vaillant,
1962; Vaillant, 1964; Wittman, 1941). Elaboration of the
concepts of process and reactive schizophrenia and definition of factors indicating poor and good prognosis in schizophrenia are the results of their work.

We have recently re-examined the association of various
predictor variables with outcome (Strauss & Carpenter, 1974;
Strauss & Carpenter, in press). As part of a special project involving the Washington Center IPSS patients, we developed a 15-item prognostic scale using information contained
in the psychiatric history and social description interview
schedules (Strauss & Carpenter, 1974). Using a methodology

that analyzes sign and symptom diagnostic data separately
from prognostic variables, we determined that a diagnosis of
schizophrenia, based on manifest psychopathology, regardless
of stringency of criteria or whose diagnostic system was
used, was a poor predictor of outcome (Strauss & Carpenter,
1974; Hawk et al ., 1975). Non-diagnostic prognostic
variables, however, did predict key aspects of outcome
(Strauss & Carpenter, 1974; Strauss & Carpenter, in press).
In fact, three prognostic variables, taken together, held
most of the predictive power of the 15-item scale. These
three items (duration of hospitalization prior to the
current admission, and social function and work function
during the year preceding admission) provide a simple means
of determining a patient's prognostic status.

It is obviously important to control for prognostic
status in any study comparing outcome on the effect of
intervention in two patient groups. The variables reported
above are readily useable for a general prognostic statement,
but more specialized meaures are often needed as well. For
example, if two neuroleptics are compared to schizophrenic
patients, childhood asociality is a critical control variable
(Klein & Rosen, 1973). If capacity to experience pleasure
is weighted heavily at outcome assessment, then comparative
study groups need to be similar on anhedonia measures at the
outset.


Assessment of Outcome

The third element in longitudinal studies is the
assessment of course and outcome. It is obvious, but often
forgotten, that there is no adequate method for measuring a
person's fate. This is especially true in schizophrenia
research where the disorder involves the total personality
of the patient and improvement in one aspect of living may
be accompanied by worsening in another. Symptom remission may
be achieved with a drug regimen that lowers motivation or
impairs social function. Psychological insight or the
loosening of pathological bonds in relationships may be
accompanied by considerable subjective distress or exacerbation of accessory symptoms. These examples illustrate the
complexity of outcome assessment, a point to which we will
return after discussing an even more basic· issue.

In evaluating what happens over time with patients, a distinction between course and outcome must be kept in mind. Course implies sequential functioning over time, focusing on the succession of happenings. This can involve any time period, such as course in the hospital or course from discharge to five years later. Outcome, on the other hand, implies status at some point of time and is cross-sectional, although in cross-sectional studies of outcome, some variables can represent a substantial rather than brief period of time. Even though outcome is obviously related to the course of disorder, a cross-sectional measure is not adequate for describing disorders with remittant or otherwise vacillating courses. Although evaluation of course has many advantages over cross-sectional outcome evaluation, it is more complex and expensive so that efficiency often dictates that cross-sectional studies be made until the variables and relationships of major importance can be clearly identified.

In earlier reports, we reviewed key issues in identifying outcome criteria for schizophrenia (Strauss & Carpenter, 1972; Strauss and Carpenter, 1974). Perhaps the most common shortcoming in defining such criteria has been the failure to appreciate the complexity of outcome function. Far too many investigations have assumed that either one reliable measure (usually some measure of hospital status during the outcome period) or one undefined measure (often some global judgment rated as good, fair or poor) provides a satisfactory assessment of a patient's life during the outcome period.

In an effort to cope with the problem of outcome complexity in our two-year follow-up study, we defined outcome as comprised of hospitalization, social relations, work, and symptom status. This scale is reliable, readily scored, and represents important areas of outcome functioning. Although total outcome can be described by summing the ratings on these four items, findings based on assessment of the four areas have demonstrated the limited degree of association between the four areas of outcome (Strauss & Carpenter, 1972). A person may be only briefly hospitalized during the follow-up period, but have practically no social relationships; or he may have psychotic symptoms and yet maintain an exemplary work record.

Although the four item outcome scale is valuable in many respects, it fails to assess such vital areas as a

person's happiness. At the time of our five-year follow-up
studies, to expand the scope of the outcome scale, we
evaluated additional areas of functioning attempting to
assess the quality of work and social functioning as well as
their quantity, and attempting to estimate the patient's (or
former patient's) capacity for a full life. This scale and
its reliability is presented in Appendix 1 to this chapter.
At five-year follow-up, limited association among the
various outcome areas was again demonstrated, reinforcing
the concept that outcome in schizophrenia is, indeed, a
complex phenomenon (Strauss & Carpenter, in press).

Our assessment of outcome in schizophrenia is far from
adequate even though it touches on several important areas
of functioning. We need better methods for judging an illness'
effect on the quality of life, perhaps using such important
information as that provided by Manfred Bleuler's detailed
account of decades of experience with many patients and
their families (Bleuler, 1968). More sensitive measures of
outcome would be even more valuable if population norms were
available to provide estimates of specific disability and
deficit. Nonetheless, studies of the course and long-range
outcome in the psychoses and studies of treatment need to
move beyond evaluating that which is most readily assessed,
such as hospital or symptom status. Clinical observations
in schizophrenia have always suggested that more personal
features such as inhibition of the will, curbing of curiosity,
loss of gratification in social relations, the inability to
share percepts, and the freezing of affective responsivity
are crucial in the life course of such patients. We measured
fullness of life reliability, and this may estimate such
psychopathologic impairment in a general way. But we cannot
yet specify what is being rated by this measure.


## SUMMARY AND CONCLUSIONS

We have discussed the three phases of longitudinal
studies which begin with the sick patient: assessment of
status at entry to the study, assessment of premorbid and
past history information, and assessment of course and
outcome. Recent methodological advances in collecting and
processing data were discussed, and application of these
methods to diagnosis and description of patients in longitudinal studies was illustrated. Emphasis was placed on

collection of reliable data, the use of operationalized,
replicable diagnostic systems, techniques for comprehensive
descriptions of patient samples, assessing prognostic
variables independently of diagnostic variables, and evaluating the main aspects of outcome function.

Methodologic shortcomings in each of the three phases
of longitudinal studies have contributed to serious miscon-
ceptions in our field. The failure to pay appropriate
attention to each phase - the present, past, and future -
has often confounded the roles of the important variables.
Concern over these problems has combined with recent methodologic advances to increase the sophistication of study
designs. The increasing recognition of these issues enriches
the potential in this area for understanding treatment
effects and other factors determining the course and outcome
of psychopathology.

## REFERENCES

Astrachan, B.M., Harrow, M., Adler, D., Brauer, B., Schwartz,
A., Schwartz, C., and Tucker, G. A checklist for the
diagnosis of schizophrenia. British Journal of
Psychiatry, 1970, 121, 529-539.

Astrup, C., and Noreik, K. Functional psychoses: Diagnostic
and prognostic models. Springfield, Ill.: Charles C.
Thomas Publisher, 1966.

Bartko, J.J., Strauss, J.S., and Carpenter, W.T., Jr. Expanded
perspectives for describing and comparing schizophrenia
patients. Schizophrenia Bulletin, 1974, 11, 50-60.

Bleuler, M. A 23-year longitudinal study of 208 schizophrenics
and impressions in regard to the nature of schizophrenia.
in D. Rosenthal and S. Kety (Eds.), The transmission of
schizophrenia. Oxford: Pergamon Press, 1968, pp. 3-12.

Carpenter, W.T., Jr., Strauss, J.S., and Bartko, J.J. Flexible
system for the diagnosis of schizophrenia: Report from
the WHO International Pilot Study of Schizophrenia.
Science, 1973, 182, 1275-1278.

Carpenter, W.T., Jr., Strauss, J.S., and Bartko, J.J. Use
of signs and symptoms for the identification of schizophrenic patients:  A report from the International
Pilot Study of Schizophrenia. Schizophrenia Bulletin,
1974, 11, 37-49.

Carpenter, W.T., Jr., McGlashan, T.H., and Strauss, J.S.  Dru
free treatment of acute schizophrenia. American Journal
of Psychiatry. In press (a).

Carpenter, W.T., Jr., Bartko, J.J., Langsner, C.A., and Strau
J.S.  Another view of schizophrenia subtypes:  A report
from the International Pilot Study of Schizophrenia.
Archives of General Psychiatry, 1976, 33, 508-516.

Cooper, J.E., Kendell, R.E., Gurland, B.J., et al. Psychiatr
diagnosis in New York and London - A comparative study o
mental hospital admissions. london:  Oxford Universitie
Press, 1972.

Endicott, J., and Spitzer, R.L.  Current and past psychopathology scales (CAPPS):  A rationale, reliability and
validity. Archives of General Psychiatry, 1972, 27,
678-682.

Feighner, J., Robins, E., Guze, S., Woodruff, R., Jr., Winoku
G., and Munoz, R.  Diagnostic criteria for use in
psychiatric research. Archives of General Psychiatry,
1972, 26, 57-63.

Fischer, M.  DIAX:  Development and validity of a computerized method for diagnosis of functional psychoses.
Acta Psychiatria Scandinavia, 1974, 50, 243-288.

Garmezy, N.  Process and reactive schizophrenia:  Some con-
ceptions and issues.  In M. Katz, J. Cole, and W. Barton
(Eds.), The role and methodology of classification in
psychiatry and psychopathology.  Government Printing
Office, 1965.

Glick, I.D., Hargreaves, W.A., Raskin, M., et al. Short
versus long hospitalization:  A prospective controlled
study. II.  Results for schizophrenic inpatients.
American Journal of Psychiatry, 1975, 132, 389-390.

Gunderson, J.G., Carpenter, W.T., Jr., and Strauss, J.S. Borderline and schizophrenic patients: A comparative study. American Journal of Psychiatry, 1975, 132, 1257-1264.

Hawk, A.B., Carpenter, W.T., Jr., and Strauss, J.S. Diagnostic criteria and five-year outcome in schizophrenia: A report from the International Pilot Study of Schizophrenia. Archives of General Psychiatry, 1975, 32, 343-356.

Klein, D.F., and Rosen, B. Premorbid social adjustment and response to phenothiazine treatment among schizophrenic inpatients. Archives of General Psychiatry, 1973, 29, 480-485.

Langfeldt, G. The prognosis in schizophrenia and the factors influencing the course of the disease. Copenhagen: Munksgaard, 1937.

Nuttall, R., and Solomon, L. Factorial structure and prognostic significance of premorbid adjustment in schizophrenia. Journal of Consulting Psychology, 1965, 29, 362-372.

Phillips, L. Case history data and prognosis in schizophrenia. Journal of Nervous and Mental Disease, 1953, 117, 515-525.

Phillips, L. Social competence, the process-reactive distinction, and the nature of mental disorder. In P.H. Hoch, and J. Zubin (Eds), Psychopathology of schizophrenia. New York: Grune & Stratton, 1970, pp. 471-481.

Raman, A., and Murphy, H. Failure of traditional prognostic indicators in Afro-Asian psychotics: Results of a long-term follow-up survey. Journal of Nervous and Mental Disease, 1972, 154, 228-247.

Schneider, K. Clinical psychopathology. Translated by M.W. Hamilton. New York: Grune and Stratton, 1959.

Spitzer, R.L., and Endicott, J. Diagno II: Further developments in a computer program for psychiatric diagnosis. American Journal of Psychiatry, 1969, 125, 12-21.

Stephens, J.H., and Astrup, C.  Treatment outcome in "process
    and "nonprocess" schizophrenics treated by "A" and "B"
    types of therapists.  Journal of Nervous and Mental
    Disease, 1965, 140, 449-456.

Strauss, J.S., and Carpenter, W.T., Jr.  The prediction of
    outcome in schizophrenia. I. Characteristics of out-
    come.  Archives of General Psychiatry, 1972, 27, 739-
    746.

Strauss, J.S., Bartko, J.J., and Carpenter, W.T., Jr.  The
    use of clustering techniques for the classification
    of psychiatric patients.  British Journal of Psychiatry,
    1973, 122, 531-540.

Strauss, J.S., and Carpenter, W.T., Jr.  Characteristic
    symptoms and outcome in schizophrenia.  Archives of
    General Psychiatry, 1974, 30, 429-434.

Strauss, J.S., and Carpenter, W.T., Jr.  The evaluation of
    outcome in schizophrenia.  In M. Roff, and D. Ricks
    (Eds), Life history research in psychopathology.
    Vol. 3.  Minneapolis:  University of Minnesota Press,
    1974, pp. 313-335.

Strauss, J.S., and Carpenter, W.T., Jr.  The prediction of
    outcome in schizophrenia. II.  Relationships between
    predictor and outcome variables:  A report from the
    WHO International Pilot Study of Schizophrenia.  Archives
    of General Psychiatry, 1974, 31, 37-42.

Strauss, J.S., and Carpenter, W.T., Jr.  Prediction of outcome
    in schizophrenia. III.  Five-year outcome and its pre-
    dictors:  A report from the International Pilot Study
    of Schizophrenia.  Archives of General Psychiatry.  In
    press.

Swensen, C., and Pascal, G.  Duration of illness as a prognost
    indicator in mental illness.  Journal of Consulting
    Psychology, 1954, 18, 363-365.

Vaillant, G.  The prediction of recovery in schizophenia.
    Journal of Nervous and Mental Disease, 1962, 135, 534-543

Vaillant, G.  Prospective prediction of schizophrenic remissic
    Archives of General Psychiatry, 1964, 11, 509-518.

Wing, J.K., Cooper, J.E., and Sartorius, N. The measurement
   and classification of psychiatric symptoms. London:
   Cambridge University Press, 1974.

Wittman, M.P. Scale for measuring prognosis in schizophrenic
   patients. Elgin State Hospital Papers, 1941, 4, 20-33.

World Health Organization. The International Pilot Study of
   Schizophrenia. Vol 1. Geneva: World Health Organization Press, 1973.

APPENDIX I

Strauss-Carpenter Levels of Function Scale and Item Reliabili

INSTRUCTIONS: RATE THE MOST USUAL FUNCTION IN PAST YEAR,
EXCEPT FOR ITEM 4.

1.  DURATION OF NON-HOSPITALIZATION FOR PSYCHIATRIC DISORDER
    (r=.95)

    Not in hospital in past year (exclude hospitali-
        zation at time of first interview if less than
        one month duration following interview)...........4
    Hospitalized less than 3 months in past year.........3
    Hospitalized 3-6 months during past year.............2
    Hospitalized over 6 months up to 9 months during
        past year........................................1
    Hospitalized more than 9 months in past year.........0

2A. FREQUENCY OF SOCIAL CONTACTS (r=.90)

    NUMBER OF SOCIAL RELATIONS (Meets with friends or does
    things with social groups, bowling, meetings, etc.
    EXCLUDE dates with opposite sex or social activities
    only with spouse. Use pertinent data from BOTH
    Social Data and History Forms.)

    (Do not include meetings with friends at work or "over
    the back fence.")

    Meets with friends on average of at least once
        a week...........................................4
    Meets with friends about once every two weeks........3
    Meets with friends about once a month................2

---

INCLUDE ALL ACQUAINTANCES

    Does not meet with friends except "over the back
        fence" or at work or school......................1
    Does not meet with friends at all under any
        conditions.......................................0

2B.  QUALITY OF SOCIAL RELATIONS (In relations, described
     in 2A, what has he had most usually in past year?)
     (r-.73)

     One or more close relationships......................4
     One or more rather close relationships...............3
     One or more moderately close relationships...........2
     Only rather superficial relationships................1
     Only very superficial relationships (e.g., only
         relationship is saying hello to neighbors).......0


3A.  QUANTITY OF USEFUL WORK IN PAST YEAR (Include as job:
     paid work, student, housewife. Excluded time in hosp-
     ital. Any hospitalization in past year would not con-
     tribute to lower score. Working as a student for a full
     academic year would be rated "4." (r=.74)

     "Employed" full-time continuously....................4
     "Employed" for about 3/4 of the year's working
         hours (e.g., full-time work for about 9
         months.......................................... 3
     "Employed" for about 1/2 of the year's working
         hours (e.g., employed half-time continuously
         or full time for 6 months........................2
     "Employed" for about 1/4 of the year's working
         hours (e.g., half-time work for 6 months)........1
     No useful work.......................................0


3B.  QUALITY OF USEFUL WORK (Consider in regard to person's
     age, education, training, and opportunities available
     - but not compensating for his psychopathology, how he
     is functioning in the area of work in regard to expec-
     table level of complexity and competence of which he
     should be capable.)

     Very competent.......................................4
     Competent............................................3
     Moderately competent.................................2
     Marginally competent.................................1
     Incompetent..........................................0

4.  ABSENCE OF SYMPTOMS (IN PAST MONTH) (r=.73)

    No signs or symptoms..................................4
    Slight signs or symptoms most of the time or
        moderate signs and symptoms on rare occasions.....3
    Moderate signs and symptoms some of the time.........2
    Severe signs and symptoms some of the time or
        moderate signs and symptoms continuously..........1
    Continuous and severe signs and symptoms.............0


5.  ABILITY TO MEET OWN BASIC NEEDS IN PAST YEAR (FEED
    SELF, KEEP CLEAN)*

    Needs no help with these things.....................4
    Needs a little help with these things...............3
    Needs some help with these things...................2
    Needs considerable help with these things...........1
    Needs total help with these things..................0


6.  FULLNESS OF LIFE IN PAST YEAR (r=.79)

    Very full life......................................4
    Full life...........................................3
    Moderately full life................................2
    Relatively empty life...............................1
    Vegatative existence................................0


7.  OVERALL LEVEL OF FUNCTION IN PAST YEAR (r=.85)

    (Consider as baseline a hypothetical "normal" person
    with full employment, meaningful social relationships,
    no symptoms, etc.)

    No impairment.......................................4
    Slight impairment most of the time or moderate
        impairment on rare occasions....................3
    Moderate impairment some of the time ...............2
    Severe impairment some of the time or moderate
        impairment continuously.........................1
    Continuous and severe impairment....................0


*Insufficient variance for intraclass correlations.  Ratings
of "4" made by both raters in 25 of 29 comparisons.

8.    TOTAL OUTCOME SCORE (SUM OF ALL THE RATINGS ON ABOVE ITEMS) RANGE 0-36 ($r=.95$)

Open Discussion


Sells:  You have 12 diagnostic symptoms that identified
people as schizophrenic and this is the optimal list; but do
you have any way of being confident that the sample that
qualifies on these criteria is truly homogeneous with regard
to some process, so that when you compare your outcome you
can have confidence that your results reflect the operation
of a common process?  Is it not possible that there may be
more than one process going on associated with the key diagnostic criteria?

Carpenter:  You are right.  I assume, in fact, that you
identify a very heterogeneous group of people using any mental status criteria for a schizophrenic diagnosis.  There
are various ways you can reduce the homogeneity of your population to fit various needs.  For example, if you're doing
a biologic study of a presumably heritable defect, you may
require a first-degree relative be diagnosed schizophrenic
in an attempt to increase genetic homogeneity.  If the purpose of the study were to look only at people who have a
chronic course, you'd have to put variables into the diagnostic scheme that will predict chronicity.  We assume that there
are multiple processes involved in any schizophrenic cohort
identified by sign and symptom criteria.

Sells:  I appreciate why you're doing this, and I applaud
it, but I am voicing what I would consider to be a doctrin-
aire opposition to the tendency to ignore individual differences in cultural background, age, and numerous other factors.
I feel that everyone who has symptoms of this kind has some
pattern of functioning which reflects selectivity attributable
to cultural rules, values attached to various outcomes and the
like; that people who have been deprived of opportunity look
at the world differently than people who haven't been deprived
and that the whole domain of individual differences is relevant.  Both in the high-risk studies and in these studies I
haven't seen any evidence that people are considered as
differing or varying, but just that anybody with a particular
set of symptoms is alike.  Eventually this must be corrected.

Carpenter:  I had hoped that this point had been made
in my presentation.  We think that using certain symptom
criteria for diagnosis, a group of patients is identified
with some important similarities, but quite diverse in other

respects such as outcome or premorbid features. As for age, culture, and other such factors, these must always be taken into account by the clinician in making his judgements as to the presence and nature of psychopathology.

Strauss: We have, in fact, been interested in multiple processes and are working on a multiaxial diagnostic system which will do just the kind of thing you're saying. In that system the symptoms would be one axis, but then social relations functioning would be a separate diagnostic axis, work functioning another, chronicity another, and so forth. The kind of point you're making may be best conceptualized in that framework.

Wynne: This study actually emphasizes the importance of looking at variables other than symptoms, because of the limited information that you get from symptoms alone; I believe there is consensus on this point.

Harrow: In relation to the question of homogeneity and heterogeneity, we have a similar situation with our New Haven Schizophrenia Index. There is no knowledge of what the schizophrenic "process" is, or if there is such a thing. So there is no final criteria for any of the Strauss-Carpenter work, for Spitzer's work, or ours, or any of the others; but at least what these approaches do is ensure replicability. Namely, when someone in Nigeria or someone in Texas wants to study schizophrenics to see whether they get the same results, they can at least use the scale. Now whether you're really dealing with "true" schizophrenics, that's a different question since as of now there are no absolute criteria. But at least with the use of an automatic index you are talking about the same people, and in the past that hasn't even been the case.

Zubin: I think the beauty of the International Pilot Study of Schizophrenia is the fact that despite the claims that schizophrenia doesn't occur in some cultures, that despite the fact that it appears differently, there were 12 diagnostic items which really existed throughout all these 9 cultures. I think that's something we shouldn't lose sight of.

Now on the other side, on the side of outcome, I'm sure that employment doesn't mean the same thing in Nigeria that it means in Washington; and so I think, the point is whether

you can begin to develop profiles of outcome indices, just
as we have profiles in psychopathology, across these different aspects of outcome which you have pointed to in your
correlational table.  Maybe outcome can be viewed not only b
the psychiatrists but from the point of view of the patient,
the point of view of the family, and the point of view of
society, to see if we can get some sort of typology of outco
which we can then use.  If you have 1200 patients, you ought
to be able to develop some typology that might reflect struc
tures of outcome which can then begin to mean something.

Tsuang:  I would also like to make the same point.  I
think Dr. Zubin mentioned a very important issue.  When we
participated in the International Pilot Study of Schizophren
investigators from each center rated Social History schedule
and also rated the outcome of their own study samples from
each of the 9 participating centers.  So with all the data
available, we ought to be able to design an outcome scale
that will be applicable cross-culturally.

Strauss:  Unfortunately, cross-cultural evaluation of
outcome function is much more complicated, I think, even
than comparing symptoms.  It's harder because you have more
serious problems of cultural relativism.  I described in a
recent paper in more detail how the specific social norms
and situations are particularly troublesome.

Bruce Dohrenwend:  It seems to me that a lot of the
problem with using social function as a measure of outcome
is that the exclusive focus on patients virtually forces you
into arbitrary decisions.  You either consider only such extreme disability that nobody's going to argue with you, or
you introduce ideal criteria that may lead you to a measure
of social functioning or dysfunctioning that is only in small
part due to the psychiatric condition.  The apparent disability could actually be due to a large number of other social
and cultural factors and have nothing to do with psychiatric
conditions.  It seems to me that the problem here comes from
failure to use normative data on social functioning from general population samples drawn from the particular social and
cultural group that corresponds to the patient group that
you're working with.  I know this is somewhat difficult practically.  It means you have more people to see, more intervie
to do and so on, but theoretically it's not a problem.  I
think part of the problem here is too restricted a focus on
your patient groups and not enough on the wider community.

# GENERAL DISCUSSION OF SECTION IV

Formal Discussant:  Gerard E. Hogarty

Several results reported today dramatically demonstrate
that the effects of treatment would be obscured if potentially confounding design and measurement problems, as those
identified by Dr. Carpenter were not systematically controlled.
For example, Dr. Carpenter stressed the importance of timing
one's evaluation. In our study, we looked at timing from two
points of view. One was repeated measurement over a 2-year
period. If we had settled on a study of outcome only at 6
and 12 months regarding the effects of treatment on performance and adjustment, we would have come away empty handed.
Those analyses, by and large, were a wasteland. The second
point, regarding timing is even more relevant and has to do
with setting. Traditionally, the prediction of long-term
outcome among schizophrenic patients has been based on earlier measures of inpatient adjustment, as well as upon other
background and historical characteristics. These prior
attempts at predicting outcome particularly using inpatient
ratings have not been rewarding. This has been demonstrated
both in a comprehensive review of the literature by Elsworth
back in 1968, and from the work of Drs. Carpenter and Strauss,
at least as I understand their 2-year and 5-year data.

Dr. Goldberg, on the other hand, demonstrates that sufficient residual variance needed for long term prediction does
exist on clinical measures made at the point of the patient's
admission to a clinic following hospital discharge. This is
somewhat remarkable in that all these patients were at least
in partial remission. Since these pre-treatment measures
were related to outcome in general, and specifically to a
negative outcome on sociotherapy, I think a clear message
exists; that prediction from one setting to another is not
very productive, but that prediction within the same setting
over time is relatively productive. I think Elsworth's work
also underscores that fact.

Regarding the interpretation of Dr. Goldberg's findings,
one could argue, as people have, that the positive and negative effects of social therapy may not be so much a function
of how "good" or "poor" the patients are prognostically
(in terms of premorbid characteristics), but are a function

371

of how "symptomatic" patients were following hospital discharge.

Another important methodologic point is one that Leff
and Wing make: that good prognostic patients often do not
enter controlled after-care trials, especially those involving drugs.  Dr. Goldberg's data suggest that good prognostic patients do not profit from chemotherapy; but it is
possible that the good prognostic patients described by Leff
were not represented in any great number in Dr. Goldberg's
study.  I'm not saying that this is a unique characteristic
of this study; it may be a function of studies done with any
sample of formerly hospitalized patients from public institutions in the United States.  For example, it is possible
that with the increased availability of community treatment
resources, that the acute, good premorbid, young, first-
episode, rapid-onset patients are screened out at the commun:
ty level, leaving an intermediate or poor prognostic group
of patients to enter public mental hospitals.  What is
useful then for predicting outcome for this group is the
level of residual symptomatology at hospital discharge and
not necessarily the traditional prognostic signs which may
well be poorly represented.

Another potential methodological problem is the obvious
one of defining the characteristics of study patients.
These must be clearly delineated before comparisons can be
made across studies.  John Strauss has made a good case for
the use of commonly agreed upon criteria for classifying
patients along dimensions other than diagnosis.  Within the
concept of diagnosis, we have included such measures as
premorbid history, social effectiveness, and similar variables.  Because of the problems in comparability, I shall
not argue with anybody else's work regarding the outcome of
schizoprhenia because I think we have all been dealing with
different parts of the elephant, so to speak.

Another comment on the methodological problems of
follow-up studies has to do again with whether the studies
are naturalistic or controlled.  While numerous justificatior
have been made for naturalistic studies, I would concur with
the statement made earlier that the principal contribution
of the naturalistic follow-up study is in hypothesis generating, and not in hypothesis testing.  This is especially true
when the effects of treatment are at issue, and when evidence

exists that more of the variance on outcome can be explained by interim treatment experiences than by patient background characteristics.

Further, I think that when we look at community tenure (that's probably a bad word to use in an academic setting) it seems more fruitful to view personal characteristics and treatment conditions in an interactive manner. Rather than univariate comparisons, the interactive model is more satisfactory. Unfortunately, there is also a problem: the interactive model is potentially maddening. As the number of significant interactions increases, particularly the higher order ones, our ability to reliably test and validly interpret findings decreases.

Another methodological note appropriate to follow-up studies argues against pooling outcome measures of relapse with the outcome measures of adjustment. In controlled follow-up studies involving treatment comparisons, most variance on behavioral measures is associated with relapse, as it was in our study. Relapse in our study was largely attributed to placebo. Knowing that the greater proportion of variance in adjustment ratings is due to relapse on placebo, then pooling ratings (as in the end point analyses), of both relapses and survivors, will obscure important treatment effects not due to relapse. We demonstrated the value of separate analyses by our results which describe the patients.

A final methodologic note on follow-up studies has to do with the selection of assessment instruments. In the absence of an experimental control, as in the naturalistic study or in controlled trials where the psychotherapy condition is not capable of being blinded, multiple observations from many points of view are necessary: from patients; psychiatrists; social workers and family members. They provide an opportunity to cross validate results from one observer to another. I'm at a loss to think of any other way to proceed when you can't double blind your treatment condition. The impact of treatment upon adjustment reported by Dr. Goldberg at 18 and 24 months, was not only replicated across 3 clinics, but was substantiated by observations made by the patients, the doctors, the social workers, and the family members.

Formal Discussant:   Martin Harrow

    Considering the results presented here and follow-up
research in general, a number of points emerge about methodology, and we should try to keep a reasonable perspective
about the real advances we have made in the last 40 years.
Despite our hesitant, apologetic approach, there has been a
good deal of progress in methodology over the years, especially since the 1930's. If you look back on the literature
in this area, you find that in the late '30's and early
'40's people were conducting extremely primitive follow-up
studies. Even well-known people were directing studies where
they would send a social worker out to ask a group of patient
"are you better, worse, or the same," and they would jot
down what the patient would say:  and the patient would
sometimes say, "well, actually, it isn't that simple," and
the patient would try to go on and they would say "no, I'm
sorry I just want to know whether you're better, worse, or
the same." We've come a long way since then.

    There are a number of areas where our methodology has
improved. For one, we have standardized scales for evaluating specific areas, such as social functioning. Myrna
Weissman has written a very nice review article on that
recently. We owe it to Strauss and Carpenter here for
providing evidence that social and work functioning levels
may not always be as closely related to each other as was
once thought. We have much greater potential replicability
in diagnosis now, too, as a result of new diagnostic scales.
The Carpenter-Strauss scale is one such instrument, another
is our own New Haven Schizophrenia Index; the St. Louis
group has done a very good job in this area, and Spitzer has
also contributed markedly. I think we've all been caught in
the bandwagon, a constructive bandwagon. Even though it
does not get at the final word on what is schizophrenia, at
least we're all talking about the same samples and variables;
and there is the potential of replicability across different
groups.

    Recently, we have become increasingly aware of more
subtle problems that we should also be trying to solve. One
of the very perplexing ones is the problem in longitudinal
studies of how to control for initial scores when you're
comparing groups that are not equated initially that way in
nature. It's a problem for which there may be no perfect
solution. It has some similarity with comparing the lion

with the moose for hunting ability. Believing that one has
to correct for the moose not having a big jaw and big teeth,
one gives the moose big teeth to equate the two, but then
finds out that we are not dealing with a moose any more. So
although there are statistical corrections, equating groups
who are not really equated in nature does not always result
in a realistic solution.

Another issue is that there are many disparities between
recent findings and previously accepted beliefs that we may
be able to resolve now with improved methodology. In the old
days, we used to know for sure that schizophrenics did very
much worse than non-schizophrenics; now we have the Strauss-
Carpenter and Carpenter-Strauss findings showing that there
is some difference, but the difference may not be as large
as was once believed. It isn't clear, though, as to why
we're getting different results from those of the past. One
feature which is absolutely clear is that we need more long-
term studies being conducted to analyze various aspects of
outcome more closely.

Our own research on disordered thinking has also produced a number of disparities from the previous literature.
There was the old belief that schizophrenic thought disorders
are permanent, that once you see someone with a schizophrenic
thought disorder, this is something that continues over
time. That may be the case for some schizophrenics, but we
have found a good number for whom it wasn't true. These and
other results of ours suggest to us that during the early
phases, schizophrenia may be a phasic, rather than a continuous disorder for many patients. Perhaps these kinds of
disparities between old and new results can be resolved with
the newer research techniques. At any rate, if we compare
our present methodologies with those of 40 years ago we find
marked advances in technology, with our newer methodologies
holding considerable promise.

Tsuang: I'd like to talk more about prognosis in
schizophrenia and long-term follow-up. We have some data
from our 35-year follow-up of schizophrenics selected according to the Feighner criteria and use the outcome criteria of
"recovered;" that a person has no psychiatric symptoms at the
time of follow-up, is working, not institutionalized, and
married. Twelve percent of schizophrenics are classified as
"recovered" 35 years later. So far we have information on

80% of our 200 schizophrenics. And it's very interesting
that we are not very far from Kraepelin's report that 13% of
schizophrenics recovered.

Harrow: I don't think it's the criteria. I would
agree with your results. What I would say is that there are
no longer as large a percentage of schizophrenics who go
drastically downhill as there may have been in Kraepelin's
time. What you have instead is a moderate to large percentage of schizophrenic patients who are functioning more
poorly than the average citizen, but are not deteriorating
drastically.

Carpenter: If you build chronicity into your diagnostic
system, as with the St. Louis criteria, you will find a
chronic population at outcome. If chronicity measures are
omitted from the initial diagnostic criteria, you may or may
not end up with a chronic population.

Tsuang: At least you know what kind of schizophrenics
we're talking about. Feighner criteria require 6 months
continuous symptoms for a diagnosis of schizophrenia.

Carpenter: Yes, but those findings just might not be
relevant to acute schizophrenics.

Vaillant: I think some of the controversy regarding
the outcome of schizophrenia can be pushed aside if we
realize that we aren't going to be able to answer these
questions without looking at very long-term follow-ups more
than 2 or 3 years. One of the things that happens with the
Feighner criteria is that you exclude most of the schizophrenics who could be expected to go on to a complete remission. Conversely, if you take the group of schizophrenics
that have recovered, the remitting schizophrenics, who were
excluded by the Feighner criteria - the schizophrenics will
remit according to predictable criteria, like acute onset,
good premorbid adjustment, and heredity positive for manic-
depressive psychosis. In talking about different results,
it is important to have the diagnostic criteria clearly
spelled out in advance and also to talk about schizophrenics
looked at for not 5 or 10 years, but for longer periods of
time.

# Section V

# Relationships among Variables Affecting
# Development and Course of Psychopathology

# DETECTING PREDICTORS OF RARE EVENTS: DEMOGRAPHIC, FAMILY, AND PERSONAL DEVIANCE AS PREDICTORS OF STAGES IN THE PROGRESSION TOWARD NARCOTIC ADDICTION

Lee N. Robins, Darlene H. Davis, and Eric Wish
Department of Psychiatry
Washington University Medical School
4940 Audubon Avenue
St. Louis, Missouri

Demographic characteristics, family patterns, and personal history are the three tools we use most in attempting to explain life history outcomes, whether favorable or unfavorable. These explanatory variables usually serve us well, if somewhat monotonously, so long as the outcome is neither close to invariate nor extremely rare. Most forms of psychopathology, fortunately for society and unfortunately for solving questions of causation, tend to be rare events. When we try to predict these rare events, our variables often do not perform well at all. Finding explanatory variables means accounting for the variance, but the rarer the event we wish to explain, the less variance is there to explain. The resulting small target is hard to hit. Thus we can predict arrests, which are common, but not the particular charge for which arrested, because each is relatively rare. When the demographic, family, and personal predictors describe large segments of the population, they are certain to be poor predictors of rare events, since they select more people than will have the rare event. We can sometimes improve their specificity by requiring multiple predictors, but even this maneuver often fails because the predictors are sufficiently intercorrelated so that their intersections still select too large a proportion of our sample. Indeed, if the event is sufficiently rare, we often find that a prediction that the event will not occur at all works better than trying to specify the persons to whom it will happen.

One way out of this dilemma is to decompose rare
events into a series of developmental stages, and apply
our predictors to the transitions from one stage to the
next, rather than trying to predict the final event immediately. This technique successively reduces the population
at risk of the next transition, by restricting it to those
who made the preceding transition. In this way, predictors
of the final transition can be distinguished from predictors of antecedent steps. Since the population at risk
declines as the events to be predicted becomes less common,
the event that is rare in the population at large is no
longer rare in the restricted population immediately at
risk.

There is nothing new about defining the "population
at risk" in which one is to search for predictors of an
outcome. What is less common is sequentially defining
successively diminishing "populations at risk." A productive use of this idea is seen in the work by Fink, Shapiro,
et al. (1969), who undertook to explain which groups came
to psychotherapy under the HIP medical care program. They
started with the observation that members in psychiatric
treatment were disproportionately formerly married, Jewish,
female, young, and college educated. They then decomposed
the process of entering psychiatric treatment into the
steps of (1) seeing the family physician, (2) the physician's
making a psychiatric diagnosis, (3) his decision to refer
the diagnosed patient to a psychiatrist, and (4) the
patient's seeking treatment and being treated by the
psychiatrist. They called this decomposition the "filter-
down" process. They found that some of the correlations
they had observed as related to psychiatric treatment had
effects only at early stages in the process, while others
had an effect only at the later stages. For instance, the
reason that being Jewish was associated with more psychiatric treatment was not because there was an increased rate
of psychiatric diagnosis by the family physician, but only
because Jews were more likely to visit the family physician
in the first place. Young females, on the other hand, were
likely to be perceived as having a psychiatric diagnosis
by the family physician, although they had no special tendency to seek medical care initially, nor to be accepted
for psychiatric treatment if such a diagnosis was made.

Entering psychiatric treatment under the HIP program was an appropriate outcome to study by means of decomposition into stages, because the only route to psychiatric care under this health plan was by progressing through the whole series of stages, each of which selected successively smaller populations as at risk. It is not clear that most rare life history outcomes require progression through equally clear stages. Such a progression through stages was suggested for alcoholism by Jellinek, but there is still no general agreement that there is a necessary, inviolable order of progression through his symptom list. However, at the grossest level, one necessary transition is clear: one cannot become an alcoholic without considerable drinking. And considerable drinking in turn, requires a transition out of the state of teetotaler. In our society, the transition from teetotaler to drinker is so nearly universal that including that transition is not very helpful in reducing the population at risk of becoming problem drinkers. In an earlier paper (Robins et al., 1962), however, we showed that it was useful to decompose problem drinking as an outcome into the transition into heavy drinking and the transition from heavy drinking to problem drinking. While both demographic and personal history characteristics predicted problem drinking, we found that the power of the demographic characteristics ended once they contributed to heavy drinking: being male and being of Irish descent were related to heavy drinking but not to the progression to problem drinking among heavy drinkers.

Decomposition of rare behaviors into various stages may be useful in informing public policy as well as in satisfying our curiosity about the genesis of rare events, because it may identify predictors that apply only to that sub-population for whom the risks of psychopathology are very great. Public intervention is seen as legitimate to the extent that the portion of the population at high risk of pathology constitutes a large proportion of the persons affected by the policy. Prohibition of alcohol, for instance, is offensive to most of the public not only because it is difficult to enforce but also because alcoholism is so rare as compared with the frequency of drinking itself. Reducing alcohol consumption by raising prices via taxation, while less noxious than total prohibition because the tax paid is proportionate to the quantities consumed, still discriminates economically by preventing drinking among

those no more likely to become alcoholics but less able to
afford liquor taxes.

Narcotic addiction, the form of psychopathology to
which I will attempt to apply the principle of decomposition into developmental stages in the present paper, is a
more appealing candidate than is alcoholism for public
intervention by reducing supplies without regard to the
users' likelihood of addiction. While narcotic addiction
is even rarer than alcoholism, addicts represent a substantial proportion of all who use narcotics at all, since any
illicit narcotic use is still unusual in our society. Nonetheless, discriminating predictors of progression from one
developmental stage of narcotic addiction from predictors
of progression into the next may point to loci where intervention is more feasible than drying up the sources of all
illicit narcotics has proved to be.

Descriptions of narcotic addicts arrested or in treatment tell us what kind of predictors to look for. Addicts
tend to be young, minority group, inner-city males, often
from disrupted homes, with a personal history of poor job
records, school dropout, and arrests for a variety of
offenses, who began their drug careers with marijuana or
glue, and progressed to a variety of other drugs before
becoming involved with narcotics. These demographic,
family, and personal history characteristics of addicts
have been observed by comparing their characteristics with
census and arrest data for the population as a whole. It
is also known from interviews with addicts that they came
to narcotics at the end of a progression from one illicit
drug to the next. These findings suggest that there are
four types of predictors of narcotic addiction: demographic
factors, parental factors, personal deviance-proneness,
and prior drug exposure. However, there are three important questions about these predictors that cannot be an-
swered by studying samples consisting entirely of addicts:
to what extent are these four types of predictors independent of each other, to what extent are the elements making
up each type (i.e., age, sex, race, city size in the demographic factor) mutually independent, and at what stages
in the addiction process does each type of predictor
operate? To answer these questions, one needs a general
population, only some of whom become addicts.

A recent follow-up of returned Vietnam soldiers allows us to investigate these issues because it provides both addicted and nonaddicted subjects. Thus, we can see which characteristics led to a transition from one stage to the next and which did not. In looking at addiction among veterans shortly after their return from Vietnam, we found not only the obvious necessary prior stage, that all addicts had used narcotics since their return, but an additional necessary stage prior to that one--that they had also used narcotics in Vietnam. No man used narcotics within the first ten months after return who had not also used them in Vietnam, no doubt reflecting the fact that the great availability of narcotics in Vietnam exhausted the market of potential users. Thus, for men addicted since their return, we have three stages of involvement that can be examined: use of narcotics in Vietnam, continuation of use after return among those who used them in Vietnam, and addiction to narcotics after return among men who continued their use in the United States. We considered adding a fourth stage-- addiction in Vietnam among Vietnam users--because most of those addicted since their return had also been addicted in Vietnam. However, there were a few who reported addiction in the United States who had used narcotics in Vietnam without becoming addicted there, so that earlier addiction was a common but not a necessary stage in the development of addiction after return.

One of the most striking findings from the study of Vietnam veterans was how rare addiction was in the first year after return. Only 1.5 percent of veterans were addicted in that first year, even though 20 percent reported having been addicted in Vietnam. Addiction in this paper is defined as meeting three out of four of the following criteria: Use of narcotics more than once a week, feeling dependent on narcotics, having at least two of four classic symptoms of withdrawal when narcotics were discontinued for a day or more--chills, stomach cramps, insomnia, muscle pain--and these withdrawal symptoms lasting for at least two days.

As we shall see, decomposition of the addiction process into its three component stages was helpful, as shown by the fact that the proportion of variance explained at each stage was greater than the proportion of variance explained overall. However, decomposition does not

magically increase the number of addicts available for
the paucity of positive cases. Fortunately, not only was
our sample reasonably large, but we heavily over-sampled
that portion of the veteran population that turned out to
produce most of the post-Vietnam addicts, those soldiers
detected as drug positive at departure from Vietnam.  If
we had not done so, even our sample of 898 Army enlisted
men would have yielded only 13 or 14 addicts in the first
year after return.  Instead we have 38 men who met our
criteria for addiction within the first eight to twelve
months after return, four from a simple random sample of
451 veterans and the remainder from a sample of 469 men
detected as drug positive at departure.  To adjust for
our oversampling of the high risk group, we will weight
the soldiers detected as drug positive appropriately so
that our results pertain to enlisted Army men who left
Vietnam for the United States in Septebmer, 1971 as a
whole.  We will, however, provide unweighted N's throughout, so that it will be clear on how many interviews each
calculation was actually based.


                          THE STUDY


        The results presented here come from a follow-up study
of 943 Army enlisted men who served in Vietnam and departed for the United States in September, 1971 (Robins, 1974).
Military records were obtained for 99 percent and interviews from 96 percent of those surviving (six had died).
Urine samples were obtained at the end of the interview to
validate the reports of current drug use.  The low incidence
of positive urines and high level (97%) of self-reported
heroin use in Vietnam among those whose military records
showed them to be known heroin users, plus the high rate of
self-reported addiction (74%) among men detected as drug
positive in urine screening at departure from Vietnam, make
it reasonable to have confidence in self-reports of drug
use and addiction both in and after Vietnam.  The very minimal loss of interviews by refusal or failure to locate assures
us that results are representative for our population.

        The information used to discover predictors of addic-
tion since Vietnam came mainly from the interview.  Men
were asked about the size of the city in which they grew
up; their parents' history of drinking problems, arrests,

and drug use; whether they lived with both parents until
they were age 16 and if not how the home was broken; their
own preservice history of drug use; and their preservice
history of a variety of types of non-drug deviance, including reasons for leaving school prematurely, truancy,
fighting, early drunkenness, and arrests. Information
about their race and age came from their military records.
Parent's occupation was also asked about, but turned out
to be so weakly related to preservice drug use or use in
Vietnam that it seemed improbable that it would add to our
ability to predict later use. This failure of family
occupational status to predict drug taking has been noted
in previous studies (Johnston, 1973; Robins and Murphy,
1967).

The preservice variables were grouped into four predictor scales: Demographic, including age, race, and
whether reared within the core city of a metropolitan area;
Parental, including whether the home was broken by divorce,
separation, or non-marriage, and arrests, drug use, and
drinking problems in parents; Own Behavior, consisting of
nondrug deviance including arrests, school dropout and
expulsion, truancy, fighting, and early drunkenness; and
Prior Drug Experience, including the use of marijuana,
amphetamines, barbiturates, or narcotics. The Prior
Drug Experience can be regarded as a trend predictor which
requires no theoretical interpretation. It is a general
observation that people who have done something before are
more likely to do it again than are persons who have not
done it before. Scale scores were obtained by summing the
scores on each element included within a scale.

This report describes the investigation of four
questions: (1) Does the procedure of summing scores produce coherent and reasonably independent predictors? We
evaluated this by contrasting the correlations among elements within scales with the correlations among elements
from different scales and by the level of correlation between pairs of scales. (2) What is the effect of each
component element and of the scale of which it is a member on post-Vietnam drug addiction overall, and on progression through the three developmental stages we have
outlined: use of narcotics in Vietnam, continuation of use
after Vietnam among those who used in Vietnam, and
addiction after Vietnam among those who used after Vietnam?

(3)   What is the joint contribution of the four predictor
scales as determined by multivariate techniques?  We used
these techniques to learn how much each predictor scale
contributes independently of the others to predicting post-
Vietnam addiction and its three development stages.  (4)
Finally, are the predictors of addiction liability dependent on the social setting?  This was evaluated by comparing
the contribution of these predictors to explaining addiction
in the United States with their contribution to explaining
addiction liability in Vietnam.


RESULTS

Intercorrelations Among Preservice Variables

The preservice predictor scales were created in the
conventional way, by putting together items which seemed
conceptually similar.  It is possible that items which
seemed conceptually similar to us are really not highly
associated with each other.  On the other hand, they may be
so highly associated as to be redundant.  In this section,
we will examine the extent of their association and the
possibility of redundancy.

Table 1 shows the results of intercorrelating all four
scales and all their elements.  Definitions of the elements
and their scale values can be found in the stub of the lower
section of Table 2.

Each scale was found to be positively correlated with
each of the other three.  The three largest correlations all
involved the Own Behavior scale.  The largest of all was
between Own Behavior and Drug Use.  That this should be the
largest relationship is not surprising, since both the Drug
and Own Behavior scales reflect personal deviant behavior.
We kept them separate in order to distinquish the continuation of drug behavior itself from the effect of other behaviors on narcotic use.

While all scales are positively correlated, the correlations are low and similar to each other, verying only from
a gamma of .20 to a gamma of .35.  Since none is so strong
as to suggest redundancy, their contributions to explaining
any outcome should be roughly additive.  We will test this

Table 1

Intercorrelations (Gammas) Among Pre-Service Variables

A. Scales

| | Parent | Own Behavior | Demography | Drugs |
|---|---|---|---|---|
| Parent | | .28 | .20 | .26 |
| Own Behavior | | | .33 | .35 |
| Demographic | | | | .27 |
| Drugs | | | | |

B. Scale Elements

| | | Parent | Behavior | | | | | Demography | | | Drugs |
|---|---|---|---|---|---|---|---|---|---|---|---|
| | | Prob | School | Arrest | Drunk | Truant | Fight | Central City | Black | Young | |
| Parent | Div/Sep | .64 | .34 | .20 | + | .32 | + | .41 | .28 | + | .21 |
| | Problems | | .29 | .31 | + | .22 | + | + | + | + | .27 |
| Behavior | School | | | .48 | .39 | .69 | .34 | + | − | .41 | + |
| | Arrest | | | | .48 | .45 | .38 | − | − | .33 | .27 |
| | Drunk | | | | | .47 | .38 | − | −.22 | .47 | .43 |
| | Truant | | | | | | .22 | .25 | + | .25 | .29 |
| | Fight | | | | | | | + | − | .28 | .25 |
| Demography | Central City | | | | | | | | .57 | −.23 | .24 |
| | Black | | | | | | | | | −.25 | .22 |
| | Young | | | | | | | | | | .21 |

inference when we combine them in multivariate analysis of their contribution to narcotics addiction.

These correlations were calculated for the whole sample. We also examined correlations among these scales for the reduced samples at risk of entering the latter two stages in the development of addiction, i.e., among narcotic users in Vietnam, which is the sample at risk of continuing their use on return, and among men using narcotics after Vietnam, which is the sample at risk of addiction after Vietnam. None of these correlations was higher than the highest value of .35 in the total sample, and all but two were below .20. Thus, these scales are less closely associated among users of narcotics than in the sample as a whole.

The lower section of Table 1 shows the intercorrelations among the scale elements, both within scales and
across scales. We observe that there is always at least
one within-scale correlation larger than any correlation
between an element of that scale and an element from a
different scale. Furthermore, each element except "Young"
is more strongly correlated with some item within its
scale than with any element from another scale. These
findings suggest that the scales' conceptual homogeneity
is indeed reflected in actual relationships.

While the correlations among the scales were all
positive, not all correlations between elements are
positive. Every element is positively correlated with
drug experience and with both elements of the Parent scale.
However, two of the three intercorrelations within the
Demography scale are negative. Being Young is negatively
associated with being Black and with living in a Central
City. These negative associations apparently reflect the
fact that Blacks are disproportionately represented among
career soldiers, and career soldiers are older than
draftees and first-term volunteers, since induction is at
about the same age for all, but career soldiers sign up for
longer enlistments and then re-enlist. Blacks presumably
re-enlist more readily than whites because of the low
level of occupational opportunities for them in American
society outside the military. Because the Army is more
"color-blind" than most of American industry, it serves
as a "career of last resort" for competent men who cannot
find good jobs elsewhere. The negative correlation between
the item "Young" and the item "Central City" reflects the
fact that these black career soldiers come more from urban
ghettos than from the rural South, where poor education
opportunities prevent their qualifying for careers in service.

Being black is also negatively correlated with four out
of five of the Own Behavior scale elements and inner city
residence with two of the five. Again urban blacks' over-
representation among career soldiers is the probable explanation. Opportunities to remain in service are awarded to
those who conform to regulations, and ability to conform in
service is almost certainly well predicted by an absence of
the deviant preservice behaviors that make up the Behavior
scale. In the military, then, correlations between elements

of the Demographic scale and elements of the Own Behavior
scale are either trivial or the opposite of what one would
expect in a general population of young men.  Rather than
the high rates of deviance usually associated with being
black and living in the inner-city, men with these characteristics have low rates of deviance.  On the other hand,
the usual positive association between being black with
coming from a broken home, having problem parents, and early
drug experience remains, because these characteristics are
irrelevant to the Army's decision processes.  Among black
veterans then, there are a considerable number who have been
exposed to the classic preservice predictors of deviance--
broken homes, large cities, parents with drinking and
arrests--but have somehow managed not to become deviant
themselves.  They are indeed "invulnerables" in Dr. Garmezy's
term.

The opposite side of this coin is that the youngest men
in service are the most deviant.  They are men who volun-
teered because they are unemployable or because they are
restless and use the Army as a means to leave home and
travel.  Sometimes they are "volunteers" in name only,
bargaining with a judge to choose the Army in preference to
jail.

It is conventional in social research to think of
demographic variables as "first causes"--ascribed statuses
that from birth influence subsequent careers.  In fact,
sample selection factors, as in this case entry into service
and selection for remaining in service, can powerfully
influence the nature of relationships between demographic
variables and their supposed consequences.  Demographic
variables act clearly as first causes only in samples
selected in such a way that outcome behaviors cannot influence
the chances of appearing in the sample.  Obviously, a sample
selected from the military does not fulfill this requirement.
(Neither, incidently, do samples selected on the basis of
residence in a geographic sub- area within a larger society.
Both military occupation and neighborhood of residence are
forms of status achievement.  Whenever achievement influences
chances of entry into a sample, the relationship between
demographic variables and variables supposed to be their
consequences should be suspect).  In a military sample, the
demographic variables can be seen as effects as much as
causes: antisocial behavior in youth selects the youngest

men for entry into service, and the absence of antisocial
behavior before service selects certain blacks to remain in
service and thus become the older soldiers.


Association of Preservice Variables with Post-Vietnam
Addiction.

    The first column of Table 2 shows the relationship of
each preservice predictor scale and each element of that scale
to post-Vietnam addiction, taking the sample as a whole.  As
we had expected with an outcome as rare as addiction, none
of the scale scores is associated with a high level of
addiction.  At all levels of all scales and their elements,
addiction remains a rare event.  Among the scales, the top
of the parent scale provides the single highest rate of
addiction, with 4.9 percent addicted. The analysis by scale
element in the lower part of Table 2 shows that this is
attributable mainly to the small group both of whose parents
have had arrests or drinking problems. Sons of such parents,
those expelled from school, and those with multiple arrests
before service are the only categories of soldiers among
whom more than 5% were addicted in the first year back from
Vietnam.

    The best scale predictor of freedom from addiction is
found in the Own Behavior scale, where those without deviant behavior before service are entirely free of addiction.  While the Parent scale provides the best predictor
that addiction will occur and the Own Behavior scale the
best predictor that it will not, the Drug Experience scale
is the best predictor overall, because at its lower end, with
only 0.2% addicted among men who came to Vietnam with no
illicit drug experience, it is almost as useful as the Own
Behavior Scale, and at the upper end, with 4.3% addicted
after return among men who entered service with some familiarity with hard drugs, it is almost as good as the Parent
scale.  The Demographic scale is the weakest, although its
relationship to addiction is positive as hypothesized.

    If we were to do no further analysis of these findings,
they would seem to support the statement a psychiatrist at
the Veterans Administration made to me not long ago.  After
I reported on veterans' experience with drug treatment programs in the VA, this physician said to me "You left out the

Table 2

Pre-Service Predictors of Post-Vietnam
Addiction and its Development

| Pre-Service Scales | Post-Vietnam Addiction | | Developmental Stages | | | | | |
|---|---|---|---|---|---|---|---|---|
| | | | Narcotic Use in Vietnam | | Continuation after Return | | Addiction if Continued | |
| | N | % | N | % | N | % | N | % |
| Drug  0. None | 469 | 0.2 | 469 | 27 | 245 | 13 | 49 | 5 |
|       1. Marijuana only | 130 | 2.5 | 130 | 66 | 110 | 15 | 26 | 24 |
|       2. Hard | 299 | 4.3 | 299 | 77 | 274 | 29 | 114 | 19 |
| Parent  0 | 520 | 0.7 | 520 | 37 | 327 | 20 | 87 | 9 |
|       1 | 263 | 2.0 | 263 | 54 | 212 | 21 | 71 | 18 |
|       2-3 | 115 | 4.9 | 115 | 59 | 90 | 23 | 31 | 36 |
| Own Behavior  0-1 | 152 | 0.0 | 152 | 17 | 59 | 15 | 11 | 0 |
|       2-3 | 308 | 1.6 | 308 | 44 | 209 | 15 | 47 | 25 |
|       4-5 | 260 | 2.2 | 260 | 52 | 201 | 21 | 58 | 21 |
|       6+ | 178 | 2.1 | 178 | 74 | 160 | 30 | 73 | 9 |
| Demographic  0-1 | 128 | 1.3 | 128 | 21 | 51 | 14 | 12 | 45 |
|       2 | 356 | 1.0 | 356 | 40 | 216 | 14 | 50 | 19 |
|       3 | 288 | 2.2 | 288 | 64 | 242 | 25 | 82 | 13 |
|       4 | 126 | 3.0 | 126 | 80 | 120 | 43 | 45 | 9 |
| **Scale Elements** | | | | | | | | |
| Parent | | | | | | | | |
| A.  Drink, Arrest, Drug Problems | | | | | | | | |
|     0. Neither | 639 | 1.0 | 639 | 40 | 426 | 21 | 118 | 12 |
|     1. One | 238 | 2.0 | 238 | 55 | 185 | 16 | 63 | 22 |
|     2. Both | 21 | 16.1 | 21 | 58 | 18 | 59 | 11 | 47 |
| B.  Divorced/Separated | | | | | | | | |
|     0. No | 677 | 0.7 | 677 | 40 | 450 | 12 | 130 | 10 |
|     1. Yes | 221 | 4.2 | 221 | 59 | 179 | 37 | 59 | 36 |
| Own Behavior | | | | | | | | |
| A.  School Completion | | | | | | | | |
|     0. Graduated High School | 552 | 0.6 | 552 | 38 | 348 | 15 | 82 | 11 |
|     1. Dropout | 312 | 2.6 | 312 | 55 | 251 | 24 | 90 | 20 |
|     2. Expelled | 34 | 11.7 | 34 | 74 | 30 | 67 | 17 | 24 |
| B.  Age First Drunk | | | | | | | | |
|     0. After 18, Never | 105 | 0.1 | 105 | 19 | 46 | 5 | 9 | 12 |
|     1. 15-18 | 402 | 1.9 | 402 | 41 | 267 | 19 | 72 | 23 |
|     2. Before 15 | 391 | 1.6 | 391 | 58 | 316 | 24 | 108 | 12 |

Table 2 (Con't.)

| | Post-Vietnam Addiction | | Developmental Stages | | | | | |
|---|---|---|---|---|---|---|---|---|
| | | | Narcotic Use in Vietnam | | Continuation after Return | | Addiction if Continued | |
| | N | % | N | % | N | % | N | % |
| **C. Arrests** | | | | | | | | |
| 0. None | 599 | 0.9 | 599 | 37 | 387 | 19 | 98 | 14 |
| 1. One, two | 202 | 1.0 | 202 | 57 | 157 | 20 | 54 | 8 |
| 2. Three + | 97 | 7.3 | 97 | 68 | 85 | 30 | 37 | 36 |
| **D. Truancy** | | | | | | | | |
| 0. None | 708 | 1.4 | 708 | 40 | 466 | 17 | 123 | 21 |
| 1. Last school year only | 71 | 1.3 | 71 | 58 | 59 | 24 | 16 | 10 |
| 2. Earlier | 119 | 1.7 | 119 | 71 | 104 | 32 | 50 | 8 |
| **E. Fighting** | | | | | | | | |
| 0. Never after 16 | 300 | 2.0 | 300 | 37 | 173 | 23 | 45 | 27 |
| 1. Occasional | 200 | 0.4 | 200 | 48 | 141 | 19 | 38 | 4 |
| 2. Regular | 398 | 1.5 | 398 | 49 | 315 | 19 | 106 | 14 |
| **Demography** | | | | | | | | |
| **A. Central City** | | | | | | | | |
| 0. No | 677 | 1.5 | 677 | 42 | 442 | 21 | 126 | 18 |
| 1. Yes | 225 | 1.2 | 225 | 58 | 183 | 19 | 59 | 12 |
| **B. Black** | | | | | | | | |
| 0. No | 689 | 1.5 | 689 | 42 | 451 | 19 | 126 | 18 |
| 1. Yes | 209 | 1.6 | 209 | 54 | 178 | 30 | 63 | 10 |
| **C. Young at Return** | | | | | | | | |
| 0. No – 23+ | 206 | 1.1 | 206 | 24 | 98 | 11 | 17 | 41 |
| 1. 21, 22 | 461 | 1.2 | 461 | 48 | 330 | 17 | 79 | 14 |
| 2. Yes – <21 | 217 | 3.3 | 217 | 70 | 193 | 35 | 44 | 13 |

most important thing, which is that all the drug patients
used drugs before they ever came into the service." Indeed,
from these data, one would have to say that we know very
little about the prediction of addiction after Vietnam, and
that the only finding that we could report with confidence
is that men who used drugs before service are more likely to
become addicts than those who did not.

However, when we look at the relationships between the
preservice scales and the three stages in the development of
addiction, we find that all the scales have made important
contributions at some stage in the addictive process. Own
Behavior, Demography, and Drugs made important contributions
to narcotic use in Vietnam, where men high on those scales

were about twice as likely to use narcotics as the average
soldier, and men low on those scales were less than half as
likely to use narcotics as the average soldier. Demographic
factors also made an important contribution to the continuation of narcotic use after return. Again, men at the top of
that scale were more than twice as likely to use narcotics
after return as was the average soldier.

When we come to the final step in the development of
post-Vietnam addiction, the liability to addiction after
return if use continued, new patterns emerged. Parents'
behavior, which had been the poorest predictor of use in
Vietnam and of continuation after return, is the only scale
which predicts liability to addiction in a positive linear
fashion. Among men who used narcotics after return and came
from families characterized by divorce and arrest, drinking,
or drug problems in the parents, the risk of addiction was
no longer trivial. More than a third of the narcotic users
from such a background became addicted.

The most surprising finding, however, was the fact that
the Demographic scale, which had predicted use of narcotics
both in and after Vietnam, had a negative relationship to
liability to addiction. The highest liability to addiction
found among any of these predictor scales was found for
users who were atypical users by Demographic criteria.
Almost half (45%) of the older white users outside central
cities became addicts. The fact that demographic determinants acted in opposite fashion when predicting use and when
predicting liability to addiction if one uses accounts for
their low overall effect on post-Vietnam addiction in Column
1. The lower section of Table 2 shows that each individual
element of the Demographic scale behaved in the same way:
High scores for each element favored narcotic use in Vietnam
and after and protected against liability to addiction if
narcotics were used after Vietnam, although the most dramatic reversal is found for the element "Young."

The Own Behavior scale, which had been linearly and
positively related to use in and after Vietnam, was not
related to addiction liability among users in a linear
fashion. Among narcotic users after return, the moderately
antisocial had the highest liability to addiction. None of
the few men who used narcotics after return without any
history of behavior problems before service became addicted,

but addiction liability was also low for the most antisocial
group. A look at the elements of the Own Behavior scale
shows that this irregularity results from averaging elements
that are related to addiction liability in diverse fashions.
Failure to complete high school continued to be associated
with addiction liability in a positive and linear fashion,
just as it had been with earlier stages in the development
of addiction, but Truancy showed the reversal of direction
that we had noted for the Demographic elements. This is not
surprising, since Truancy was the one form of deviance
positively associated with Central City residence (See Table
1). Arrests, Fighting, and Age First Drunk are each associated with addiction liability in a nonlinear fashion, and
highest risks occur at different levels of each of these
variables. High addiction liability occurs for those
arrested three or more times, for those who became drunk for
the first time in the middle age category, i.e., between 15
and 18, and for those who were not fighters before they went
into the service. Any attempt to explain these nonlinear
patterns is inevitably post-hoc, but it is possible that the
relatively low narcotic addiction liability for those who
started serious drinking very early in life may be explained
by their preference for alcohol as their addictive drug.
The relatively high rate of addiction for men who have never
been fighters may have something to do with the association
of addiction with passivity, although at this moment we have
no way of testing this hypothesis.

The contribution of each of our predictor scales to the
overall level of post-Vietnam narcotic addiction (Column 1)
was small, as expected given the rarity of addiction, but
positive and reasonably linear. These scales' contribution
to the first step in addiction, use of narcotics in Vietnam,
was also positive and linear and quite strong as well.
Their contribution to the second developmental step, continuation of narcotics after return, was less strong but continued to be positive and linear. Their contribution to the
final step, liability to addiction if narcotic use continued
in the United States, was reasonably strong but not linear
in two cases (Drug and Own Behavior) and not positive in
another (Demography). The scale least associated with use,
Parents Behavior, was the strongest predictor of addiction
liability and the only scale related to addiction liability
in a positive linear fashion.

In sum, the overall prediction of addiction on return
to the United States was weak only in part because of the
rarity of the outcome variable.  To a large extent it was
weak because the strong positive effect of the Demography
scale on use was cancelled out by its equally strong negative relationship to addiction liability, and because the
highest level of deviance in the Own Behavior scale was also
associated positively with use and negatively with addiction
liability.  In short, with the exception of the Parent
scale, our predictors of narcotic addiction succeed to the
modest extent that they do only because they predict use of
narcotics, not because they are good predictors of addiction
liability.  If the proportion of addicts among users should
drop, we might find them of little further utility.


## Multivariate Analysis

We noted in Table 1 that all the preservice scales were
moderately positively intercorrelated for the overall sample.
This should mean that any attempt at finding their individual
contribution through multivariate analysis should show a
moderate decrease in the contribution of each scale when the
effect of other scales is held constant. To learn the extent
to which an independent contribution was made by each scale
both to post-Vietnam addiction in toto and to its stages of
development, we entered the four scales into a multiple
classification analysis, a system similar to dummy-variable
multiple regression analysis, but not requiring that the
scales be linearly related to outcome (Sonquist, Baker, and
Morgan, 1973).

Table 3 compares percentages from Table 2 with percentages obtained after each scale had been adjusted for the
effects of the other three scales.  (Since we are dealing
with dichotomous outcomes assigned values of 1 or 0, the
adjusted mean is identical with the adjusted percent
positive for the outcome).  The adjusted percentage for each
scale score is an estimate of what that percentage would
have been if persons with that scale score had been distributed exactly like the whole sample on the three other
scales.  As expected, controlling on the effects of the
other scales generally modestly reduced the contribution
attributable to each scale, without chancing the relative
importance of one scale as compared with another. Only one

Table 3

## Multiple Classification Analysis Compared with Cross-Tab Analysis of Effects of Pre-Service Scales on Post-Vietnam Narcotic Addiction

| Pre-Service Scales | Post-Vietnam Narcotic Addiction (N=898) | | Stages in the Development of Post-Vietnam Addiction | | | | | |
| | | | Narcotic Use in Vietnam (N=898) | | Continued Use after Return (N=629) | | Addicted after Return if Use Continued (N=189) | |
| | Cross-Tab % | MCA Adj. % | Cross-Tab % | MCA Adj. % | Cross-Tab % | MCA Adj. % | Cross-Tab % | MCA Adj. % |
|---|---|---|---|---|---|---|---|---|
| Percent Positive | 1.5% | | 44% | | 20% | | 16% | |
| **Drug** [†] | | | | | | | | |
| 0 | 0.2 | 0.3 | 27 | 35 | 13 | 13 | 5 | 9 |
| 1 | 2.5 | 2.3 | 66 | 65 | 15 | 17 | 24 | 23 |
| 2 | 4.3 | 4.0 | 77 | 74 | 29 | 28 | 19 | 18 |
| **Parent** | | | | | | | | |
| 0 | 0.7 | 0.8 | 37 | 42 | 20 | 21 | 9 | 8 |
| 1 | 2.0 | 1.7 | 54 | 46 | 21 | 18 | 18 | 18 |
| 2-3 | 4.9 | 4.4 | 59 | 52 | 23 | 27 | 36 | 39 |
| **Own Behavior** | | | | | | | | |
| 0, 1 ˙ | 0.0 | 0.8 | 16 | 32 | 15 | 15 | 0 | 13 |
| 2, 3 | 1.6 | 1.8 | 44 | 46 | 15 | 16 | 24 | 24 |
| 4, 5 | 2.2 | 1.9 | 52 | 61 | 21 | 21 | 20 | 17 |
| 6+ | 2.1 | 0.8 | 74 | 70 | 30 | 28 | 9 | 11 |
| **Demography** | | | | | | | | |
| 0, 1 | 1.3 | 1.7 | 21 | 33 | 14 | 14 | 44 | 41 |
| 2 | 1.0 | 1.1 | 40 | 46 | 14 | 14 | 19 | 19 |
| 3 | 2.2 | 1.9 | 64 | 61 | 25 | 25 | 13 | 16 |
| 4 | 3.0 | 1.4 | 80 | 70 | 43 | 42 | 9 | 4 |

[†]For N's, see Table 2.

relationship was strengthened when the effect of other scales was taken into account. Parental Behavior showed an even stronger relationship to liability to addiction among users after Vietnam when the effects of other scales were held constant. With the general small reduction in relationships resulting from holding the other predictor variables constant, a few of the weakest relationships became nonlinear. This occurred for Own Behavior and Demography as related to post-Vietnam narcotic addiction in the sample as

a whole (Column 1) and for Parents' effects on continuation
of narcotics after return (Column 3).

The relative importance of a given scale compared to
other scales at each stage in developing addiction, and
changes in each scale's own predictive power at one stage
compared to another stage, are shown in Figure 1 by the B2
value of each scale at each stage in the development of
addiction, and for post-Vietnam addiction overall. The
B2 value is a measure provided by MCA of each predictor's
ability to explain variation in the outcome variable after
adjusting for effects of other variables. Note that three
of the four predictor scales are virtually ineffective for
predicting post-Vietnam addiction overall. It now becomes
clear that the prediction of post-Vietnam addiction is weak
because no single variable is a strong positive predictor at
all stages of the development of addiction. Parental Behavior
makes little contribution overall because it is important
only in the final stage, predicting addiction liability if
narcotic use is continued in the United States. Own Behavior is not powerful overall because it has very little
effect on the chances of continuation of narcotic use among
those who used narcotics in Vietnam. The effect of the
Demographic variable ends up being negligible because its
positive effects on use both in and after Vietnam are counter-
balanced by its negative effects on addiction liability.
Preservice drug experience appears as the best predictor
mainly on the basis of its strong contribution to use in
Vietnam and its more moderate contribution to continuation
after Vietnam.

The use of MCA has two important limitations. First it
assumes an additive model. If interactions between the
predictors are present, this summing of effects is inappro-
priate. Second when the outcome variable is very rare or
almost universal, MCA analysis may produce invalid results
(Fienberg, 1975). Thus MCA, like other statistical techniques, has major shortcomings when the problem involves
finding multiple predictors of rare events.

In the present example, it is reassuring to note that
the MCA results are essentially identical with those of
simple cross-tab analysis. However, to check the validity
of the MCA results further, we attempted to perform a stepwise logit analysis on the same data, using methods suggest-

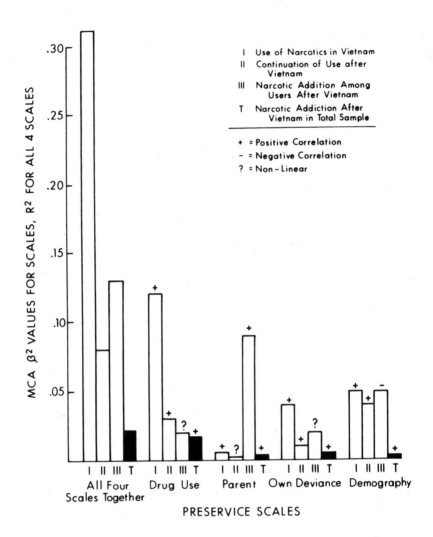

Figure 1

The Explanatory Power of Preservice Predictors

of Narcotic Addiction After Vietnam

(Over All and Decomposed into 3 Stages)

ed by Goodman (1971). To use this method, it was necessary
to dichotomize the predictor variables to reduce the number
of cells in the contingency tables. Sensible results could
be produced for predicting use either within Vietnam or
after Vietnam, but not for predicting post-Vietnam addiction
either in the sample as a whole or in those who used narcotics after leaving Vietnam. Addiction was simply too rare a
phenomenon to analyze via a multidimensional contingency
table. Thus it was not possible to test fully the findings
concerning predictors of addiction by this second method of
multivariate analysis. However, there were no significant
interactions among predictors with respect to narcotics use,
thus eliminating one potential source of invalidity in the
MCA findings. Moreover, the predictors of narcotics use in
Vietnam and after were ranked in the same order by logit
analysis as by MCA. A model using only the independent
additive effects of the three best predictors of narcotics
use in Vietnam, Drug, Demography, and Own Behavior, was
sufficient to predict the observed cell frequencies of use
in Vietnam well (unexplained $X^2$ was reduced to an insignifi-
cant 14.80, df = 13). The logit analysis therefore provides
support for the MCA findings concerning predictors of use in
and after Vietnam, even though it could not test the MCA
finding on addiction.


Further Exploration of the Roles of Demography and Drugs as
Predictors of Addiction

     a. Demography in Vietnam and the United States. It
is not clear whether the relative invulnerability to addiction among users with demographic characteristics associated
with high probabilities of narcotics use is a general
finding. One might suspect that it is merely an artifact of
the demographic peculiarities of this military sample, i.e.,
the fact that a large portion of the black, inner-city men
were career soldiers, whose very endurance in the military
is evidence of their resistance to all forms of deviance,
including narcotic addiction. However, examination of the
scale elements individually showed that this relative invulnerability to addiction among users held for young men as
well as for inner-city blacks. Since the young were highly
deviant and not career soldiers, the paradoxical reverse
effect on addiction of demographic variables favoring use
may be a general phenomenon, and not merely an accidental

correlate of the Army's selection criteria for military careers. This possibility is further substantiated by the fact that the paradoxical effect of the Demographic scale survived multiple classification analysis, which controlled for the contributions of deviance, drug experience and parent behavior. Therefore, the lower vulnerability of the inner-city black veteran user cannot depend entirely on his being generally nondeviant.

Indeed, this paradoxical effect of demographic variables on addictability seems to make sense at a more general level. The chief contribution of demographic variables to addiction is probably their facilitating exposure to opportunities and pressures to use narcotics. The young inner-city black uses narcotics for a variety of reasons -- because his friends urge him to, for relaxation and companionship, to satisfy his curiosity, as well as to achieve euphoria or narcotize pain. Men who live in environments in which none of their peers uses narcotics are not being urged by friends to use them for social purposes. Indeed, if they use narcotics at all, they are violating local norms and most expend great effort to maintain their supply, since narcotics in their area are very scarce. Presumably older whites who live outside of the central city and still use narcotics must be driven to this use by an unusual compulsion to achieve euphoria or by serious subjective problems. It appears, therefore, that use against demographic odds implies a greater need, a need so great that it overrides considerations of control and moderation.

Similar findings have been reported for drinking behavior. In tee-totaling environments such as the Southern Bible Belt, alcoholism rates overall are low, but among drinkers they are high (Cahalan and Room, 1974; Globetti, 1967). Presumably, in the absence of a strong personal need for alcohol, the normal individual in a tee-totaling environment adapts to local customs and refrains from drinking altogether, leaving as those who drink, individuals whose needs are so great as to override local customs. In the United States, except for the urban black ghetto, virtually the entire country is a "Bible Belt" so far as narcotics go, where the norm is abstention and the supply is low. In Vietnam, in contrast, narcotics were available to all, even more available than in the urban ghetto. Under these circumstances of plenty, demographic variables

favoring use were <u>not</u> negatively related to addiction liability (Table 4). In Vietnam, men without any of the demographic
characteristics favoring use were also unlikely to become addicted if they used, and for the rest, there was no relationship between demographic characteristics and addictability.

      b.  <u>Interpreting the role of early drug experience</u>.
Preservice drug experience was included as a trend predictor.  One would expect a trend predictor to have its maximal
effect at the nearest point in time.  As expected, the
importance of preservice drug use was greatest in Vietnam,

Table 4

Effect of Pre-Service Predictors on Narcotics Users'
Liability to Addiction in Vietnam Compared
with Post-Vietnam (MCA)

| | Narcotics Users | | | | | |
|---|---|---|---|---|---|---|
| | In Vietnam | | | After Vietnam | | |
| Pre-Service Scales | N | Adj. %<br>Addicted | $\beta^2$ | N | Adj. %<br>Addicted | $\beta^2$ |
| <u>Drugs</u> | | | .02 | | | .02 |
| 0 | 245 | 44 | | 49 | 9 | |
| 1 | 110 | 34 | | 26 | 23 | |
| 2 | 274 | 51 | | 114 | 18 | |
| <u>Parents</u> | | | .001 | | | .09 |
| 0 | 327 | 47 | | 87 | 8 | |
| 1 | 212 | 44 | | 71 | 18 | |
| 2, 3 | 90 | 43 | | 31 | 39 | |
| <u>Own Behavior</u> | | | .03 | | | .02 |
| 0, 1 | 59 | 33 | | 11 | 13 | |
| 2, 3 | 209 | 37 | | 47 | 24 | |
| 4, 5 | 201 | 53 | | 58 | 17 | |
| 6+ | 160 | 52 | | 73 | 11 | |
| <u>Demography</u> | | | .02 | | | .05 |
| 0, 1 | 51 | 27 | | 12 | 41 | |
| 2 | 216 | 45 | | 50 | 19 | |
| 3 | 242 | 50 | | 82 | 16 | |
| 4 | 120 | 47 | | 45 | 4 | |

shortly after entering the service, and declined markedly
thereafter. In Vietnam, preservice drug experience had a $B^2$
value of .12, even after the effect of the other three
scales was controlled. But once men had narcotic experience
in Vietnam, having had the earlier drug experience as well
produced a $B^2$ value of only .03 in explaining whether or not
they would ever use narcotics again in the United States
after service. And if they did use narcotics again after
service, a history of having used drugs before service had
a $B^2$ value of only .02 in explaining whether or not they
were to become addicted. Thus, once a man had used drugs
recently, his earlier drug experience became largely irrelevant.

    It is interesting that, despite the decline in power of
preservice drug experience to predict progressing to the
second and third stages of post-Vietnam addiction, the
statement by the Veteran Administration physician mentioned
earlier remains technically correct. Almost all post-
Vietnam addicts had had experiences with illicit drugs
before service. Among the post-Vietnam addicts in this
report, 87 percent had tried hard drugs before service and
an additional three percent had tried marijuana before service. But what should one make of this fact? It seems that
the physician interpreted it to mean the Vietnam experience
was irrelevant, that the veterans he treated were addiction-
prone and would have become addicts in any case. These data
would not support that view. Preservice drug experience was
actually the weakest predictor of liability to post-Vietnam
addiction among users. It was the best predictor of addiction in the total sample because it was the only predictor
which at all three stages showed men in the top category
having twice the likelihood of passing through that stage on
the way to addiction as had men in the lowest category. The
probability of being addicted after return from Vietnam is
the product of the probabilities of passing through each of
the three stages of development of addiction that have been
discussed: P (Ad p V) = P (Adp V/Use p V) . P (Use p V/Use
in V) . P (Use in V).* When the three probabilities of
progression from one stage to the next are multiplied to-

*Read as: "The probability of addiction after Vietnam is the
probability of addiction after Vietnam among users after
Vietnam times the probability of use after Vietnam among
users in Vietnam times the probability of use in Vietnam."

gether for each category of the preservice drug scale, men
in the top category of the preservice Drug scale end up with
13 times the probability of addiction as do men in the
bottom category, i.e., those without any pre-Vietnam drug
experience. Thus, the strong association this physician
noted between preservice drug use and post-Vietnam addiction
depends on the regularity of the positive relationship of
preservice drug use to use in both Vietnam and the United
States and to addiction liability, rather than to the strength
of preservice drug experience as a predictor of addiction
liability itself.


Implications of Decomposition of Predictors for Policy

     How can these observations be translated into policy?
If one wants to select for intervention those narcotics-
using veterans who are at the highest risk of becoming
addicts, one might choose atypical users, i.e., those who do
not have the demographic characteristics that are normally
associated with exposure to drug use. One would be particularly concerned about such atypical users who come from
families that are also atypical for men of favorable demographic backgrounds, that is, families with drinking problems, arrests, and divorces.

     If the process of addiction had not been decomposed
into stages, it would have appeared instead that men with a
history of drug use before Vietnam were most at risk of
addiction, since this is the result obtained from looking at
the total population. And this would be the best choice if
one were forced to nominate men for intervention knowing
nothing about them except that they had served in Vietnam.
But, the choice of individuals with whom to intervene is not
likely to be made for Vietnam veterans as a whole, but
rather for those who happen to be detected as current narcotics users--either because they come to the attention of
the police or because they report narcotics use during an
intake interview for some medical problem, or in similar
circumstances. To be detected as Stateside users, they must
already have passed through the first two of our three
stages of development of addiction, and it is irrelevant to
pay attention to predictors of these earlier stages that lie
behind them.

Not only is it probable that consideration of possible
intervention will be delayed until Stage Two has been entered,
but from both the public's and the individual's point of view,
this delay may be preferable.  If one were to select all preservice drug users, a third of all veterans would need to be
selected for intervention in order to forestall an event that
would occur in only 6% of those selected, obviously an inefficient procedure.  On the other hand, this intervention
would reach almost every potential addict (92%).  The procedure
suggested here would select only a tiny group for intervention,
0.6% of all veterans, but would obtain a group in which almost
half (45%) can be expected to become addicts.  However, it
would reach only a small portion of the potential addicts (19%)
Whether one should opt for massive intervention in order to
reach almost all addicts or for minimal intervention, settling
for reaching only those with high risks of addiction in order
to avoid inconveniencing those with low risks, depends on how
one estimates the costs and benefits of intervention.  At this
moment, the costs of such intervention appear more impressive
than the benefits.  If new and less obtrusive methods of intervention are discovered, this judgment would change.  Research
findings help to inform, but obviously cannot settle policy
questions.

## CAUTIONS AND OVERVIEW

What has been discovered about the relative importance
of preservice factors in predicting addiction to narcotics by
Vietman users after their return to the United States is based
on a relatively few addicts, and therefore, results may be unstable.  At best they apply in environments where there are
vastly differing opportunities for use among different subpopulations, as there are in the United States.

This study has shown a way to help solve the problem that
has harrassed most who attempt to predict psychiatric disorder.
It is well known that when events are very rare, they are difficult to predict.  Narcotic addiction is no exception to this
observation, not even in a population of young veterans whose
liability to addiction is somewhat higher than that in the population at large.  Without an ability to predict addiction,
there is little that can be done to choose a high risk population with whom to attempt prevention or early intervention.

What this report has tried to do is show that even when
predictors of a rare final outcome are weak, if one
can identify a set of necessary stages in progression
toward the rare event, it may be possible to assess at what
stage intervention is most feasible and acceptable and to
identify the characteristics of persons who, having progressed to that stage, are at high risk of progressing to the
next stage. If our observations turn out to have some
generality, a reasonable public policy with respect to
narcotics users might be to invite into early treatment only
those with a high risk of addiction, rather than following
the current policy which seems to be trying to identify and
treat every user. At the present time these findings suggest
that one way to identify a high risk population of users
might be to choose those without the demographic characteristics associated with the high risk of narcotics use but
who come from disturbed families. Such a group is a small
one, but at least among Vietnam veterans, it is a population
that has an addiction risk two to four times that of the
average user. This may be a particularly hopeful population
to work with because of their use can be interrupted, they
are not likely to be again invited to relapse, since the
world in which they move has few opportunities to obtain
narcotics nor to participate in their use with peers.

## REFERENCES

Cahalan, D. and Room, R. Problem drinking among American
    men. Monograph of the Rutgers Center of Alcohol
    Studies, New Brunswick, 1974.

Fienberg, S.E. Reivew of F.M. Andrews, J.N. Morgan, J.A.
    Sonquist, and L. Klem: 1973 Multiple Classification
    Analysis (Second Edition), Institute for Social Re-
    search, University of Michigan, Ann Arbor. Social
    Indicators Research I (1975), pp. 40-47.

Fink, R., Shapiro, S., Goldensohn, S.S., and Dailey, E.F.
    The "filter-down" process to psychotherapy in a group
    practice medical care program. American Journal of
    Public Health, 1969, 59, 245-260.

Globetti, G.  A comparative study of white and Negro teenage drinking in two Mississippi counties.  Phylon, 1967, 28, 131-138.

Goodman, L.A.  The analysis of multidimensional contingency tables:  Stepwise procedures and direct estimation methods for building models for multiple classifications.  Technometrics, 1971, 13, 33-61.

Johnston, L.  Drugs and American youth.  Institute for Social Research, University of Michigan, Ann Arbor, 1973.

Robins, L., Bates, W.M., and O'Neal, P.  Adult drinking patterns of former problem children.  In Pittman, D.J., and Synder, C.R. (Eds.), Society, culture, and drinking patterns.  John Wiley and Sons: New York, 1962.

Robins, L., and Murphy, G.E.  Drug use in a normal population of young Negro men.  American Journal of Public Health, 1967, 56, 1580-1596.

Robins, L.N.  The Vietnam drug user returns.  Special Action Office Monograph, Series A, No. 2, Wash. D.C., 1974

Sonquist, J.A., Baker, E.L., and Morgan, J.N.  Searching for Structure.  Institute for Social Research, University of Michigan, Ann Arbor, 1973.

PROBLEMS OF CONCEPTUALIZATION AND DESIGN IN RESEARCH ON THE

EVALUATION OF TREATMENT FOR DRUG ABUSE

S.B. Sells
Institute of Behavioral Research
Texas Christian University
Fort Worth, Texas

Beginning in 1969, the staff of the Institute of Behavioral Research (IBR) undertook responsibility for a large-scale, prospective study to evaluate the effectiveness of treatment for drug abuse (Sells, 1974; Sells and Simpson, 1967). In the course of this research, 43,943 patients were tracked from admission to termination of treatment, an interval varying from one day, in some cases, to over three years, in others. During treatment-evaluation, studies have been completed for three cohorts, as follows:

Cohort 1, 11,383 patients, 23 agencies, admissions between 6-1-69 and 5-31-71

Cohort 2, 15,831 patients, 35 agencies, admissions between 6-1-71 and 5-31-72

Cohort 3, 16,729 patients, 53 agencies, admissions between 6-1-72 and 3-31-73

In the fall of 1974, a follow-up study of the first two cohorts was initiated, with samples of approximately 2000 patients from each cohort. The field work for Cohort 1 is currently in progress.

The patient reporting mechanism that provided the data base has been called the Drug Abuse Reporting Program and the research program based on the resulting files has been generally identified by the acronym DARP. It is believed that the problems identified in the DARP research program, the approaches considered in their conceptualization, and the methodological decisions adopted at various points in

the program may have implications generalizable to other
large-scale longitudinal studies. These topics are addressed
in the present paper. The first portion of the presentation
is in effect a historical review of the long-term large-
scale, multifaceted, longitudinal DARP research program,
with emphasis on its methodological aspects. This sets the
context for the entire discussion and places the major
issues in perspective with respect both to the types of
problems that required consideration and the sequential
order in which various solutions were attempted, usually in
successive cohorts. In the later sections, several of the
more salient problems are discussed in finer detail.


### HISTORICAL REVIEW OF THE DARP RESEARCH PROGRAM

The DARP was developed in 1968 under a grant administered by the Division of Narcotics and Drug Abuse and field
tested in late 1968 and early 1969. Data collection began
formally in June, 1969 under a contract administered by the
Narcotic Addict Rehabilitation Branch (NARB) and continued
for more than 5 years through the transition to the National
Institute on Drug Abuse (NIDA). In 1971 a contract under
NARB authorized the implementation of the evaluation research.
These activities have reflected a close working relationship
between the NARB and IBR staffs that undoubtedly contributed
to the productivity of the program. The cooperation of
personnel throughout the agencies that comprised the reporting
network further reflects the serious concern of a large
number of people, in government and at the treatment agencies,
for the objective evaluation of treatment.

At the inception of the DARP in June, 1969, the expan-
sion of Federal support of treatment facilities for opiate
addicts was already accelerating, with the prospect (that
subsequently materialized) of extremely large-scale invest-
ment in methadone maintenance as a therapy of choice; at the
same time very little objective information was available on
the effectiveness of methadone, or for that matter, any
other treatment approach for habitual users of opioid or
other illicit drugs. With great wisdom, those who contributed
to the design of the reporting program, and who authorized
and protected its continuation, realized the importance of
prospective, longitudinal tracking of persons entering
treatment and rejected retrospective, cross-sectional
approaches to evaluation as misleading and often inaccurate.

The information required for research on the evaluation
of treatment was viewed in 1968, when the DARP forms were
created and pretested, as involving (1) patient descriptors,
in order to investigate differential patient prognosis for
different types of treatment, (2) baseline measures, to
reflect status at the outset of treatment on factors to be
measured as outcome criteria, (3) treatment delivery data,
specifying the treatment paradigms as well as participation
in significant components, and (4) outcome measures to serve
as criteria. This general prescription remains unchanged
after 8 intensive years, although if possible some of the
items incorporated in the forms, would be revised in the
light of experience.


## The Admission Report

Most of the information reported on the data collection
forms was obtained in interviews with the patients by trained
interviewers assigned for this purpose. The reliability and
validity of these data are discussed below. The Admission
Report incorporates both patient background and baseline
data. In the former category, it includes items on demographic characteristics (age, ethnicity, sex, socioeconomic
level, education, and occupation), family background,
criminal history, employment history, alcohol and drug use
history. In addition, it provides information on drug use,
alcohol use, employment, living arrangements, sources of
support, and criminality during the 2 months preceding
admission. This information as well as that reported on the
Status Evaluation Form, below, is identified only by Agency
code numbers and elaborate provision are implemented for
protection of the confidentiality of the entire file.

The Admission Report was revised in the middle of the
third year of its use. The revision clarified a number of
item definitions, dropped some unproductive items, added a
few new items, and tightened up the definition of an admission,
which had some ambiguities in the previous version.


## The Status Evaluation Report (SER)

This form was submitted at bimonthly intervals up to
termination and reported treatment components in which the
subject participated during each period as well as patient

performance in respect to drug and alcohol use, living
arrangements, employment, role activities, sources of support,
and criminal activities.  It was used also to indicate
patient status at the close of each period (in treatment,
deceased, terminated, or other statuses, such as hospitalized or jailed).  It was revised and shortened at the same
time as the Admission Report.

Although the Status Evaluation Report identifies treatment received and components attended by patients in each
report period, it does not define the treatment paradigms
involved.  This would not have been feasible for two reasons.
First, only the general treatment modalities, such as methadone maintenance or therapeutic community, but not the
specific treatment paradigms within modalities, were known
at the start of the DARP; the analysis of characteristics of
the various treatment programs and determination of specific
treatment types within each of the major modalities represented
among the agencies reporting was accepted as a research
problem and such types could only have been reported on the
DARP forms if generally accepted labels had been available.
Second, the characteristics of treatment programs represented
data at a different level and were not appropriate for
individual patient reports.  As discussed later, such data
were collected directly from the treatment programs by site
visit.

## Reporting Organizations

DARP reports were obtained from treatment agencies
funded by the NIMH (and more recently, NIDA) under legislation related to the treatment and rehabilitation of opioid
addicts, and, later, other habitual drug abusers.  In June,
1969, six agencies, providing treatment services for addicts,
were the first to report.  These were located in New Haven,
Manhattan, Philadelphia, St. Louis, Chicago, and Albuquerque.
Six additional agencies were included in the system by the
end of the first year.  At the end of the second year, the
number had increased to 23. In the third year it reached 36
and at the end of the fourth year, 51.  One agency included
in Year 3 was discontinued after a brief period.  The
reporting of new admissions was discontinued on March 31,
1973, when a new Federal reporting program, CODAP, was
initiated, but Status Evaluation Reports for patients then

Table 1

Agencies Reporting to DARP by Region and
Year of the Program

| Region | Year | | | |
| | 1 | 2 | 3 | 4 |
| --- | --- | --- | --- | --- |
| New England | 2 | 3 | 5 | 8 |
| Middle Atlantic | 7 | 10 | 11 | 13 |
| South Atlantic | 0 | 1 | 2 | 5 |
| East South Central | 0 | 0 | 1 | 1 |
| West South Central | 0 | 2 | 2 | 3 |
| East North Central | 1 | 2 | 6 | 8 |
| West North Central | 1 | 2 | 2 | 2 |
| Mountain | 1 | 2 | 2 | 2 |
| Pacific | 0 | 0 | 4 | 8 |
| Puerto Rico | | 1 | 1 | 1 |
| Total | 12 | 23 | 36 | 51 |

in treatment were continued for another year.  The distribution of reporting agencies by year and region is shown in
Table 1.  It is apparent that the major locations of the
reporting agencies were in New England, the Middle Atlantic
States, and the Midwest, with the Pacific region fairly well
represented only in the fourth year.

## The Total DARP Population

As shown in Table 2, the total DARP file contains
records on 43,943 adminissions.  The percentages of this
total by year were 7% in Year 1, 18% in Year 2, 36% in Year
3, and 38% in Year 4.  The regional distribution by year is
roughly comparable to that of the reporting agencies.
Although this is a large file, the organizations designated
to report were selected for a number of administrative
reasons, and it is not a random epidemiological sample of
drug users in the United States.

Table 2

DARP Population
New Admissions by Region and Year of the Program

|                     |      | Year |      |      |       |
|---------------------|------|------|------|------|-------|
| Region              | 1    | 2    | 3    | 4    | Total |
| New England         | 300  | 1324 | 2028 | 1721 | 5573  |
| Middle Atlantic     | 1293 | 4026 | 6271 | 4912 | 16502 |
| South Atlantic      | 0    | 48   | 887  | 2050 | 2985  |
| East South Central  | 0    | 0    | 403  | 425  | 828   |
| West South Central  | 0    | 397  | 676  | 518  | 1591  |
| East North Central  | 787  | 570  | 1208 | 2086 | 4651  |
| West North Central  | 268  | 678  | 868  | 633  | 2447  |
| Mountain            | 266  | 540  | 890  | 844  | 2540  |
| Pacific             | 0    | 0    | 1535 | 3379 | 4914  |
| Puerto Rico         | 0    | 686  | 1065 | 161  | 1912  |
| Total               | 3114 | 8269 | 15831| 16729| 43943 |

For the purposes of the evaluation research, 5510 admissions, representing (1) non-users of drugs reported by prevention programs at some of the agencies, and (2) persons who went through the admission process but did not enter treatment, were eliminated from the research file. Detailed information has been published on the characteristics of the sample (Curtis, Simpson, and Joe. 1976). The following is a brief review of trends in the total research sample of 38,433 drug users who entered into treatment, in respect to sample composition by age, sex, and race-ethnic status. These data are shown in Table 3 taken from Curtis, Simpson, and Joe (1976).

Over the 4 years during which new admissions were reported, the major trends in the DARP population were toward increased proportions of females, youth, particularly in the under-18 category, and whites. There were corresponding decreases in the proportions of males, older persons, particularly in the range between 31 and 40, and Blacks. An important implication of these changes, which in part

Table 3

Sex, Age, and Race-Ethnic Status of Patients
by the Year of Admission
(After Curtis, Simpson, & Joe, 1976)

| | Percentage of Patients | | | | | % of |
| | Year 1 | Year 2 | Year 3 | Year 4 | Patients | Total |
|---|---|---|---|---|---|---|
| **Sex** | | | | | | |
| Male | 81 | 80 | 76 | 72 | 29007 | 75 |
| Female | 19 | 20 | 24 | 28 | 9426 | 25 |
| No. of Patients | 2673 | 7341 | 13987 | 14432 | 38433 | |
| **Age** | | | | | | |
| Under 18 | 6 | 8 | 8 | 15 | 4107 | 11 |
| 18-20 | 13 | 17 | 19 | 17 | 6679 | 17 |
| 21-22 | 13 | 16 | 17 | 16 | 6134 | 16 |
| 23-25 | 14 | 17 | 20 | 18 | 7112 | 18 |
| 26-30 | 18 | 18 | 17 | 16 | 6439 | 17 |
| 31-40 | 27 | 18 | 14 | 13 | 5838 | 15 |
| Over 40 | 9 | 6 | 5 | 5 | 2124 | 6 |
| No. of Patients | 2673 | 7341 | 13987 | 14432 | 38433 | |
| **Race-Ethnic Status** | | | | | | |
| Black | 54 | 50 | 44 | 40 | 17077 | 44 |
| Puerto Rican | 6 | 13 | 11 | 5 | 3445 | 9 |
| Mexican-American | 8 | 8 | 7 | 9 | 3046 | 8 |
| White | 30 | 28 | 36 | 44 | 14295 | 37 |
| Other | 2 | 1 | 2 | 2 | 570 | 2 |
| No. of Patients | 2673 | 7341 | 13987 | 14432 | 38433 | |

reflect administrative response to legislation affecting
treatment program support and admission policies, is a shift
from services primarily for heroin and other opiate addicts,
in the first 2 years, to the inclusion of increasing numbers
of polydrug users in Years 3 and 4.


Data Organization

Although data collection began in June, 1969, two years
passed before a sufficient number of patients had an opportunity to spend a full year in treatment to equable construction of a research sample. During that period the major

effort was devoted to development of the master computer
file and the preparation of the data for analysis.  The
first research contract was authorized in June, 1971.

The evaluation research is organized by patient cohorts,
consisting of samples admitted during a designated period of
time and followed for a uniform period to allow all patients
an equal opportunity to pass through treatment.  The evaluation is conceptualized as involving two phases.  The first
is the period during treatment, while the patient was under
the surveillance of the treatment program, and the second,
post-treatment, after he returned to unsupervised community
living.

For the during-treatment evaluation studies, the major
analyses necessarily focused on comparison of treatments
within the four modalities represented in the DARP file:
methadone maintenance, outpatient drug-free treatments,
therapeutic communities, and detoxification programs.
Differences between these treatment approaches, with respect
to clientele served as well as duration of treatment, made
cross-modality comparisons difficult.  In addition, except
for measures of retention of patients, which were studied
separately, most of the behavioral measures built into the
SER for criterion purposes were suitable primarily for
outpatient programs, in which the patients could be at risk
to use drugs, commit crimes, and participate in illegal
activities, in the community. Their use was limited with
respect to residential (therapeutic community) and inpatient
(hospital) programs.  Finally, the analysis relating to
short-term patients, who dropped out with only one SER, and
that often incomplete for those who chose to be evasive,
were necessarily limited in the during-treatment studies.
As a result, the during-treatment evaluation results have
been restricted by the analytic opportunities provided in
the situation.  Most of these restrictions are inoperative
in the post-treatment studies, however, where risk is not
differentiated in relation to type of treatment and in which
the short-term patients provide important comparison groups.

## METHODOLOGICAL ISSUES

### Research Design Problems in During Treatment Studies

The significant questions which the DARP research has
addressed are concerned with the differential assessment of

outcomes of treatments with respect to discrete components of the patient population. In order to accomplish the required assessment, it has been necessary to specify treatments to be evaluated, patient groupings that could serve as discrete components of the population, and the outcome variables and measures to represent them. The specification of these elements, which were preliminary to research design consideration. was one of the major challenges of this program.

The DARP research staff, mainly research psychologists oriented to large-scale field studies and multivariate analysis, were in the position of pioneers when these issues were first considered, for there were virtually no satisfactory guidelines in the literature. However, with supreme confidence in their research methodology and resolute commitment to the task, they explored previously uncharted domains and created structures that enabled systematic and sophisticated analyses of the data. These will be summarized briefly.

Data Management. Discussion of the elaborate methods employed to insure reliability of data are included because of the firm belief that data management is an important element of design even though it is rarely mentioned in textbooks. Since DARP is a large-scale, field, data collection enterprise, patient reports presented problems of missing data, logical inconsistencies, extreme values, and other types of error. All reports received were screened by data editors who checked omissions and obvious errors before any data were recorded. From the editors the forms went through data processing where they were checked further by extensive editing programs that identified errors, inconsistencies, and extreme values and these were referred to the sources for explanation and correction. The IBR maintained a staff that worked closely with and visited the agencies continually. File maintenance procedures were followed that enabled insertion of revised data on a routine basis. There may still be an unverified male housewife or teenage father of five in the file, but the consistency of this file overall is remarkable.

In view of the use of agency code numbers instead of names, as a means of maintaining confidentiality, there was no adequate check on the authenticity of the patients reported. This was taken largely on faith, although the continuing contacts with the agencies provided repeated

assurance of the rationality of the system.  However, once
the field work of the follow-up study got under way, it
became possible to determine whether or not the patients
reported were real people and to what extent the information
on them was accurate. The discrepancies found were relatively
few and confidence in the file continues at a high level on
the basis of information available thus far.

In addition to the efforts to achieve completeness and
consistency, most of the data entered into analyses were
either standardized composites derived from cluster or
factor analyses or scaled to index numbers that reflected
desirable properties in statistical analyses in comparison
with the raw measures.  In many cases, scaling corrected for
extreme values without doing violence to the distributional
properties of the variables.  Comparisons of correlations
based on raw data with those based on such transformations
verified the superiority of the transformation.  Examples of
these operations will be presented in the subsequent dis-
cussions.

Finally, there has been much concern with the validity
of the DARP patient report data.  Comparison with documen-
tary sources is subject to error also.  Such comparisons are
often prohibited by law, as in the case of invasion of
privacy.  In the present study, since the data were reported
anonymously, any efforts to verify would have involved an
enormous task, even if sanctioned.  The evidence supporting
validity is of three types.  First, comparisons of individual
records have been reported with other research data on DARP
patients (Maddux, 1973).  These have shown close agreement
on most items when collected independently, each without
knowledge of the other.  Results on similar populations have
been reported with sufficient frequency in the literature
(Ball, 1967; Stephens, 1972; Cox and Longwell, 1974; and
others) that lend further support to the validity of the
data.  Secdon, in numerous instances, complex analyses
of DARP data have been replicated on samples from
several cohorts, with highly similar correlation structures and other relationships that would not be expected
by chance.  And third, there have been a few opportunities
to compare interview data with objective reports.  One of
these involves the comparison of drug use reports with
reports of urine tests.  Another has involved comparison of
death reports on SER's with other sources, such as reports
from NIMH.  In both cases, the results, while not in perfect

agreement, reflect levels of validity of acceptable magnitude and comparable with that accepted in most social science research.

Patient Classification. In order to implement the design requirements mentioned earlier, it was necessary to address taxonomic problems with respect to the specification of patient types and of treatments. Otherwise the generalizability of the data would have been ambiguous and the evaluation results would necessarily have fallen short of their primary goal, to facilitate learning from experience in order to plan more effective programs thereafter. This section summarizes the approaches followed with respect to patient classification.

Prior to this program, there were no systematic quantitative efforts to deal with patient typology, although classification by age, sex, and race-ethnic status has been commonplace. Several authors had proposed qualitative typologies of street addicts (for example, see Feldman, 1973) but these were rejected in the present program both because of lack of empirical objectivity and because they involved considerations not included in the DARP data base.

In the studies of Cohort 1, McRae (1974) developed a patient typology based on cluster analysis of a profile of patient background indices, drug use, and demographic variables. This involved 12 patient types, 4 black, 3 Puerto Rican, 2 Mexican-American, and 3 White, in which every individual was located in the type representing his minimum profile distance (Table 4). This typology was used in the evaluation study of Cohort 1 and was effectively replicated for Cohort 2 in a study by Joe and Simpson (1976a). However, in the Cohort 2 evaluation research, it was decided to shift to the greater flexibility of classification by the complete profile. There were several reasons for this. First the McRae types proved to be less homogeneous than had been thought. Second, the types were unfamiliar to treatment staff members and other workers in the field and their acceptance, at least in the short run, appeared doubtful. And third, despite the fact that the types had advantages in communication of results, their complexity made it difficult to assess the sources of variance associated with patient type results. This shift required some change in analytic design, more in specific

Table 4

Patient Types Defined for Cohort 1
(From McRae, 1974)

| Patient Type Description | Percent of Cohort 1 |
|---|---|
| 1.  Black, young, male heroin preaddicts | 18 |
| 2.  Black, young polydrug users | 5 |
| 3.  Black, female heroin and polydrug users | 9 |
| 4.  Black, older male heroin addicts | 21 |
| 5.  Puerto Rican, young heroin and polydrug users | 2 |
| 6.  Puerto Rican, older male heroin addicts | 7 |
| 7.  Puerto Rican, young delinquent referrals | 2 |
| 8.  Mexican-American, young heroin and poly-drug users | 1 |
| 9.  Mexican-American, older male heroin addicts | 5 |
| 10. White, older opiate and poly drug users | 3 |
| 11. White, young polydrug users | 7 |
| 12. White, opiate addicts | 21 |

algorithm than in concept, and introduced problems in
reporting.  These are discussed below.

Treatment Specification and Classification.  Although
there were only a few guidelines for patient classification,
there were none for the critical issue of treatment classification.  For the most part, treatment was described as
represented mainly by four modalities, short-term in-patient
detoxification, outpatient drug-free treatment, residential
therapeutic community, and the now popular, but then new,
outpatient methadone maintanence treatment.

In order to identify distinctive treatment approaches
within modalities, a field study was initiated for Cohort 1
and staff visits were made to the 38 agencies involved in
the first three years of the DARP.  At each agency all
treatment locations were observed, key staff interviewed,
and a schedule of questions completed concerning philosophy,
goals, policies, procedures, staff, organization, facilities,
records, and research.

These data were analyzed for trends while at the same time, the treatment modality assignments were reported on the bimonthly status Evaluation Reports (SER's) by agency by report period. The latter provided good support for the reliability of the data in that the correspondence between types of treatment offered (from site visit information) and the type of treatment reported (from SER's) was very high. The treatment typology developed by Watson, Simpson, and Spiegel (1974) which was used in the Cohort 1 evaluation study, specified three distinctive types of methadone maintenance treatment, three types of therapeutic community, three types of outpatient drug-free treatment, and two types of detoxification treatment in which most of the DARP programs could be fit.

This first study was nevertheless regarded as preliminary and further studies were scheduled. The Watson typology did not have the benefit of extensive consultant advice, which was precluded by the deadline pressures experienced during the first year of this annually funded research contract. However, at the outset of the following contract year, as a first step in reviewing and updating the treatment typology for Cohort 2, this was corrected. Changes were made that gave higher priority to goals and treatment processes than to procedural and organizational factors, which were more salient in the Watson et al. typology. These changes resulted in a revised treatment typology (Cole and Watterson, 1976). Table 5 enumerates the two sets of treatment types.

In an effort to strengthen this typology further all of the treatment type descriptors were quantified. Raw score factor analyses of clinic profiles were carried out for each modality. The types resulting from these studies supported the Cole and Watterson typology, although data on a larger number of clinics are needed before certain ambiguities can be clarified (James, et al., 1976, a & b).

Criterion measures. While it is an axiom in evaluation research that criterion design should reflect program goals, the DARP program reflects a network of treatment programs, with differing goals in many cases, and at the same time required uniform measures for all programs. As a result, program goals were incorporated in treatment paradigm definitions and system goals were adopted representing the Federal (and generally the public) expectations concerning rehabili-

Table 5

Treatment Types Defined for Cohort 1 and for Cohorts 2-3*

| Treatment Type Description | Percent of Patients |
|---|---|
| Cohort 1 | |

Methadone Maintenance Programs:

| | | |
|---|---|---|
| 1. | Emphasis on maintenance, with supportive use of counseling | 13 |
| 2. | Emphasis on resocialization through therapeutic group activities | 19 |
| 3. | Emphasis on improving personal functioning through individual counseling | 33 |

Therapeutic Communities:

| | | |
|---|---|---|
| 4. | Traditional (Synanon) model, using hierarchical social structure and peer pressure in residential setting to achieve resocialization | 12 |
| 5. | Medical orientation and setting, using chemical detoxification, with traditional TC model | 2 |
| 6. | Modified-traditional orientation, with emphasis on positive reinforcement and prescribed activities for personal growth | 1 |

Outpatient Drug-Free Programs:

| | | |
|---|---|---|
| 7. | Orientation similar to traditional therapeutic community model, using full-time therapeutic activities during the day, but without residential facilities | 5 |
| 8. | Designed primarily for patients who work or attend school, emphasizing reality-oriented and problem-solving therapies | 5 |
| 9. | Special drug-free programs within methadone maintenance clinics, with supportive use of individual counseling | 2 |

Detoxification Programs:

| | | |
|---|---|---|
| 10. | Inpatient, short-term use of supportive chemicals in detoxification | 4 |
| 11. | Outpatient, short-term, methadone-assisted detoxification | 4 |

Table 5 (Con't.)

| Treatment Type Description | Percent of Patients |
|---|---|
| Cohorts 2-3 | |

**Methadone Maintenance Programs:**

1. Emphasis on resocialization and eventual drug-free living, with well-defined phases of treatment and mandatory counseling — 15
2. Emphasis on a supportive therapeutic approach, with minimum structure and control over patients, and use of methadone maintenance as protection against illicit drug use and hazards of "street life" — 19

**Therapeutic Communities:**

3. Traditional orientation, designed to achieve resocialization using a highly structured and disciplined residential environment — 9
4. Modified-traditional orientation, with emphasis on the development of practical (work-related) skills — 5
5. Short-term treatment emphasizing social and work skills — 3

**Outpatient Drug-Free Programs:**

6. Emphasis on resocialization, using a highly structured day-time schedule similar to traditional therapeutic community model — 14
7. Emphasis on a supportive use of counseling, focused on immediate problems, using minimum structure and control over patient — 12

**Detoxification Programs:**

8. Inpatient, short-term use of supportive chemicals in detoxification — 9
9. Outpatient, short-term, methadone-assisted detoxification — 14

* Based on Watson, Simpson, and Spiegel, 1973 and Cole and Watterson, 1974.

tation of drug abusers.  These involve mainly treatment
outcomes reflecting changes in patient behavior in the
direction of conformity to standards of citizenship, such as
discontinuance of use of illicit drugs, work and self-
support on legitimate jobs, elimination of criminal activities
and assumption of appropriate role responsibilities.

Extensive research has been carried out on the development of criterion measures that meet rigorous standards of
statistical acceptability (Demaree, 1974; Demaree and Neman,
1976).  These studies dealt with problems of combining
measures over successive report periods, correcting for
extreme responses, compensating for missing data, and
development of index values that represented well the distributional properties of the raw data and at the same time
were sensitive to trends over time.  Table 6 shows the
scaling of the criterion indices employment, alcohol use,
opioid drug use, nonopioid drug use, and criminal activities;
based on Demaree and Neman (1976).  In the Cohort 1 study,
it was realized that the base rate for employment among
females was much lower than that for men and that a new
measure was needed that would reflect outcomes for women at
a level comparable to those for men.  For Cohort 2, a measure
designated productive activities was used in which several
appropriate role activities, such as homemaking and school
attendance were equated with legitimate employment for
positive scores.

Evaluation Design in During-Treatment Studies.  Again,
as a result of contract requirements, certain restrictions
were accepted in the research.  The most important restric-
tion was to limit the during-treatment evaluation to the
first 12 months following admission. Evaluation then focused
on three aspects of treatment effectiveness: (1) retention,
which involves the length of time that patients remain in
treatment and also on reasons why they leave; this is
assumed to reflect motivation, conformity, and participation
in the treatment process; (2) patient death rates and causes
of death, and (3) patient outcomes on criterion measures.
In the retention studies, time in treatment is a dependent
measure, while in the criterion outcome studies it is an
important covariate; there are major differences between
modalities in time in treatment.

In these studies, as in all longitudinal human research,
the isolation of variance attributable to a particular set

Table 6

Scaling of Criterion Measures for Employment, Alcohol Use,
Opioid Drug Use, Nonopioid Drug Use, and
Criminal Activities*

| Criterion Variable | Scale Value | | | |
|---|---|---|---|---|
| | 1 | 2 | 3 | 4 |
| Employment (days worked) during a two-month period) | Over 30 | 16-30 | 1-15 | 0 |
| Alcohol Use (ounces per day of 80-proof liquor equivalent) | 0 | 0 to 4 | 4 to 8 | Over 8 |
| Opioid Use (days use of opioids) | 0 | 1-2 | 3-8 | Over 8 |
| Nonopioid Use (days use of any nonopioid drug) | 0 | 1-2 | 3-8 | Over 8 |
| Criminal Activities (based on 3 indicators: arrests, days in jail, illegal activities as source of support) | None | Any 1 | Any 2 | All 3 |

* Based on Demaree and Neman, 1974.

of variables, such as treatment is extremely complex. A
treatment episode is only a brief interval in each person's
life and is preceded, accompanied, and followed by many
events that may have signficant and in some cases greater
influence on each of the dependent variables than the
particular independent variables of central interest to the
investigator. The additional factors, by domain, include at
least the following: (1) demographic factors, including time
period, region, city, age, race, sex, socio-economic status,
and the like, (2) individual background, including family
experience, drug history, criminal history, education and
work history, and related factors, (3) pretreatment legal
status and status with respect to each of the criterion
measures, and (4) during-treatment performance on each
criterion measure, as well as the concurrent total life
space outside of the treatment program. In follow-up
studies, subsequent to termination of treatment, events that

occur between termination and time of assessment, including
subsequent treatment, are also relevant.

The DARP data collection schedule represented a tradeoff
between the social scientist's impossible dream of a comprehensive protocol and the reality of a feasible and fundable
program.  Demographic and background data were built into
the Admission report along with pretreatment baseline measures
The SER provided bimonthly data points on treatment participation and criterion performance, but not on other events
outside the treatment program.  School and employment
records, psychological evalatuion of attitudes, feelings,
and values, and other relevant intrapsychic data could not
be included in the data base.  More extensive data in these
areas were incorporated in the follow-up interview  schedules, which are subject to a different set of restrictions.

The design strategy in the evaluation studies has
followed the general linear model, computing hierarchical
analyses of variance and analyses of covariance by multiple
regression methods, such as those described by Overall and
Spiegel (1969).  The Cohort 1 studies, in which the patient
types and treatment types involved categorical classification, were implemented using a procedure that partitioned
the sum of squares of each dependent variable (for example,
opioid use) into mutually exclusive subsets, each attributable to some independent variable or factor (for example,
patient type) in the design.  Some analyses utilized only
one independent factor, as when criterion scores were
compared across patient types.  In others, involving more
than one independent factor, the factors were ordered
hierarchically and the sum of squares attributed to any
factor was only the portion attributed to it that had not
been accounted for by an earlier factor in the present
sequential order.  In these analyses, main effects (attributable to factors) take precedence over interactions (effects
attributable to combinations of factors).

The Cohort 1 studies by Spiegel and Sells (1974) investigated three independent factors: time in treatment, patient
type, and treatment type.  Pretreatment background and
status and demographic classification were not considered
separately because they were part of the fabric of the
patient typology.  This procedure was disarmingly simple
both to compute and to report, but in reality it obscured

the effects of many variables concerning which more detailed
information would have been enlightening.

The analyses that were undertaken in this context were
limited by several restrictions imposed by factors beyond
the control of the investigators.  Three of these were
particularly important.  First, the distribution of patient
types by treatment types was biased; instead of at least
minimum numbers in the cells representing the patient type
matrix, many cells were extensively over- or under- represented, consequently accounting for unwanted, systematic
interactions.  Second, the patients in residential (therapeutic community) and inpatient (e.g., detoxification)
treatments were not comparably at risk, with respect to
criteria such as drug and alcohol use, criminality, and
employment, with outpatients in methadone maintenance and
drug-free treatments.  Only retention could be compared
equitably across all treatments for the during-treatment
phase.  Finally, limitations of computer capacity required
that certain adjustments, such as limitation of the number
of factors, be made.  As a result, analyses were split and
undertaken sequentially that might have been undertaken in a
more unified manner.  Most of the analyses related to
criteria were repeated on single criteria.

The substitution of the profile of patient classification variables for patient types, in the Cohort 2 studies,
required adaptation of the analytic design although the
logic was essentially unchanged (Gorsuch, Abbamonte, and
Sells, 1976).  Instead of time in treatment, patient type,
and treatment type, as in Cohort 1, the analyses in Cohort 2
involved six factors: pretreatment (baseline level) for each
criterion, ethnic group, age, (pretreatment) drug use pattern,
treatment type (within modality), and time in treatment,
plus interactions.  In this context, it was possible to
assess the total amount of variance on each criterion, on
the six factors, and to arrange them sequentially so that
the variance attributed to baseline levels could be extracted first, followed by ethnic group and age, and finally
treatment type and time in treatment.  Sex was not included
as a factor because separate analyses were run for male and
female samples.  Although very similar conceptually to the
Cohort 1 results, the Cohort 2 results proved to be more
informative because of their explicit elucidation of points
that could only be inferred in the earlier study.

Criterion-Oriented Designs. Over several years of the
DARP research, considerable staff discussion has been devoted
to the possibilities of finding more efficient computational
schemes to implement the designs, which have been described
very generally above. One approach that appeared promising
involved the construction of criterion path groups to
reflect criterion performance dynamically over time rather
than as a cross-sectional, mean statistic. The design that
evolved consisted first of classifying all patients into
path groups reflecting the mean levels and patterns of
criterion performance, as illustrated in Table 7, for heroin
use during treatment (Demaree and Neman, 1976). The second
step involved the investigation of differences in background,
demographic, baseline, and during treatment characteristics
and performance among the groups, by multiple discriminant
analyses. Table 8 shows illustrative results from a report
by Demaree, Neman, Long and Gant (1976) which studies the
during-treatment employment of methadone maintenance patients
(exclusive of students and housewives) who remained in
treatment six months or longer.

Retention Studies. Patients leave drug abuse treatment
programs for a variety of reasons: many quit on their own
and against program advice; some are expelled for violation
of rules or failure to cooperate; some are referred to other
programs for substantive reasons; some complete treatment
and are released to independent community living; others are
dropped from the rosters when they are hospitalized or
jailed for long periods, or die. Some return to the same
agency after a period following termination, and are treated
as readmissions. In the present study, readmissions were
not considered and all data were based on the first treatment episode. In calculating time in treatment, referrals
and completions must receive special consideration. Referrals
are not strictly terminations, although they must be so
regarded technically. Completions reflect favorable outcomes
but may occur at any time, since treatment curricula are
more flexible than those of schools.

In assessing time in treatment, when all categories of
terminations are combined, it was necessary to resort
to index transformations. Joe and Simpson (1976) utilized a
tenure index, with a 5-point scale in which the highest
score was given to completion. Their studies as well as an
earlier one by Joe (1974) have shown interesting relations
of termination categories to this type of index and have

Table 7

Percentage of 3,496 Outpatients in Cohort 2 With
Particular Mean Levels and Patterns of Heroin
Use Over the First Year in Treatment*

| Mean Level | Pattern | | | | % of Total |
|---|---|---|---|---|---|
| | Steady | Increasing | Decreasing | Fluctuating | |
| Little or no use | 65.9 | | | | 65.9 |
| Light | 3.7 | 0.9 | 8.0 | 14.8 | 27.4 |
| Moderate | 0.6 | 0.8 | 1.9 | 2.5 | 5.8 |
| Heavy use | 0.9 | | | | 0.9 |
| % of Total | 71.1 | 1.7 | 9.9 | 17.3 | 100.0 |

* Based on Demaree, Neman, Long, and Gant, 1974.

Table 8

Employment Path Groups Showing Mean Levels and Patterns of Employment
Over Time in Treatment, Percentage of the Sample of 2615 in
Each Group, and Typical Paths of Employment*

| Path Group | Mean Level of Employment | Pattern of Employment | % of Sample | Typical Path of Employment |
|---|---|---|---|---|
| 1. High employment | High | Steady | 22.0 | Worked during more than half the number of days in each 2-month period |
| 2. Moderate, steady | Moderate | Steady | 1.1 | Worked 16-30 days |
| 3. Moderate, drop | Moderate | Decreasing | 2.4 | Dropped from > 30 to ≤15 days |
| 4. Moderate, gain | Moderate | Increasing | 8.4 | Increased from ≤15 days to > 30 days |
| 5. Moderate, fluctuating | Moderate | Fluctuating | 8.0 | Fluctuated around 16-30 days, but with little or no trend |
| —[1] Low, steady | Low | Steady | — | Worked 1-15 days |
| 6. Low, drop | Low | Decreasing | 4.4 | Dropped from 15 days to unemployed |
| 7. Low, gain | Low | Increasing | 9.7 | Went from unemployed to >15 days |
| 8. Low, fluctuating | Low | Fluctuating | 12.0 | Fluctuated around 1-15 days, but with little or no trend |
| 9. Unemployed | Very low or none | Steady | 32.0 | Unemployed but may have had some employment in certain periods |

[1] This group contained only 6 patients; these were put in Group 8.

* Based on Demaree, Neman, Long, and Gant, 1974.

investigated predictors of tenure as well as background, demographic, and treatment differences related to tenure.

Death Rate Studies. The DARP file has offered an unusual opportunity to study death rates of addicts; it has proven to be the only source thus far in which the population at risk was determined and for which accurate measures of time at risk were available. Three studies have been completed for successive years, summarized in Watterson, Sells, and Simpson (1976). In these studies, the man-days at risk were calculated for the base populations and differential rates for the deceased samples were computed by age, race, sex, treatment modality, and combinations of these, as well as for the total samples.

Death rates for patients under the surveillance of treatment programs are believed to be lower than for addicts "in the street" and support for this was found in comparison with British data (Pierce, 1967; Bewley et al., 1968). This implies that the DARP results are underestimates of the true rates. However, the advantages of a specified base were also apparent in the comparisons of residential and inpatient treatment situations, where risk was low, with out-patient treatments. The differential rates were instructive for the other factors as well. However, these were unstable from year to year despite the fact that the samples were large, ranging from 10,000 to 23,000 persons.

Limitations of the Research. As in many field studies, the present research has involved a large scale, quasi-experimental investigation in which the distribution of subjects across treatments was not under the control of the investigators. In fact, the assignment was not only not random, but in many cases systematically biased as a result of medical, professional, or administrative policies. Assignment in some cases involved no choice, as when a treatment program was both the only one available and limted to only one type of treatment. Varying acceptance rules, based on residence and other factors, were practiced at all agencies and assignment rules, where choice were available also varied among agencies. Assignment to methadone programs was also restricted by Federal Guidelines, which set a minimum age limit and admission criteria involving length of addiction and previous treatment. As a result there is no balanced distribution, but rather an imbalance that posed challenging problems in analysis. In general, younger patients, who were also more frequently nonopioid users, were assigned to drug-free programs, while a disproportionate number of older patients were assigned to methadone programs. There were also linkages of ethnic groups to particular treatments; for example, most of the Mexican-American methadone patients were in one treatment type, while most Puerto Rican methadone patients were in another. Finally it was not feasible, within the limits of the DARP to obtain control groups. Indeed, with most patients in treatment under some form of coercion, it would have been impossible to obtain comparable samples not in treatment on whom reports could have been obtained.

The during-treatment studies undertaken thus far have tracked patients only during the first full year following admission. This was partly a matter of administrative convenience in relation to contract schedules but, at least initially also reflected the belief that within one year most of the patients would have terminated. This belief has proven to be true for drug-free and detoxification treatments and to a large degree for therapeutic communities, but not for methadone maintenance.

Early in the investigation of Cohort 1, a study was made by Simpson and McRae (1974) to determine whether patients with one or more readmissions differed in any significant way from those who did not have readmissions. The results, in agreement with a related investigation by Ball, Thompson, and Allen (1970) indicated: (1) that multiple treatment episodes at the same or different agencies are quite common among drug dependent and addicted persons, and (2) that there were not discriminable differences between the sample of readmissions (about 15% of the total sample) and the remainder of the patients. In view of the complications that would have been necessitated by including data for succeeding treatment episodes, it was decided to base the during-treatment studies on the first treatment episode only.

The followup study of Cohort 1 involves a sample of approximately 2000 patients to be approached for interviews between four and six years past admission, depending on when, between June 1, 1969 and May 31, 1971, they entered treatment. Some of these patients terminated their association with the treatment agency within a few days following admission, while others remained in treatment status without

any break over the entire time period covered.  It is expected that both time in treatment and time elapsed between
termination and interview, in addition to the multitude of
other relevant factors, will affect the rate of location of
sample patients and also their willingness to be interviewed.

The design of the follow-up sample is complex.  While
it was necessary to exclude many categories from the during-
treatment studies (for example, residential and hospital
patients, who were minimally at risk, early dropouts,
for whom inadequate data were available, and certain groups,
particularly females for whom numbers were inadequate), the
constraints that operated earlier were not relevant to the
follow-up study.  For the residential patients and inpatients,
the follow-up study data provide the only outcome evaluation
information comparable to those for other treatments (except
for retention).  For the short-term patients, the follow-up
study provides not only an opportunity to evaluate abortive
and short-term participation in treatment in comparison
with the effects of longer participation, but also it
provides important comparison groups that in many ways can
be called notreatment groups, although not random controls.

With respect to the small-size groups scattered throughout the sample, our decision was to exclude them also from
the follow-up studies.  It may, however, be feasible later,
to pick up some of these by combining cohorts. The sampling
plan includes random selections from subgroups identified by
age, sex, ethnic group, time in treatment, treatment type,
and agency, for whom there were sufficient numbers in the
treatment sample to generalize the results.  As a matter of
policy, the remainder who were inadequately represented were
excluded.

The design of the follow-up interview follows the
content of the DARP forms, but provides for chronological
reporting over the period from termination to interview.
Since the DARP forms were received from the treatment
agencies identified only by code numbers, while names,
addresses, and other identification were never obtained,
elaborate negotiations were necessary with the treatment
agencies in most cases with superordinate state and local
agencies to obtain names and addresses.  In the long run,
this will undoubtedly be advantageous to the research, but
it is worthy of note that the maneuvers currently required

by human research legislation and regulation, while un-
questionably necessary in many cases, are arduous and have
added a new dimension of frustration and expense to the
rigors of field research.

   Advantages of the Longitudinal Design. Perhaps the
most important advantages of the longitudinal design for the
type of evaluation research addressed by the DARP program
are (1) that the total population of persons admitted to
treatment constitutes the data base for the research and
that no retrospective biases resulting from inadequate
records or administrative amnesias are permitted to intervene in definition of the study sample, and (2) that periodic
current reporting enables assessment of status at every
point so that an overall design is permitted in which early
performance can be evaluated as a precursor of later performance and, more particularly, outcome during treatment can
be evaluated in relation to outcome subsequent to treatment,
which is the payoff in this type of research. It is true
that budgetary and humanitarian realities limit the number
and timing of post-treatment follow-up assessments, but this
is not intrinsic to the longitudinal design.

   Finally, in relation to the entire strategy of follow-
up study methodology, there are a number of points that
deserve serious consideration. First, people in treatment
for drug abuse are mainly alienated, rejected, frustrated,
and frequently in legal jeopardy. To the extent that they
are successfully rehabilitated and reenter the mainstream of
society, they must frequently conceal their past in order to
avoid the prejudice and distrust that is still widespread
among employees, associates, and other citizens. Field
studies to locate these people frequently disturb their
efforts to camouflage their former identities and are likely
to be viewed as highly threatening. Even though investigators may go to the most extreme lengths to prevent inadver-
tent disclosure, accidents have happened and regretably may
occur again. For this reason, it is essential to use whereever possible, unobtrusive, nonreactive methods of data
collection in this area. At this time, the prospects look
favorable in terms of feasibility, but the entire idea tends
to be viewed with suspicion from the viewpoint of safeguards
in human research.

## CONCLUSION

We have reviewed the goals, scope, design, problems, advantages, and limitations of the DARP research program on evaluation of drug abuse treatment. To those accustomed to the refinements of design under laboratory conditions, it presents some difficult and perhaps distressing problems. On the other hand, it has also presented an opportunity to investigate, under realistic, operational conditions, issues of the most serious concern in contemporary society. Despite the limitations noted, the DARP population does represent: (1) a major segment of the treatment effort supported by the Federal government, (2) almost the entire spectrum of treatment approaches practiced in the late 1960's and early 1970's (certain religious programs, acupuncture, and experimental new pharmacological agents are not included), (3) substantial samples from about 50 major metropolitan areas of the United States of the principal ethnic groups involved in addiction, and (4) probably the most comprehensive, most reliable, and most valid set of data on a drug using population that is available today. When the follow-up data are incorporated, the value of the project will be further enhanced.

## REFERENCES

Ball, J.C.  The reliability and validity of interview data obtained from 59 narcotic drug addicts. American Journal of Sociology, 1967, 72, 650-654.

Ball, J.C., Thompson, W.O., and Allen, D.M.  Readmission rates at Lexington Hospital for 43,215 narcotic addicts. Public Health Reports, 1970, 85, 610-616.

Bewley, T.C., Ben-Arie, O., and Pierce, J.I.  Morbidity and mortality from heroin dependence. British Medical Journal, 1968, 1, 725.

Cole, S.G., and Watterson, O.  A treatment typology for drug abuse in the DARP: 1971-1972 admissions.  In S.B. Sells and D.D. Simpson (Eds.), The effectiveness of drug abuse treatment. (Vol. 3).  Further studies of drug users treatment typologies and assessment of outcomes during treatment in DARP.  Cambridge, Massachusetts: Ballinger, 1976.

Cox, T.J., and Longwell, B.  Reliability of interview data
    concerning current heroin use from addicts on methadone.
    International Journal of Addiction, 1974, 9, 161-165.

Curtis, B., Simpson, D.D., and Joe, G.W.  Description of drug
    users entering treatment in the DARP during 1969-1973.
    In S.B. Sells and D.D. Simpson (Eds.), The effectiveness
    of drug abuse treatment. (Vol. 3.)  Further studies of
    drug users treatment typologies and assessment of outcomes
    during treatment in the DARP.  Combridge, Mass: Ballinger,
    1976.

Demaree, R.G.  Behavioral measures and related criterion for
    assessment of outcomes during treatment for drug users
    in the DARP:  1969-1971 admissions.  In S.B. Sells (Ed.),
    The effectiveness of drug abuse treatment. (Vol. 1).
    Evaluation of treatments.  Cmabridge, Mass.: Ballinger,
    1974.

Demaree, R.G., and Newman, J.F.  Behavioral criteria for
    assessments of outcomes during treatment for drug users
    in the DARP:  1971-1972 admissions.  In S.B. Sells &
    D.D. Simpson (Eds.), The effectiveness of drug abuse
    treatment. (Vol. 3).  Further studies of drug users
    treatment typologies and assessment of outcomes during
    treatment in the DARP.  Cambridge, Mass.: Ballinger,
    1976.

Demaree, R.G., Neman, J.F., Long, G.L., and Grant, B.L.
    Patterns of behavioral outcomes over time in methadone
    maintenance treatment.  In S.B. Sells & D.D. Simpson
    (Eds.), The effectiveness of drug abuse treatment.
    (Vol. 4). Evaluation of treatment outcomes for the
    1971-1972 admission cohort.  Cambridge, Mass.: Ballinger,
    1976.

Feldman, H.  Street status and drug users.  Society, May-June,
    1973, 32-38.

Gorsuch, R.L., Abbamonte, M., and Sells, S.B.  Evaluation
    of treatments for drug users in the DARP:  1971-1972
    admissions.  In S.B. Sells and D.D. Simpson (Eds.),
    The effectiveness of drug abuse treatment. (Vol. 4).
    Evaluation of treatment outcomes for the 1971-1972
    admission cohort.  Cambridge, Massachusetts: Ballinger,
    1976.

James, L.R., Hammond, T.J., Hartment, E.A., and Sells, S.B.
    Treatment processes associated with drug treatment
    modalities:  An application of multiple discriminant
    analyses.  In S.B. Sells & D.D. Simpson (Eds.),
    The effectiveness of drug abuse treatment. (Vol. 3).
    Further studies of drug users treatment typologies
    and assessment of outcomes during treatment in the
    DARP.  Cambridge, Mass.: Ballinger, 1976 (a).

James. L.R., Hammond, T.J., Hartman, E.A., and Sells, S.B.
    A typology of treatment process for drug abuse.  In
    S.B. Sells and D.D. Simpson (Eds.), The effectiveness
    of drug abuse treatment. (Vol. 3.), Further studies
    of drug users treatment typologies and assessment of
    outcomes during treatment in the DARP.  Cambridge,
    Massachusetts: Ballinger, 1976 (b).

Joe, George W.  Retention in treatment of drug users in the
    DARP:  1969-1971 admissions.  In S.B. Sells (Ed.),
    The effectiveness of drug abuse treatment. (Vol. 1),
    Evaluation of treatments.  Cambridge, Mass.: Ballinger,
    1974.

Joe, G.W., and Simpson, D.D.  Classification of drug users
    based on the DARP treatment population.  In S.B. Sells,
    and D.D. Simpson (Eds.), The effectiveness of drug abuse
    treatment. (Vol. 3).  Further studies of drug users
    treatment typologies and assessment of outcomes during
    treatment in the DARP.  Cambridge, Mass,: Ballinger,
    1976 (a).

Joe, G.W., and Simpson, D.D.  Retention in treatment of drug
    users admitted to treatment during 1971-1972.  In S.B.
    Sells, and D.D. Simpson (Eds.), The effectiveness of
    drug abuse treatment. (Vol. 4).  Evaluation of treat-
    ment outcomes for the 1971-1972 admission cohort.
    Cambridge, Mass: Ballinger, 1976 (b).

Joe, G.W., and Simpson, D.D.  Treatment retention for drug
    users:  1972-1973 DARP admissions.  In S.B. Sells,
    and D.D. Simpson (Eds.), The effectiveness of drug abuse
    treatment. (Vol. 5).  Evauation of treatment outcomes
    for the 1972-1973 admission cohort.  Cambridge, Mass.:
    Ballinger, 1976 (c).

McRae, D.J.  The development of a patient typology.  In S.B.
    Sells (Ed.), The effectiveness of drug abuse treatment.
    (Vol. 2).  Research on patients, treatments, and outcomes.
    Cambridge, Mass.:  Ballinger, 1974.

Maddux, J.F., and Desmond, D.D.  Reliability and validity of
    information from chronic heroin users.  Presented at the
    annual meeting of the Committee on Problems of Drug
    Dependence, National Research Council, Chapel Hill,
    North Carolina, May, 1973.

Overall, J.E., and Spiegel, D.K.  Concerning least squares
    analysis of experimental data.  Psychological Bulletin,
    1969, 72, 311-322.

Pierce, J.I.  Suicide and mortality amongst heroin addicts
    in Britian.  British Journal of Addictions, 1967, 62,
    391.

Sells, S.B. (Ed.),  The effectiveness of drug abuse treat-
    ment.  Vol. 1.  Evaluation of treatments.  Vol. 2.
    Research on patients, treatments, and outcomes.
    Cambridge, Massachusetts: Ballinger, 1974.

Sells, S.B., and Simpson, D.D. (Eds.),  The effectiveness
    of drug abuse treatment.  Vol. 3.  Further studies of
    drug users treatment typologies and assessment of out-
    come during treatment in the DARP.  Vol. 4.  Evaluation
    of treatment outcomes for the 1971-1972 admission cohort.
    Vol. 5.  Evaluation of treatment outcomes for the 1972-
    1973 admission cohort.  Cambridge, Mass.:  Ballinger,
    1976.

Simpson, D.D., and McRae, D.J.  Readmissions to treatment
    of drug users in the DARP: 1969-1971 admissions.  In
    S.B. Sells (Ed.), The effectiveness of drug abuse
    treatment.  (Vol. 1).  Evaluation of treatments.
    Cambridge, Mass.:  Ballinger, 1974.

Spiegel, D.K., and Sells, S.B.  Evaluation of treatments for
    drug users in the DARP: 1969-1971 admissions.  In
    S.B. Sells (Ed.), The effectiveness of drug abuse treat-
    ment.  (Vol. 1).  Evaluation of treatments.  Cambridge:
    Mass.:  Ballinger, 1974.

Stephens, R.  The truthfulness of addict respondents in research projects.  International Journal of Addiction, 1972, 7, 549-558.

Watson, D.D., Simpson, D.D., and Spiegel, D.K.  Development of a treatment typology for drug use in the DARP: 1969-1971 admissions.  In S.B. Sells (Ed.), The effectiveness of drug abuse treatment. (Vol. 2).  Research on patients, treatments, and outcomes.  Cambridge, Mass.: Ballinger, 1974.

Watterson, O., Sells, S.B., and Simpson, D.D.  Death rates and causes of death for opiate addicts in treatment during 1972-1973.  In S.B. Sells and D.D. Simpson (Eds.), The effectiveness of drug abuse treatment. (Vol. 5).  Evaluation of treatment outcomes for the 1972-1973 admission cohort.  Cambridge, Mass.:  Ballinger, 1976.

Open Discussion

Zubin: In a recent study of another deviant group, high class call girls, an attempt was made at classifying the men that visit them by observers behind a voyeur screen. About a thousand observations were made, an attempt at classifying the men seemed to yield very little in terms of the statistical evidence it was possible to gather, but the classification by the call girls themselves based upon the sexual objectives that demanded different roles, yielded a much better analysis of the results than any attempt at the analyses of observer data. The girls classified the men in accordance with their expectations into the romantic type, and they charged much more; the Lolita type and behaved accordingly, the businessman type who would say "I have only 10 minutes," and so on. I wonder whether there is any way of getting the self-classification of the drug addict which might also help in the analysis.


Sells: There have been similar attempts to classify drug addicts; the hippie type, etc. It seems to me that these have been more relevant to social relationships on the street than to prognosis in treatment. For purposes of large-scale treatment evaluation, it is necessary to obtain measures that can be collected routinely that are reliable and also accurate. Such qualitative classifications are almost unmanageable in a data system such as the DARP.

Formal Discussant:  Monica Blumenthal


One question that arises from these presentations is
how do these two populations, the one described by Dr.
Robins and the one described by Dr. Sells relate to each
other.  How do both these groups fit into the population in
general?  At the current moment I live in a national survey
research organization and I'm always very happy when I can
talk about American men; in fact, I'm very happy if I can
just talk about people living in the Detroit metropolitan
area.  But when I have to talk about people who come from
A, B, C, D, and E, I begin to wonder what it is that I'm
really talking about, particularly when the populations in
these places have not been selected by random, representative sampling techniques.

Both Dr. Robins and Dr. Sells raised some really very
interesting issues, vis-a-vis how we look at variables and
what they mean in relationship to a person's life, but I would
like to remind you about things that all of you already know.
We begin with a person's birth.  One of the important things
that happens when a person is born, he becomes a member of a
cohort.  I'm sure that all of us who have worked with young
people over the last half dozen years or so are profoundly
aware of the fact that cohort characteristics can change
extremely rapidly.  That person has a sex, he has a set of
parents who have certain socioeconomic characteristics.
The person also has a birth process, which is something that
turns out to be important sometimes, particularly in relation
to the genetics with which he also arrived in the world.
The person goes on to have a childhood.  Presumably many
things happening in childhood are influenced by the factors
present when that person was born.  Further changes occur as
a result of both factors present at birth and occurring in
childhood.  The individual arrives in adolescence, and in
adolescence further change related to demographic characteristics will occur.  For example, where you happen to be
living when you're an adolescent is quite important.  If
you live in a black, urban ghetto, there is a relatively high
likelihood that you will drop out of school in the 9th or
10th grade.  That becomes a demographic characteristic which

is influenced by antecedent demographic characteristics,
which then becomes a totally independent characteristic
influencing the outcome measures that are so important for
Dr. Sells.

Another example of these complex relationships occurs
during adolescence when some people are exposed to varying
factors that are again influenced by demographic characteristics. For example stress due to life events is also
correlated with the demographic environment of the individual. If you're poor, people in your immediate vicinity are
much more likely to die, lose jobs, and become seriously
ill, than if you're not poor. These stresses in turn may
influence future outcomes.

A further complication is that Dr. Robins and Dr. Sells
began to study people after they had been selected into treatment environments. Again, the characteristics that relate to
who selects whom into a treatment environment are important.
It comes back to that same set of demographic characteristics,
but they have a different meaning. If you're black you're
more likely  to be arrested and go to court, and consequently
end up in a Methadone treatment program; if you're white
you're more likely to be selected into psychotherapy. Again,
we have to keep these factors in mind as separate variables
that we have to deal with in longitudinal studies. The order
of causality cannot be determined from data that deal with
only a limited segment of time.

Lastly, of course, comes outcome. People in the helping
professions are always very fond of thinking that treatment
accounts for the effects which occur but the effects may be
more determined by demographic factors than we think. For
example, at least one of the outcomes that you use but didn't
mention, namely death, varies according to age and according
to race. If you're a young black male, you're much more likely
to be murdered than if you are a young white female. There
is also an interaction between employment and demographic
characteristics of course. We're all terribly fond of using
employment as a measure of function that implies recovery from
illness. In fact, if you were a young black person living in
an area where the local unemployment rate is 40%, then it
does not make very much sense to use this as an outcome
measure.

I'd like to remind you of what Dr. Dohrenwend has said, that if we knew more about the characteristics of individuals living in our communities, and the characteristics of the communities, including things like treatment determinants, we might not get so very lost in our data. It's perfectly feasible to survey the community of origin of people we study and develop at least some notion of what baseline kinds of events are happening in that community, to these particular kinds of people. We really can't generalize if we withdraw ourselves from that socio-economic world out there that insists on changing constantly according to government policy.

To summarize, I believe that causal analysis must take into account the sequence of events and their influence at each point in time and that studies of outcome must carefully account for non-individual variables before they can be properly interpreted.


Formal Discussant:  John Rolf

Rather than speak specifically on the two papers that were presented, I would like to give a very brief overview of what I've been observing. It seems to me that life history research is yielding a growing list of independent variables which demand attention for their significance to questions of etiology and because they require experimental control if one tries to predict outcome in prospective research. The evolutionary course of life history research has been reviewed in the past few days, and it seems to have shifted from what was very intellectually stimulating descriptive research beginning with clinical retrospective models and to have moved on to experimental prospective designs. Apparently, now the major purpose of life history research is to try to predict outcome from known or inferred risks rather than to try to correlate known outcome to some past event. During this evolution, there have been some unfortunate tactical errors. Too often, we have chosen to study unpredictable behaviors (such as is the case with schizophrenia) and we have also chosen to study low base rate behaviors with variable periods of high risk during an individual's life. Further, the decision to use repeated measures over time and to abandon one shot cross-sectional designs has been methodologically reasonable but has also been a great stumbling block to us because we are such novices at developmental prediction. I agree with Sameroff

and Robins; it's foolish to try to predict remote outcomes
using some kind of linear model for subjects when, first of
all, the subjects are undergoing rapid developmental changes,
and secondly, the outcome events are exceedingly improbable.
I think it would be much better if we paid attention to shoring
up our very short-term predictions using the framework
of Sameroff's transactional model (one which I would prefer
to call a developmental interactional model) in which there's
always an interplay of variables over measurably observable
short periods of time.

    Perhaps what this new field of prospective life-history
research needs most is to develop some kinds of multiphasic
epidemiological measures taken at typical developmental
stages with which one can judge a specific child on his/her
typical and atypical behaviors, try to predict to the
next shortest interval, and then see if the typical behaviors
have now become atypical or if atypical behaviors have moved
back into the mainstream of the normative range.  I think
there are ways to measure the life histories of risk over
short periods of time and I would urge investigators to try
to go out of the laboratory and to establish developmental
risk norms as part of their prospective research designs.
If this were done, then one could take a child with a certain
target high-risk factor plus certain other demographic risk
attributes and compare his or her behavior to a "normative"
template of developmental progress of a control group of
children with the same accessory demographic risk attributes (sex, race, age, SES, broken homes, neighborhood experiences, etc.).  Having that kind of data would help to
put the high risk child's behavior into the appropriate
life-history developmental context.  From this context,
one could judge better the deviance of the "outcomes"
from the normative control group's at various points in
the subject's life.  One could then say, "he doesn't look
any different than those people, let's not get excited yet."
Or if he does look different at the first evaluation when you
come back for subsequent re-evaluations, you may find that
he has shifted back into the normal range again.  As Robins
demonstrated with the predictions of narcotic addiction,
the environmental context of drug usage (Vietnam vs. U.S.A.)
makes a big difference if one is attempting to predict future
drug addiction from past drug taking behavior.  The factors
which would predict being a user or deviant in one context,
may well be useless for predicting it in another context.

In another example, the outcomes of Mednick and Schulsinger's prospective studies also suggest that predictors for early breakdown may not be the best predictors for recovery or later breakdown in persons at high risk for schizophrenia. Thus, as life history research continues its evolution to a science of predicting the courses of lives, more normative epidemiologic data of developmental growth and changes must be gathered and used in the appropriate contexts of time and environment.

Schooler: We've seen during this whole conference the presentation of really good data, data collected with blood, sweat and tears and increased sophistication, data which at some level we have reason to trust. It measures something which is out there. But I also have a criticism. Nobody has noticed the fact that there has been a major revolution in data analysis in sociology. Through the work of Simon, Blalock, Duncan, and Joreskog, there has developed a whole methodology of causal analysis for non-experimental data, and also for experimental data, which involves path analysis, two stage least squares, and confirmatory factor analysis. There hasn't been a single reference to any of these methods here. This methodology was made basically for these problems, and you haven't even mentioned it.

Blumenthal: I really want to respond to that, because you know in a sense you are very right. The reason that I made the set of remarks that I made is because the model that you look at is terribly important, because the model will determine what your analysis will be; I'm not talking about mini, little 2x2 sorts of models. You must have the whole array of variables laid out, you must know how they happen in time, you must know where they affect things or else you just can't do it. But first I think we really have to think about these models and how they work. Once you lay out the model statistics...

Schooler: All right. Path analysis and its subsequent developments are not the ultimate; they involve developing models and testing out the models in terms of their goodness of fit. I don't think we have any disagreement about that.

Blumenthal: No, we don't.

Schooler: But it's a method and my God you can even have dynamic interactions. I mean there's all kinds of things you can do, and you just can't have a scientific association with goals of this one and neglect such major methodological advances.

Strauss: As chairman, I'm going to take the chairman's perogative. I've been very interested in path analysis, and when I talk with people about it, sociologists especially, maybe it's just my sampling, they say well your variables have to be perfectly reliable, well we really don't have a program for this, and so forth.

Schooler: The problem of reliability exists and is particularly important for the independent variables, which, fortunately, are generally fairly reliable. If your independent variables are reliable, your dependent variables can be slightly unreliable and won't louse you up. In any case, Joreskog's confirmation factor analysis provides what is probably the most sophisticated way presently available of dealing with the problem separating true change from unreliability.

Roff: Is this the path coefficient of Sewall Wright, do you know?

Schooler: Yes, by golly, it is, 1921.

Roff: I was raised on that when I was a boy.

Schooler: It is one of the ironies of the whole business that Sewall Wright's path coefficient for predicting the prices of hogs, developed in 1921, has gone from there, through genetics, through agriculture, to econometrics. And then, Simon, on his way from being an economist through being a sociologist to becoming a psychologist kind of dropped it off on sociology, which has picked it up and through the work of Joreskog developed to a highly sophisticated yet generally applicable tool.

Roff: I don't think it makes a lot of difference.

Harrow: I just want to note that we're talking about data analyses, and data analyses gives approximations, it doesn't give final answers and final truths about the nature of things. We have a problem of distinguishing between means and ends. I think more and better statistical analysis is

important, but statistical analysis is a means toward an
end, it's not an end in itself. So far in the history of
the world most great discoveries have not come from refined
analysis of subtle aspects of data, but from things that
have been at least moderately obvious by looking at fairly
simple raw data and by looking at average scores, and often
by conceptualizing the problem differently, or by looking at
often-observed phenomena and asking new questions about them
which people had not thought of before. I just want to note
that there are various ways of dealing with statistics, but
they are means rather than an end, and I think we should
keep that in perspective.

Schooler: My point really was that even if these forms
of analysis may turn out wrong, somehow those in this research
area should deal with it. It hasn't even been dealt with as
a possibility, and I think that is what finally drove me to
speak so strongly.

Blumenthal: As Martin (Harrow) suggested, it really
isn't so much the statistical analysis, but it has to do
with the view of the nature of the experimental problem. I
think most most of us came out of more basic sciences and
we're used to the one independent variable/dependent variable
paradigm. I think, in fact, that psychiatric phenomena
don't work that way, but that we're dealing with a very
complex model with multiple interactions and those interactions
are necessary to produce the resultant phenomena of interest.
It's not a question of the statistical analysis, it's a
question of the conceptualization of your basic experimental
paradigm. Path analysis is important in the sense that it
stresses those models and laying out what goes into your
paradigm. I think much psychiatric research, although I
must say it has improved so much in the last decade that I
can't believe it, but much psychiatric research is based on
limited and constricted paradigms and they're not going to
produce the answers.

Cromwell: I would disagree very strongly about the
notion that refined multivariate techniques (whether path
analysis, factor analysis, or some other approach) are
unimportant. I would also disagree that the major things we
learn are from the large mean differences that hit us in the
face. This has been true in the past, only because people
have not been adequately trained in multivariate statistics.

The area of multivariate experimental psychology had not advanced a great deal. There are several examples now of findings, important findings, which would never have emerged without multivariate statistics. Of course, there must be the opportunity to replicate subtle and unexpected findings with new and independent samples.

Overall: One thing I noticed in Dr. Sells' project is the amount of effort that went into planning the statistical analysis and then reanalyzing findings when you encountered new relationships.

Sells: After five or six years of working with our data, we have begun to understand some of the idiosyncracies of many of the variables that we had overlooked originally. Lee (Robins) pointed out some of the problems with her data, I can mention a few problems with ours. For example, in our data samples, Puerto Ricans, whites, Mexican Americans, and blacks differ on a confounding variable, age, that runs across these groupings in a very complex way. Since almost every variable is confounded with two or three other variables in a nasty way, when you try to do model testing, you find very often that the solution by any single analysis leads to conclusions that have a certain amount of ambiguity regarding their interpretation. As a result, we are cautious about relying on just one or another method of analysis and prefer multiple analyses to compare these models. We have been using the general linear model with a great deal of satisfaction, and we also have a new method which I call criterion-oriented analysis, in which the data are grouped according to results on the criterion and then examined by multiple discriminant analysis.

Rutter: While I agree that many studies are inadequately analyzed, I do not believe that mathematical manipulations of patterns of correlations, which is what path analysis involves, provide a sufficient answer to questions of the direction or causality of relationships. What is needed is the demonstration that waggling one variable causes another to move. In the experimental situation you can do this directly, but in the social sciences, this is less often possible. However, epidemiology provides an alternative approach in which use is made of natural variations between and within populations. The art and the science lies in the identification of population samples which differ in terms

of the independent variable to be studied, but which are
otherwise similar. If the populations also differ with
respect to the dependent variable hypothesized to be the
result of the first variable, if it can be shown that this
is not an artefact of other population differences and if
the results can be cross-validated with other independent
samples, it is reasonable to infer a probable causal connection. No amount of statistical juggling can really eradi-
cate inconvenient overlap between variables (although it can
help); a search for fresh samples which do not suffer from
the unwanted overlap is needed.